© THE ASSOCIATION OF
SUPERVISORY AND EXECUTIVE
ENGINEERS

ASEE Illustrated Guide
to the
IEE Regulations
for
Electrical Installations

(Fifteenth Edition 1981)
(including 1983, 1984, 1985, 1986 and 1987 amendments)

Produced and published by
**THE ASSOCIATION OF SUPERVISORY AND
EXECUTIVE ENGINEERS**
WIX HILL HOUSE, WEST HORSLEY, SURREY, KT24 6DZ
(Telephone: Guildford (0483) 222383)

Issued February 1984
Reprinted with amendments 1985 and 1987

© Association of Supervisory and Executive Engineers

British Library Cataloguing in Publication Data

ASEE illustrated guide to the IEE regulations
    for electrical installations.—15th ed.
    1981
    1. Institution of Electrical Engineers.
    Regulations for electrical installation
    2. Buildings—Electric equipment
    3. Electric wiring, Interior
    I. Association of Supervisory & Executive
    Engineers
    621.319′24   TK3271

ISBN 0-903511-14-2

For information about ASEE see pages 303 to 305

Printed in England by Unwin Brothers Limited, Old Woking, Surrey

CONTENTS
(The Regulations covered are shown in brackets)

The ASEE Illustrated Guide to the IEE Regulations for Electrical Installations (15th edition)

(including Amendments promulgated in 1983, 1984, 1985, 1986, 1987)

PREFACE

The 15th Edition of the IEE Regulations for Electrical Installations is the first major step towards the alignment of electrical installation principles of the United Kingdom and other European countries, but the arrangement of rules and the greater importance of safety measures in the new Regulations have changed the layout of the previous edition to such an extent that the ASEE Illustrated Guide to the 14th edition of the Regulations will no longer serve its purpose after the 30th December 1984. This new Edition of the ASEE Illustrated Guide has therefore become necessary to assist in understanding the meaning and intensions of the new Regulations which are generally arranged according to the new plan for Publication 364: Electrical Installation of Buildings of the International Electrotechnical Commission (IEC).

The Executive Council of the Association seeks to serve the Association's membership in particular and also the electrical industry in general with sound technical advice. The popularity of the previous editions of the ASEE Illustrated Guide with teaching establishments and practising engineers has proved the value of this major ASEE service. The type of presentation adopted, using simple language and illustration, should leave no doubt in the minds of both the engineer and the apprentice as to the requirements of the Regulations. But the Guide is not intended as a substitute for the "Wiring Regulations" which should be studied along with the additional information given in the Guide where a particular Regulation is not clearly understood.

Every care has been taken in the preparation of the Guide, but if there is doubt about the interpretation of any Regulation, any official interpretation issued by the Institution of Electrical Engineers must prevail.

The new Regulations allow designers of installations greater scope but for compliance with the Regulations coupled with a high standard of workmanship, reference to British Standards and Codes of Practice concerning choice of materials and equipment utilised is mandatory. Hence there is a greater need for access to the Standards and Codes of Practice for reference purposes than was the case hitherto, although alternative methods are not precluded if the same standards of safety are achieved.

The principal differences between the 14th and 15th editions of the IEE Wiring Regulations are as follows:

1. The new Edition introduces requirements which relate to the assessment of general characteristics of the source of supply and to the associated electrical installations.
2. New terminology is introduced particularly in relation to (a) types of systems (b) direct and indirect contact (c) exposed and extraneous conductive parts, and (d) circuit and other protective conductors.
3. Maximum disconnection times have been introduced.
4. There are much more detailed requirements concerning the use of residual current devices (e.g. earth leakage circuit breakers) particularly to protect certain socket-outlets.
5. Requirements for isolation and switching and concerning overcurrent protection are more detailed.
6. A new approach to the determination of conductor sizes is adopted.
7. Thermal requirements for conductors under fault conditions have been introduced.
8. Requirements for supplementary bonding have been introduced.

The numbering system used in the 15th Edition of the Regulations to identify particular Regulations is based on the first digit indicating a *Part* of the Regulations, the second digit a *Chapter* within a *Part*, the third digit a *Section* within a *Chapter* and the fourth digit indicates a

particular *Regulation* within a *Chapter*. Thus, for example the designation 413-2 indicates:
Part 4 – Protection for Safety
Chapter 41 – Protection against electric shock
Section 413 – Protection against indirect contact
Regulation 413-2 – which deals with extraneous conductive parts.

This Illustrated Guide to the Regulations does not follow the format or sequence of the 15th Edition. An attempt has been made to gather particular Regulations together in relevant subject areas. The Guide is divided into three distinct sections covering fundamental *Principles* and eleven sections which deal with areas of *Practice* each of which seeks to explain how the principles are applied. Inevitably, because some Regulations are relevant to more than one subject, some cross references to the first mention of a particular Regulation will be found. Also no attempt has been made within the Illustrated Guide to identify individual Regulations; rather the Regulations are identified in groups within particular subject areas. Reference to the Contents pages will indicate which groups of Regulations are referred to within particular Principles or Practice sections of this Guide. Further, reference to the Index should be an additional indicator to particular specialised subjects.

The Association is indebted to many people and companies too numerous to mention individually, for the ready and willing provision of assistance in the compilation of this ASEE Illustrated Guide. That assistance is readily recognised by the Association and it is hoped that this general acknowledgement of their invaluable help will be accepted in the spirit in which it is intended.

Principles 1

Scope, objectives and fundamental requirements

The 15th edition of the IEE Regulations for Electrical Installations applies to all aspects of new electrical installations and by implication requires that existing installations should be reappraised when they are extended. The scope of the Regulations applicable to the types of installations and sites is set out in Schedule 1. The voltage ranges covered by the Regulations are shown in Schedule 2. The types of installations and equipment which are excluded from the scope of the Regulations are shown in Schedules 3a and 3b. Partial exclusions from scope are shown in Schedule 4.

Schedule 1 – Scope of Regulations

(Regulation 11-1 and 11-3)

Scope of Regulation	For further guidance see
Permanent and temporary installations in and around buildings: design, selection, erection, inspection, testing, certification and maintainability. In other locations Regulations may need modification or supplementation for other uses.	Practice 10 for certification Practice 11 for inspection and testing. Aspects of the selection and erection of equipment are covered in several of the Practice Notes which follow; consult Index to identify.
Agricultural and horticultural premises*	Practice 1 (Annex 2) Practice 2 (471-40 and 471-41) Practice 3 (523-26 and 523-34) Practice 9 (554-35 to 554-40)
Construction sites*	Practice 1 (Annex 2) Practice 9 Schedule 9.2 and 9.3 Practice 3 (Annex 3) British Standard Code of Practice CP1017 "*Distribution of electricity on construction and building sites.*"
Caravans and caravan sites*	Practice 2A Schedule 2.19 Practice 10 (514-6) Practice 9 Schedule 9.2 and 554-2 IEC Document 585-1 "*Caravans, boats and yachts*"

(continued)

Scope of Regulation	For further guidance see
Telecommunication and similar circuits other than those fed from a safety source.	Practice 5

Note: There are references to these locations in the footnotes to Completion and Inspection Certificates (Practice 10)

Voltage ranges

Schedule 2 sets out the internationally agreed voltage ranges.

Schedule 2 – Voltage ranges applicable to Regulations

(Regulation 11-2)

Nominal voltage ranges	System	Voltage between conductors		Voltage conductors to earth		For further guidance see
		From	To	From	To	
Extra low voltage	AC	0	50	0	50	Practice 3 (521-7) Also Practice 2 "Functional Extra Low Voltage" (411-11 to 411-15) and "Safety Extra Low Voltage" (411-2 to 411-10)
	DC	0	120	0	120	
Low voltage	AC	over 50	1000	over 50	600	Practice 2A (471-27 to 471-33) "Reduced system voltages"
	DC	over 120	1500	over 120	900	
Higher than low voltage discharge lighting	AC	over 1000	rated Volts	over 600	5kV rms	Practice 8 – Fireman's Switches Practice 9 (554-3)
Higher than low voltage electrode boilers	AC	over 1000	rated Volts	over 600	rated Volts	Practice 9 (554-20 to 554-26)
	DC	Not applicable to dc				

Schedule 3a – Types of installation and equipment (in buildings) excluded from the Regulations

(Regulations 11-3, 11-4 and 11-5)

Type of installation or system	Notes and references
Power generation, transmission and distribution systems for public supplies	The responsibility of the designer and the installer under the 15th edition begins at the origin of the consumer's installation. Electricity Supply Regulations 1937 apply in Great Britain. In Northern Ireland the regulations made by the Secretary of State apply. Overseas the relevant requirements of the particular country are applicable. For guidance on the latter requirements refer to Technical Help to Exporters, British Standards Institution, Linford Wood, Milton Keynes, MK14 6EE.
Installations in potentially explosive atmospheres specified in British Standard Codes of Practice BS5345 and CP1003	Refer to the Electricity (Factories Act) Special Regulations 1908 and 1944. Also Practice 1 (Annex 1 and Annex 2)
Premises where fire risk is of an unusual character which requires special consideration	Refer to Highly Flammable Liquids and Liquified Petroleum Regulations 1972, The Petroleum Consolidation Act 1928, The Home Office *"Model Code of Principles for Construction and Licensing Conditions"*
Telecommunication circuits and equipment supplied from safety source including: radio, telephone bell, call and sound distribution and data transmission.	Schedule 4.
Fire detection and intruder alarm circuits supplied from a safety source.	British Standard Code of Practice BS5839, *"Fire detection and alarm systems in buildings"*. A Code of Practice on intruder alarms is in preparation.
Radio interference suppression equipment	Except where it affects safety of electrical installation. See PD6485:1980 *"Limits of radio interference and leakage currents"*.
Lightning protection of buildings	See British Standard BS6651 *"The Protection of Structures against lightning"*.

(continued)

Type of installation or system	Notes and references
Erection of prefabricated installations for temporary but frequent use	Examples are festoon lighting, prefabricated harnesses with cable couplers, etc. See *"Home Office Guide to Safety at Fairs"* (HM Stationery Office)
Prefabricated assemblies of electrical equipment which comply with an appropriate specification	Factory built assemblies of switchgear and control gear to British Standard Specification BS5486 are an example of pre-fabricated assemblies.

Schedule 3b – Types of installation and equipment (other than in buildings) excluded from the Regulations

Type of installation or system	Notes and references
Emergency lighting supplied from a safety source.	See British Standard Code of Practice BS5266, *"Emergency Lighting"*
Electric traction equipment	BS2618: 1975 *"Electric Traction Equipment"* deals with motive power units. See also BS6287: 1982 *"Code of practice for safe operation of traction batteries"*.
Motor vehicles (unless the requirements for caravans apply)	The Automobile Series of British Standards applies to Motor Vehicles. Some of these Standards refer to electrical aspects of motor vehicles.
Ship installations	See *"Regulations for the Electrical and Electronic Equipment of Ships"* published by Institution of Electrical Engineers
Off-shore installations	IEE Regulation for 'Off shore' installations are under preparation
Aircraft electrical equipment	The Civil Aviation Authority publishes *"British Civil Airworthiness Requirements"*
Mines and quarries	See Coal and Other Mines (Electricity) Regulations 1956 See Quarries Electricity Regulations 1956 See Miscellaneous Mines (Electricity) Regulations 1956

Partial exclusion from scope

Schedule 4 – Installations partially within scope of the Regulations

(Regulations 11-3 to 11-5)

Type of installation partially covered by Regulations	Notes and references
Telecommunication circuits Fire Alarm circuits Intruder Alarm circuits Emergency lighting circuits	See also the following British Standards Codes of Practice BS5839 – *"Fire Alarm Systems"* BS5266 – *"Emergency Lighting of Premises"* which also apply. Under the Fire Precautions Act, installations in designated buildings are required to comply with these Codes of Practice.
Electrical equipment	Selection and application of equipment for installation only are applicable.
Prefabricated installations for temporary use and frequent erection	Only those Regulations applicable to design and selection apply.

Objectives

The objectives which the Regulations seek to achieve are tabulated in Schedule 5.

Schedule 5 – Objectives of Regulations

(Regulations 12-1 to 12-8)

Objective of Regulation	Notes and references
To ensure installation is safe particularly against hazards i.e. shock, fire and burns	Safety for persons and animals
To cite Regulations in entirety, not in part, in contracts. To provide that qualified persons advise on difficult or special installations	
To secure compliance with statutory regulations relative to electrical installations when fundamental requirements for safety (Chapter 13 – see Schedule 6a) are met	See Practice 1 (1st Annex) for the statutory regulations covered

Objective of Regulation	Notes and references
To detail methods and practices meeting fundamental requirements for safety	See Practice 2
To ensure that departures from specified methods and practices to be noted in the completion certificate	See Practice 10
To ensure only established materials, equipment and methods are considered by designers. Not intended to discourage invention or to exclude other ways of achieving objective if equivalent degree of safety is attained	See next objective
To ensure that departures from Regulations through use of new material, invention or design to written specification of competent person, are not described as complying with the regulations and do not lead to a lower standard that that achieved by the Regulations.	See previous objective
ANT Scheme – Deleted by January 1983 Amendments to 15th edition	
To ensure that requirements of licensing or statutory authority are ascertained where necessary	See Practice 1 (first Annex)
Notes in the Regulations provide indications of way Regulation requirements can be met. Notes are not themselves part of the Regulations	The ASEE Illustrated Guide is likewise intended to assist in the expansion and clarification of the Regulation's intentions
Validity of the Regulations. This Regulation deleted by January 1983 Amendments to 15th edition.	
New cables not covered by Regulations should be subject of consideration by British Approvals Scheme for Electric Cables (BASEC) but an installation which involves BASEC Certificate of Assessment cannot be described as complying with the Regulations.	

Subjects Regulations do not cover.

The matters which the Regulations specifically state are not intended to be covered are shown in Schedule 6.

(Regulations 12-2 and 12-7)

The Regulations do not serve as:
A detailed specification
A means of instructing untrained persons
A means of dealing with every situation; for example – difficult or special installations outside the scope of the Regulations and which need further qualified guidance
An alternative to the requirements of licensing or statutory authorities

Fundamental requirements for safety *(Regulations 13-1 to 13-20)*

Regulations 13-1 to 13-20 of the IEE Regulations are important because in essence they form the basis of all the Regulations which follow. Failure to comply with the requirements of those Regulations could lead the electricity supply authority to withhold a supply of energy to an installation. Figures 1 to 3 show the application of fundamental safety requirements to a typical installation. The symbols used in Figure 3 indicate the following:

A – The circuit chart shall identify the location of all points of utilisation served by each protective device, the nominal rating and type of protective device or fuse link or gauge of fuse wire and phase shall also be clear. (Regulation 514-3)

B – A metal or other permanent warning notice shall be attached to or fixed adjacent to the point where an earth conductor connects to an earth electrode or where a bonding conductor connects to an extraneous conductor the label shall be engraved, embossed or durably marked 'SAFETY ELECTRICAL CONNECTION – DO NOT REMOVE' in letters not less than 4.75mm. (Regulation 514-7)

C – Where equipment may automatic restart when an emergency switching device is re-set a warning notice shall be provided adjacent to points of danger. (Regulation 537-16)

D – A switch or other device intended to switch off equipment or drives for mechanical maintenance shall be easily identified or marked. (Regulation 462-2)

E – Emergency switching devices shall be marked to indicate their use. (Regulation 463-4)

F – Where the enclosures of equipment, switchgear etc contain a voltage exceeding 250 volts or where two such enclosures are simultaneously accessible and would have a voltage exceeding 250 volts between them if opened a warning notice of the maximum voltage present shall be provided on the covers to give warning before access can be gained to live parts, this also applies to the covers of switchgear and fixed equipment where different nominal voltages are present, in this case the voltages present shall be made clear by warning notices. (Regulation 514-4)

G – Provide a label to indicate the purpose of control gear or switchgear where confusion could arise.

H – Protective devices should preferably be grouped, such as in a distribution board to enable the circuits and the related protective devices to be easily recognised. (Regulation 514-2)

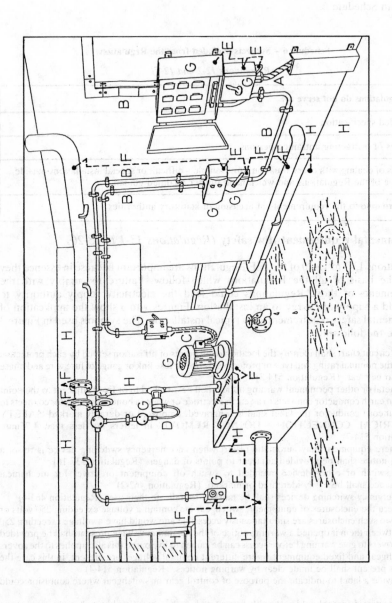

Figure 1 – Protective Conductors (see Practice 7) and Conductive Parts (see Practice 2)
A – Cable Armour (543-8), B – Metallic Conduit (543-19), C – Separate Conductor (543-1), D – Separate Core in a Cable (543-5), E – Supplementary Conductive Parts, H – Extraneous Conductive Parts.
Bonding (547-4), F – Supplementary Bonding (547-4), G – Exposed Conductive Parts (413-7), G – Exposed Conductive Parts, H – Extraneous Conductive Parts.

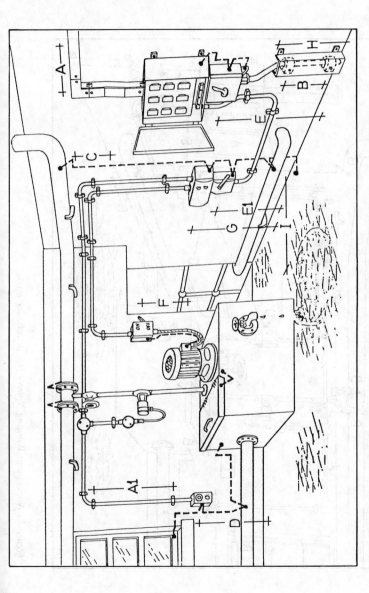

Figure 2 – A1 – Fixing Centres for Conduit (529-2), A – Fixing Centres for Trunking (529-2), B – Fixing Centres for Cables (529-1), C – Fixing Centres for Protective Conductors, D – Means of Emergency Switching to be Readily Accessible and Easily Operated, E1 – Means of Isolation for a Motor and All Equipment (476-5), E – Means of Isolation for Every Circuit or Group of Circuits (461-1), F – Means of Isolation for Maintenance of a Motor (476-7), G – Mounting Height of Starter, Isolator and Distribution Board to be Readily Accessible to the Operator and Easily Operated, H – Height of Mechanical Protection to Cables to be Not Less than 1 Metre where possible, I – Siting of Switchgear, Equipment etc to allow access for use and maintenance. Also to be separated or protected from possible hazards such as spillages, pedestrian or other traffic anticipated in normal service.

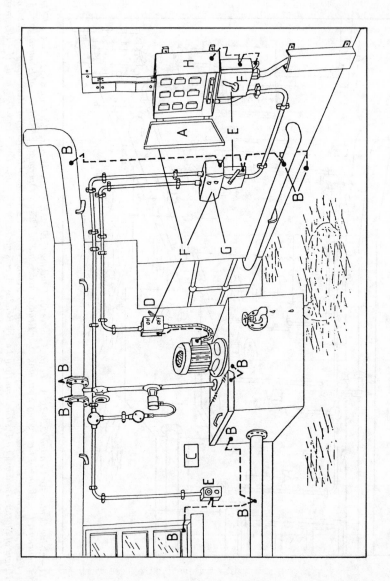

Figure 3   Notices and Warning Notices (for details, see text).

Linking material

Whilst Part 1 of the IEE Regulations and in particular Regulations 13-1 to 13-20 provide the fundamental safety requirements for electrical installations, the remainder of the Regulations deal in more detail with aspects of installation practice. For this reason this Illustrated Guide will deal with each fundamental safety requirement in the general concept of electrical installation practice to which it is primarily applicable. Schedule 6a indicates each fundamental safety requirement and shows where each subject is further covered in this publication.

Schedule 6a – Fundamental safety requirements

Regulation	Fundamental requirement	Refer to
13-1	Workmanship, materials and general requirements	Practice 1
13-2	Equipment installed, constructed and protected to prevent danger and to permit maintenance inspection and testing	
13-3	Equipment suitable for maximum power demanded	
13-4	Conductors of sufficient size and current carrying capacity	
13-5	Conductors insulated, protected, located and safeguarded to prevent danger	
13-6	Electrical joints and connections properly constructed	
13-7	Circuits protected by overcurrent devices	Practice 6
13-8	Metalwork earthed to prevent danger	Practice 7
13-9	Dangerous earth leakage currents prevented	Practice 7
13-10	Fault current protection by overcurrent protective devices or residual current or voltage operated device	Practice 7
13-11	Exposed metal parts of other services connected to earthing terminal	Practice 7
13-12	No protective device or switch in earthed neutral conductor	Practice 6 and 8

(continued)

Regulation	Fundamental requirement	Refer to
13-13	Single pole switches in phase conductor only	Practice 6
13-14	Provision of means to cut off voltage from installation	Practice 8
13-15	Provision of means easily to disconnect motors from supply	Practice 8
13-16	Provision of safe means of access and working space	Practice 9
13-17	Equipment constructed or protected to prevent danger where exposed to weather or corrosive atmosphere	Practice 1
13-18	Equipment constructed or protected to prevent danger from risk of fire or explosion	Practice 1
13-19	Existing installation adequate in all respects for any addition or alteration made thereto	Practice 1
13-20	Testing and inspection of completed installation or extension or alteration, to verify Regulations 13-1 to 13-19 have been met	Practice 1

Principles 2 — Definitions

Because the 15th edition of the IEE Regulations for Electrical Installations arises from the development of international wiring rules by the International Electrotechnic Commission, many new terms have been introduced into that edition. Reproduced below, by kind permission of the Institution of Electrical Engineers, are some of those definitions which appear in the Regulations for the first time. These definitions are fundamental for a comprehension of the intent of the relevant 15th edition Regulations.

There are, of course, many other defined terms which are used in the 15th edition and which are not reproduced below. Further guidance on the sense in which defined terms are used, can be obtained by reference to British Standard BS4727 "Glossary of electrotechnical" power, telecommunication, electronics, lighting and colour terms.

Arm's reach. A zone of accessibility to touch, extending from any point on a surface where persons usually stand or move about, to the limits which a person can reach with his hand in any direction without assistance.

Bonding conductor. A protective conductor providing equipotential bonding.

Circuit protective conductor. A protective conductor connecting exposed conductive parts of equipment to the main earthing terminal.

Current-carrying capacity of a conductor. The maximum current which can be carried by a conductor under specified conditions without its steady state temperature exceeding a specified value.

Danger. Danger to persons (and livestock where present) from:
 (i) fire, electric shock, and burns arising from the use of electrical energy, and
 (ii) mechanical movement of electrically actuated equipment, in so far as such danger is intended to be prevented by electrical emergency switching or by electrical switching for mechanical maintenance of non-electrical parts of such equipment.

Direct contact. Contact of persons or livestock with live parts which may result in electric shock.

Earth. The conductive mass of the Earth, whose electric potential at any point is conventionally taken as zero.

Earthing conductor. A protective conductor connecting a main earthing terminal of a installation to an earth electrode or to other means of earthing.

Electrical installation *(abbr: Installation)*. An assembly of associated electrical equipment to fulfil a specific purpose and having certain co-ordinated characteristics.

Emergency switching. Rapid cutting off of electrical energy to remove any hazard to persons, livestock, or property which may occur unexpectedly.

Equipotential bonding. Electrical connection putting various exposed conductive parts and extraneous conductive parts at a substantially equal potential.

Exposed conductive part. A conductive part of equipment which can be touched and which is not a live part but which may become live under fault conditions.

External influence. Any influence external to an electrical installation which affects the design and safe operation of that installation.

Extraneous conductive part. A conductive part liable to introduce a potential generally earth potential and not forming part of the electrical installation.

Functional earthing. Connection to earth necessary for proper functioning of electrical equipment.

Gas installation pipe. Any pipe, not being a service pipe (other than any part of a service pipe comprised in a primary meter installation) or a pipe comprised in a gas appliance, for conveying gas for a particular consumer and any associated valve or other gas fitting.

Indirect contact. Contact of persons or livestock with exposed conductive parts made live by a fault and which may result in electrical shock.

Isolation. Cutting off an electrical installation, a circuit, or an item of equipment from every source of electrical energy.

Live part. A conductor or conductive part intended to be energised in normal use including a neutral conductor but, by convention, not a PEN conductor.

Mechanical maintenance. The replacement, refurbishment or cleaning of lamps and non-electrical parts of equipment, plant and machinery.

Obstacle. A part preventing unintentional contact with live parts but not preventing deliberate contact.

Origin of an installation. The position at which electrical energy is delivered to an installation.

Overcurrent. A current exceeding the rated value. For conductors the rated value is the current-carrying capacity.

Overcurrent detection. A method of establishing that the value of current in a circuit exceeds a predetermined value for a specified length of time.

Overload current. An overcurrent occurring in a circuit which is electrically sound.

PEN conductor. A conductor combining the functions of both protective conductor and neutral conductor.

Protective conductor. A conductor used for some measures of protection against electric shock and intended for connecting together any of the following parts:
– exposed conductive parts,
– extraneous conductive parts,
– the main earthing terminal,
– earth electrode(s),
– the earthed point of the source, or an artificial neutral.

Residual current device. A mechanical switching device or association of devices intended to cause the opening of the contacts when the residual current attains a given value under specified conditions.

Residual operating current. Residual current which causes the residual current device to operate under specified conditions.

Simultaneously accessible parts. Conductors or conductive parts which can be touched simultaneously by a person or, where applicable, by livestock.
Notes – 1. Simultaneously accessible parts may be: live parts; exposed conductive parts; extraneous conductive parts; protective conductors; earth electrodes. 2. This term applies for livestock in locations specifically intended for these animals.

Switch. A mechanical switching device capable of making, carrying and breaking current under normal circuit conditions, which may include specified operating overload conditions, and also of carrying for a specified time currents under specified abnormal circuit conditions such as those of short circuit.
Note – A switch may also be capable of making, but not breaking, short circuit currents.

System. An electrical system consisting of a single source of electrical energy and an installation. For certain purposes of these Regulations, types of system are identified as follows, depending upon the relationship of the source, and of exposed conductive parts of the installation, to Earth:
– *TN system,* a system having one or more points of the source of energy directly earthed, the exposed conductive parts of the installation being connected to that point by protective conductors. Three types of TN systems are recognised as follows:
– *TN-C system,* in which neutral and protective functions are combined in a single conductor throughout the system.
– *TN-S system,* having separate neutral and protective conductors throughout the system.
– *TN-C-S system,* in which neutral and protective functions are combined in a single conductor in part of the system.
– *TT system,* a system having one point of the source of energy directly earthed, the exposed conductive parts of the installation being connected to earth electrodes electrically independent of the earth electrodes of the source.
– *IT system,* a system having no direct connection between live parts and Earth, the exposed conductive parts of the electrical installation being earthed.

Principles 3

Assessment of general characteristics

Those general characteristics of the energy source and the associated electrical installation which are required to be assessed are shown in Schedule 7.

Schedule 7 – Assessment of installation characteristics

(Regulation 300-1)

Characteristic (Regulation Number)	Notes and references
Purpose of the installation, its general structure and nature of supply *(311-1 to 314-4)*	Involves: maximum demand; diversity; live conductors; earthing, circuit arrangements; supply source (see Schedule 8). Consider possible installation growth when assessing maximum demand and diversity.
External influences; environmental conditions; building's use; building construction	A Chapter has been reserved in the 15th edition for future use but classification of external influences is given in Practice 1, Annex 3)
Compatibility of installed equipment with other services and the supply *(331-1)*	See Schedule 9
Maintenance of installation: frequency and quality *(341-1)*	Involves consultation with manufacturers of equipment and the maintenance staff to decide frequency and quality of maintenance operations.

Purposes, supplies and structure *(Regulations 311-1 to 314-4)*

Schedule 8 sets out the requirements of the Regulations which serve as a check list of the relevant factors to be assessed in respect of the installation's purpose, its supplies and its structure.

Schedule 8 – Purpose of installation, its structure and electricity supplies thereto (*Regulations 311-1, 311-2, 312-1 to 312-3, 313-1, 313-2, 314-1 to 314-4*)

Requirement	Notes and ASEE Comment
Assess maximum demand (amperes). Take account of diversity	For information on maximum demand and guidance on diversity, see Practice 5. Diversity factor need not be applied and in any event that factor should be applied cautiously.
Settle method of protection by assessing number and types of live conductors of energy source and installation circuits. Determine type of earthing arrangements	Supply undertakings normally provide energy through TN-S system or TN-C system (protective multiple earthing). See Figures 7.2 to 7.5 Practice 7. See Practice 2 for protection methods.
Ascertain or determine public supply (or private source) characteristics: (i) nominal (designated) voltage (see Schedule 2) (ii) frequency and current (iii) prospective short circuit current at installation origin (iv) type and rating of overcurrent device at installation origin (v) supply suitability for installation including maximum demand (vi) external earth loop impedance	The supply authority should be consulted to determine: prospective short circuit current at the origin of installation; suitability of supply for the proposed installation (including maximum demand); the value of external loop impedance. In latter connection Engineering Recommendation P23 (Electricity Council) gives typical earth fault loop impedance as follows: Protective Multiple Earthing (PME) terminal – 0.35ohm Protective Neutral Bonding (PNB) Earthing terminal – 0.35ohm Cable sheath/Earthing Wire Terminal – 0.8ohm No earthing terminal provided (PME distributor) – 21ohm* Electricity Boards normally design their distribution system to a maximum short circuit level and that maximum is 16kA for domestic installations. Further guidance on the determination of prospective fault current will be found in Practice 6.
Assess characteristics of any safety or standby supplies which must be adequately rated, have appropriate changeover time and have adequate capacity and reliability for purpose. If in parallel with public supply, consult supply undertaking as to switching arrangements.	See British Standard Code of Practice BS5266 (Emergency Lighting of Premises) and BS5829 (Fire Alarm Systems).
Divide circuits into manageable parts so as to: (i) avoid danger and minimise inconvenience in event of faults (ii) facilitate safe operation, inspection, testing and maintenance	Use more than one final sub-circuit for lighting installation. Keep power circuits separate, eg separate ways on distribution boards. See also Practice 6 on discrimination between protective devices. Practice 5 gives details of standard circuit arrangements.

Schedule 8 – Purpose of installation, its structure and electricity supplies thereto (*Regulations 311-1, 311-2, 312-1 to 312-3, 313-1, 313-2, 314-1 to 314-4*) – *continued*

Requirement	Notes and ASEE Comment
For separate control purposes of parts of installation, provide separate circuits to ensure they are unaffected when other circuits fail.	For example staircase lighting should be controlled separately. The supply to each floor of a building should be separately controlled and further sub-division may be necessary, for example corridor lighting ought to be supplied from a circuit originating at a separate way of a fuseboard.
Determine number of final circuits. Take account of: overcurrent protection; isolating and switching; conductor current carrying capacity; final circuits.	See Practice 6 See Practice 8 See Practice 3 See Practice 5 Alternative final circuit arrangements can be specified by qualified electrical engineer.
Connect each final circuit to a separate way of a distribution board. Electrically separate final circuits to prevent energising one intended to be isolated.	Separate neutral conductors are required for each final circuit. See also Practice 1, Practice 5 and Practice 7 for guidance on mutual detrimental influences and segregation of circuits.

* This value consists of resistance of neutral to earth, plus impedance of the transformer winding and line conductor, but does not include the resistance of the consumer's earth electrode.

External influences

No Chapter on external influences appear in the 15th edition as yet. Chapter 32 in that publication has been reserved for future use. Practice 1, Annex 3 gives guidance on external influences.

The "Environmental Conditions" sections of Practice 3 and Practice 4 may also be relevant.

Compatibility *(Regulation 331-1)*

The Regulations call for an assessment to be made of equipment electrical characteristics likely to impinge harmfully upon other equipment or services or the supply. Some examples are shown in Schedule 9.

Maintainability *(Regulation 341-1)*

Regulation 341-1 requires that an assessment shall be made of the likely frequency of maintenance activity, and its quality, during an installation's intended life. The requirements of the Regulations have to be applied in taking account of the expected maintenance frequency and its quality. Thus an installation should be designed so that throughout its life:

(a) it is possible to carry out readily and safely such operations as periodic inspection, testing, maintenance and repair.

(b) safety protective measures remain effective, and

(c) equipment reliability is appropriate. In the latter connection, it may be necessary to organise for the periodic replacement of equipment.

Attention is also drawn to the need to arrange equipment so that it is accessible for maintenance (further guidance on accessibility of equipment for maintance is given in Practice 9) and to the need to provide appropriate isolators and switches so that electrical and mechanical maintenance can be under taken safely (see Practice 8).

Factors which will influence the design of an installation for maintainability will include the extent to which maintenance is a discipline operated within the environment of that installation, eg there is little electrical maintenance exercised within domestic premises and the extent to which it is practised within commercial and industrial premises is variable.

Supplies for safety services *(Regulations 351-1 and 352-1)*

A storage battery, or a primary cell, or an independent generator set, or an independent separate feeder is recognised as being a safety service source. These may be classified as either automatic or non-automatic and automatic sources of safety supplies may be of the 'no-break' type or the time-delay type. Attention is drawn to the need to establish whether any statutory authority regulates the requirements for safety services in the specialist area in which that authority operates. For example, where an electrical safety service is required in a situation administered by the Petroleum Acts, regard must be had to specifications of the local licensing authority. Likewise in cinemas and places of public entertainment, regard must similarly be given to statutory requirements. Where an independent feeder, which is distinct and separate from the normal feeder, is used as the source of a safety service, there is a need to make an assessment as to whether both feeders are likely to go out of service at the same time.

Practice 1 (Regulations 561-1 to 566-1) sets out in more detail the special requirements for safety sources.

Schedule 9 Equipment characteristics: assessment of compatibility

(Regulation 331-1)

Assessment required of	Notes and references
Transient overvoltages	An overvoltage can occur in a circuit either directly, eg too high a setting on a transformer tapping, etc, or by induction from another circuit. A transient voltage can cause damage through electrical breakdown or from poor regulation of a generator.
Rapidly fluctuating loads	Lifts and welding machines give rise to fluctuating loads
Starting currents	Large motor installations can give rise to heavy starting current
Harmonic circuits	Fluorescent lighting loads and thyristor drives together with convertor equipment and some household electrical appliances and equipment (with or without electronic control devices) can introduce harmonics of the supply frequency into the systems to which they are connected. If a balanced multiphase load takes a current with a significant harmonic content, then current will flow in the neutral conductor. In this event the neutral conductor is required to have an adequate cross sectional area. For further information on harmonics see: *Limits for harmonics in the UK electricity supply system* (ERG 5/3 and ACE 73) – Electricity Council. *Harmonic distortion caused by convertor equipment* (ACE 15) – Electricity Council. *Disturbances in supply systems caused by household appliances and similar electrical equipment* (555-2) – International Electrotechnical Commission.
Mutual inductance	Magnetic flux produced by one circuit can produce linkages with another circuit and become mutually coupled or have mutual inductance between them.
Feedback (dc)	Power packs and rectifier units are sources of dc feedback
High frequency oscillations	Feedback amplifiers and closed-loop automatic control systems can oscillate under certain conditions. Radio frequency heating units are also a source
Earth leakage currents	See Practice 7
Connections to Earth to provide independent clean earths (where required)	See Practice 7
Other characteristics	No detrimental influence between protective measures should be possible. Practice 3 (Section of Annex 2 dealing with protection against metal work corrosion) Practice 3 (Environmental conditions) Particular attention should be given to the several references to mutual detrimental influences contained in the Regulations.

Practice 1

General

Fundamental requirements for safety *(Regulations 13-1 to 13-6 and 13-17 to 13-18)*

It is fundamental to the IEE Regulations that good workmanship and proper materials are used.

In this general practice Section the fundamental requirements for safety stipulated in Regulations 13-1 to 13-6 and Regulations 13-17 and 13-18 are covered. The remaining fundamental requirements are dealt with elsewhere (see Schedule 6a – Principles 1).

These general requirements for safety should be met if the questions tabulated in Schedule 1.1 and Schedule 1.2 can be answered with a definite 'YES'.

If a designer or installer intends to provide an installation which meets the fundamental requirements for safety set out in Schedule 1.1 and Schedule 1.2, regard must be had to the complementary provisions contained elsewhere in the IEE Regulations and which will be covered in the various Practice sections of this publication.

Attention is drawn to the effect of the Regulations (Schedule 5 – Principles 1) concerning new materials, inventions and designs.

Selection and erection of equipment *(Regulations 510-1, 511-1)*

Regulations relating to the way in which items of equipment shall be selected and erected are outlined in Regulations 510-1 to 515-2. Because of the wide scope of those Regulations, reference will need to be made to other provisions of the Regulations. In particular the reader is referred to Practice 9 – Equipment. In Principles 3 (Schedule 8) it is made apparent that installation designers are required to assess the characteristics of the public supply. Notes on equipment operating conditions follow below.

Particular reference is made in the Regulations to the need to comply with the relevant current British Standards. If the designer specifies equipment not covered by a British Standard it is incumbent upon him to assure himself that the equipment, so specified, meets the requirement of the Regulation in question regarding the degree of safety required.

A list of British Standards and Standard Codes of Practice will be found in Annex 1 to this Section. It is pointed out, however, that reference to other British Standard publications covering the specification of suitable materials and equipment may be necessary. It should be noted that certification schemes for equipment are operated by:
British Standards Institution
British Electrotechnical Approvals Board
British Approvals Service for Electric Cables (but see Schedule 5, page 6)
Association of Short Circuit Testing Authorities.

Schedules 1.3 and 1.4 detail the requirements of the Regulations concerning equipment operating conditions.

Schedule 1.1 – Questions on general fundamental principles

(Regulations 13-2 to 13-6)

Positive answer required to all the following questions	Notes and ASEE Comment
Is all the equipment constructed, installed and protected so as to prevent danger as far as is reasonably practicable?	"Danger" – a defined term – relates to risk of injury or death to persons or livestock which might arise from the use of electricity eg shock, fire, burns or mechanical movement.
Can the equipment be maintained, inspected and tested in safety?	Sufficient space around the equipment should be provided. Provision should be made for the isolation of sub-divisions of an installation.
Are the switchgear and cables capable of handling the maximum power demanded by connected current using equipment?	Conductors should be large enough and all contacts adequate to carry out the duties required. Apart from items intended to be replaced periodically (such as fuse links and contacts) there must be no overheating or deterioration of continuous or short term rated equipment during its expected life.
Are all conductors of sufficient size and capacity for the intended load?	The rated conductor current carrying capacity may require considerable de-rating to accommodate ambient temperature conditions, temperature rise, volt-drop, power factor, type of enclosure, cable grouping, motor starting current group starting, overload current, fault current, circulating current, harmonics, frequency, mechanical strength.
Are all conductors properly insulated, protected and safely located to prevent danger?	Protected in this instance means protected from mechanical damage, from heat, from water, from corrosive chemicals etc., as well as from touch.
Are all joints and connections correctly made, of low resistance and are they properly insulated and mechanically protected?	Joints must not work loose or stretch. They must be insulated for the system voltage with conductor insulation properly protected. Conductors must not pull out of a joint, nor run hot

Schedule 1.2 – Questions on fundamental safety requirements for precautions to be taken in adverse conditions

(Regulations 13-17 and 13-18)

Positive answer required to all the following questions	Notes and ASEE Comment
Has equipment been constructed or protected to prevent danger which might occur through exposure to weather, corrosive atmosphere or other adverse conditions?	Where standard equipment is further enclosed by a second enclosure to meet adverse conditions, care should be taken to prevent condensation, restricted ventilation or cooling. See Index for other references.
Where the surroundings are at risk from fire or explosion, has electrical equipment selected, been constructed or protected, or special precautions taken, to prevent danger?	See British Standard Codes of Practice BS5345 *"Selection, installation and maintenance of electrical apparatus for use in potentially explosive atmospheres"* and CP1003 *"Electrical apparatus and associated equipment for use in explosive atmospheres of gas or vapour"*.

Schedule 1.3 – Equipment operating conditions

(Regulations 512-1 to 512-4)

Term	Operating conditions
Voltage	In the selection of equipment the installer must assure himself of the following: (1) Equipment utilised suitable for nominal voltage (rms value, a.c.) of the installation or any section of it. (2) Equipment connected between phase and neutral of an IT system (only exposed conductive parts earthed) must be insulated for nominal phase voltage. (3) Equipment which is inductive or capacitive (such as motors and fluorescent luminaries) requires switches or circuit-breakers designed to cope with that characteristic(s). (4) Equipment in some cases requires particular regard to the highest and/or lowest voltage likely to occur in service. "Equipment" is a defined term which covers all components of an electrical installation involved in generation, conversion, transmission, distribution or utilisation of electrical energy.

(continued)

Schedule 1.3 – Equipment operating conditions

(Regulations 512-1 to 512-4) – continued

Term	Operating conditions
Current	All equipment capable of meeting load (current) requirements of circuit controlled: (a) under normal conditions; (b) under abnormal conditions, as determined by the characteristics of the protective devices employed. The current carrying components used in construction of equipment, plant, etc, should take account of the intended location, ambient temperature, type of enclosure, starting current, overload, fault current, harmonics and frequency.
Frequency	All equipment selected having regard to its rated frequency which needs to be compatible with the supply frequency. Attention: some equipment is particularly "frequency sensitive".
Power	Equipment selected having regard to its power characteristics and account taken of load factor and operating conditions of the installation or system.

Schedule 1.4 – Equipment operating conditions, other influences

(Regulations 512-5, 512-6, 515-1 and 515-2)

Term	Operating conditions
Compatibility	Equipment must be selected and installed so that failure of a component will not have harmful effects on other parts of the installation or impair the supply under normal operating conditions.
External influences	Only equipment suitable for the situation or environment in which installed to be used. In this connection see Principles 3 and the Annexures hereto, listing statutory memorands and classification of external influences.
Mutual detrimental influence	At design stage consideration to be given to possible mutually detrimental effects between electrical equipment and equipment of a non-electrical nature: for example position of gas, water, oil, telephone, bulk liquid storage tanks should be taken into account and the effect of a hot, dusty, damp or corrosive environment to be taken into consideration. When equipment having different voltages and different types of current is grouped, care must be taken that one has no adverse affect on other.

Supplies for safety services *(Regulations 561-1 to 561-3, 562-1 to 562-3, 563-1 to 563-5, 564-1, 565-1 to 565-2 and 566-1)*

The source of supply for a safety service must be chosen so that the service is maintained for an adequate duration. Statutory Authorities and other similar bodies give guidance on the duration of certain systems, (e.g. emergency lighting, fire alarm systems etc). Fire alarm battery systems are required to be protected and enclosed in fire resistant compartments. Preferred systems are those which give an audible and visible indication of a first fault.

The Regulations require that all equipment powering a safety system is permanently fixed in a location, accessible only by skilled staff and installed in such a manner that it will remain operational on failure of the normal supply. If a single source of energy is provided for a safety service, the Regulations do not permit this source of energy to be used for any other purpose. In the event of more than one source of energy being available, and provided that on failure of one or more sources the remaining sources have sufficient capacity to meet the full operating requirements of the safety system, dedicated safety sources are not required.

The foregoing arrangement generally entails providing facilities for automatic shedding of non-essential services.

If the equipment is powered by self-contained batteries the above requirement in respect of location, accessibility and dedicated service do not apply.

All safety services circuit wiring shall be kept separate from all other circuits, and are not permitted to be installed in locations having a fire risk, unless the wiring systems are of the fire resistant type. To avoid using fire resistant materials the alternative is to route the circuit wiring away from fire risk areas.

Overcurrent protective devices shall be provided and installed such that an overcurrent in one circuit will not affect the satisfactory operation of the remaining circuits in the system.

Switch and control gear shall be labelled and installed in locations accessible to skilled staff. All Alarm devices shall be clearly identified.

If two different circuits supply one piece of equipment, neither the electric shock protection provided, nor the safe operation of the other circuit, shall be affected by a fault in one circuit. This type of equipment should be bonded to the protective conductors of the two circuits which supply it.

In all cases when dealing with supplies for safety services the special requirements for parallel and non-parallel operation shall be observed. The requirements for protection against short circuit and indirect contact must also be met.

Annex 1 to Practice 1. Publications of the British Standards Institution *(IEE Appendix 1)*

Note: After 1975 the prefix BS replaced the prefix CP for Codes of Practice

Subject	Application	Number
ACCESSORIES, Electrical	General requirements	5733
ALARM SYSTEMS,	Fire detection and, alarm systems in buildings	5839
BINDING AND IDENTIFICATION SLEEVES	for use on electric cables and wires	3858
BOXES	for the enclosure of electrical accessories	4662
BROADCASTING,	Reception of sound and television	BS6330
CABLES	Armoured with thermo-setting insulation	5467
	Elastomer insulated flexible trailing types for quarries and miscellaneous mines	6116
	Impregnated paper-insulated with aluminium sheath/neutral conductor and three shaped solid aluminium phase conductors (CONSAC) 500/1000V, for electricity supply	5593
	Impregnated paper-insulated for electricity supply	6480
	Insulated flexible cables for lifts and for other flexible connections	6977
	Mineral insulated	6207
	PVC-insulated split concentric types with copper conductors for electricity supply	4553
	PVC-insulated and elastomer-insulated types for electric signs and high voltage luminous discharge-tube installations	5055
	PVC-insulated (non armoured), for power and lighting	6004
	PVC-insulated for switchgear and controlgear wiring	6231
	PVC-insulated for electricity supply	6346
	Rubber-insulated for power and lighting	6007
	Covers for, concrete and earthenware	2484
CEILING ROSES	Ceiling roses	67
CIRCUIT BREAKERS	Miniature and moulded case types	3871
	Residual current operated type	4293

Subject	Application	Number
FLEXIBLE CORDS	Insulated	6500
FLOOR WARMING	Systems, electric, for use with off peak and similar electrical supplies	CP1018
FUSES	Cartridge type for voltages up to 1000V a.c. and 1500V d.c.	88
	Cartridge fuse links, (rated at up to 5 amps) for a.c. and d.c. service	646
	Cartridge, for a.c. circuits in domestic and similar premises	1361
	Cartridge, general purpose fuse links for domestic and similar purposes (primarily for use in plugs)	1362
	Semi-enclosed, (ratings up to 100 amps and 240V to earth)	3036
GLANDS,	Mechanical, for rubber and plastics insulated cables	4121
	Mechanical, for elastomer and plastics insulated cables	6121
HEATING, ELECTRIC SURFACE	Equipment and its design and installation	6351
INDICATOR LIGHTS,	Colours for, pushbuttons, annunciators and digital readouts	4099
JOINTS PERFORMANCE OF,	Mechanical and compression joints in electric cable and wire connectors	4579
LAMPHOLDERS,	Lampholders, general	5042
LIFTS,	including service lifts	5655
LIGHTFITTINGS,	(see Luminaires)	
LIGHTING	Emergency	5266
LIGHTNING,	Protection of structures against	BS6651
LUMINAIRES,		4533
MACHINES,	Rotating, electrical, of particular types or for particular applications	5000
MOTOR STARTERS,	for voltages up to and including 1000V a.c. and 1200V d.c.	4941
PIPELINES	Identification of	1710

Annex 2 to Practice 1. Legislation and related guidance documents relevant to electrical installations *(IEE Appendix 2)*.

The Schedules below list those principal statutory regulations which are applicable to certain electrical installations in Great Britain. For further information, reference should be made to the appropriate administrative authority. The listing is not exhaustive and it should be borne in mind that some other legislation which relates to particular activity or environments, contains provisions relating to electrical installations. The documents referred to in the Schedule can be obtained from H.M. Stationery Office with the exception of those relating to Protective Multiple Earthing.

Class of installation	Title of Regulations and other related references	Administrative or legislative authority
Agricultural and Horticultural	Agriculture (Stationary Machinery) Regulations 1959	Health and Safety Commission
Buildings generally (Scotland only) subject to some exemptions	Building Standards (Scotland) Regulations with Amendment Regulation 1971-1980. See also Explanatory Memoranda on the above Regulations (1980)	Secretary of State for Scotland
Cinematograph	Cinematograph Regulations of the Cinematograph Acts 1909 and 1952	Home Office and Secretary of State for Scotland
Coal mines and stratified ironstone, shale or fireclay	Coal and Other Mines (Electricity) Regulations 1956	Health and Safety Commission
Factories, construction sites, non domestic caravans i.e. mobile workshops etc.	Electricity (Factory Act) Special Regulations 1908 and 1944. See also Memorandum by Senior Inspector of Factories on the above Regulations (SHW 928)	Health and Safety Commission
General, subject to exemptions	Electricity Supply Regulation 1937. See also Explanatory Notes on these Regulations, 1937	Secretary of State for Energy. Secretary of State for Scotland
Metaliferous Mines	Miscellaneous Mines (Electrical) Regulations 1956	Health and Safety Commission
Quarries	Quarries (Electrical Regulations) 1956	Health and Safety Commission
Explosive Atmospheres	The Electricity (Factories Act) Special Regulations 1908 and 1944.	Health and Safety Commission

Class of installation	Title of Regulations and other related references	Administrative or legislative authority
Explosive Atmospheres	The Highly Flammable Liquids and Liquified Petroleum Gases Regulations 1972	Health and Safety Commission
Explosive Atmospheres	The Petroleum (Consolidated) Act 1928	Local Authority Licence
Construction sites	The Construction (General Provisions) Regulations 1961	Health and Safety Commission
Equipment designed for household use	The Electrical Equipment (Safety) Regulations 1975. Electrical Equipment (Safety) (Amendment) Regulations 1976	Department of Trade and Industry
Safety signs	Safety Sign Regulations (SI 1980 No. 1471)	Health and Safety Executive

Guidance on legislation

Subject	Details	Source
Installations general, subject to exemptions	Explanatory notes on Electricity Supply Regulations 1937	H.M.S.O.
Installations of Factories, construction sites, non-domestic caravans etc.	Memorandum by H.M. Senior Electrical Inspector of Factories on the Electricity (Factories Act) Special Regulations (SHW 928)	H.M.S.O.
Buildings generally (Scotland only) subject to exemptions	Explanatory Memoranda on the Building Standards (Scotland) Amendment Regulations 1980.	H.M.S.O.
Protective Multiple Earthing	Protective Multiple Earthing Approval	Secretary of State for Energy.
Theatres and other places of public entertainment	Requirements of local licensing authority	Appropriate local authority
Caravan sites	Model Standards under Caravan Sites and Control of Development Act 1960	Department of the Environment

Annex 3 to Practice 1. Classification of external influences *(IEE Appendix 6)*

This Annex establishes the classification and codification of external influences which require assessment in the design and erection of electrical installations. (It is reproduced by kind permission of the International Electrotechnical Commission from IEC Publication 364).

Codification
   Each condition of external influence is designated by a code comprising a group of two capital letters and a number as follows:
The first letter relates to the general category of external influence
A = environment.
B = utilization.
C = construction of buildings.
The second letter relates to the nature of the external influence
A ...
B ...
C ...
The number relates to the class within each external influence
1 ...
2 ...
3 ...
   For example   the code AC2 signifies:
              A   = environment
              AC   = environment-altitude
              AC2 = environment-altitude > 2000 m
Note. – The codification is not intended to be used for marking equipment.

Code	Class designation	Characteristics	Applications and examples
	Ambient temperature		
		The ambient temperature is that of the ambient air where the equipment is to be installed	
		It is assumed that the ambient temperature includes the effects of all other equipment installed in the same location	
		The ambient temperature to be considered for the equipment is the temperature at the place where the equipment is to be installed resulting from the influence of all other equipment in the same location, when operating, not taking into account the thermal contribution of the equipment to be installed	
		Lower and upper limits of ranges of ambient temperature:	
AA1		$-60°C$ $+5°C$	
AA2		$-40°C$ $+5°C$	
AA3		$-25°C$ $+5°C$	
AA4		$-5°C$ $+40°C$	
AA5		$+5°C$ $+40°C$	
AA6		$+5°C$ $+60°C$	
		The average temperature over a 24-hour period must not exceed $5°C$ below the upper limits.	
		Combination of two ranges to define some environments may be necessary. Installations subject to temperatures outside the ranges require special consideration.	
	Atmospheric humidity		
	(Under consideration)		
	Altitude		
AC1		≤ 2000 m	
AC2		> 2000 m	

Code	Class designation	Characteristics	Applications and examples
	Presence of water		
AD1	Negligible	Probability of presence of water is negligible	Locations in which the walls do not generally show traces of water but may do so for short periods, for example in the form of vapour which good ventilation dries rapidly
AD2	Free-falling drops	Possibility of vertically falling drops	Locations in which water vapour occasionally condenses as drops or where steam may occasionally be present
AD3	Sprays	Possibility of water falling as a spray at an angle up to 60 from the vertical	Locations in which sprayed water forms a continuous film on floors and/or walls
AD4	Splashes	Possibility of splashes from any direction	Locations where equipment may be subjected to splashed water; this applies, for example, to certain external lighting fittings, construction site equipment
AD5	Jets	Possibility of jets of water from any direction	Locations where hosewater is used regularly (yards, car-washing bays)
AD6	Waves	Possibility of water waves	Seashore locations such as piers, beaches, quays, etc.
AD7	Immersion	Possibility of intermittent partial or total covering by water	Locations which may be flooded and/or where water may be at least 150 mm above the highest point of equipment, the lowest part of equipment being not more than 1 m below the water surface
AD8	Submersion	Possibility of permanent and total covering by water	Locations such as swimming pools where electrical equipment is permanently and totally covered with water under a pressure greater than 0.1 bar

Code	Class designation	Characteristics	Applications and examples
		Presence of foreign solid bodies	
AE1	Negligible	The quantity or nature of dust or foreign solid bodies is not significant	
AE2	Small objects	Presence of foreign solid bodies where the smallest dimension is not less than 2.5 mm	Tools and small objects are examples of foreign solid bodies of which the smallest dimension is at least 2.5 mm
AE3	Very small objects	Presence of foreign solid bodies where the smallest dimension is not less than 1 mm *Note:* In conditions AE2 and AE3, dust may be present but is not significant to operation of the electrical equipment.	Wires are examples of foreign solid bodies of which the smallest dimension is not less than 1 mm
AE4	Dust	Presence of dust in significant quantity	
		Presence of corrosive or polluting substances	
AF1	Negligible	The quantity or nature of corrosive or polluting substances is not significant	
AF2	Atmospheric	The presence of corrosive or polluting substances of atmospheric origin is significant	Installations situated by the sea or industrial zones producing serious atmospheric pollution, such as chemical works, cement works; this type of pollution arises especially in the production of abrasive, insulating or conductive dusts
AF3	Intermittent or accidental	Intermittent or accidental subjection to corrosive or polluting chemical substances being used or produced	Locations where some chemical products are handled in small quantities and where these products may come only accidentally into contact with electrical equipment; such conditions are found in factory laboratories, other laboratories or in locations where hydrocarbons are used (boiler-rooms, garages, etc.)
AF4	Continuous	Continuously subject to corrosive or polluting chemical substances in substantial quantity	For example, chemical works

Code	Class designation	Characteristics	Applications and examples
	Mechanical stresses		
	Impact		
AG1	Low severity	*Note:* Provisional classification. Quantitative expression of impact severities is under consideration.	Household and similar conditions
AG2	Medium severity		Usual industrial conditions
AG3	High severity		Severe industrial conditions
	Vibration		
AH1	Low severity	*Note:* Provisional classification. Quantitative expression of vibration severities is under consideration.	Household and similar conditions where the effects of vibration are generally negligible
AH2	Medium severity		Usual industrial conditions
AH3	High severity		Industrial installations subject to severe conditions
	Other mechanical stresses		
AJ	(Under consideration)		
	Presence of flora and/or mould growth		
AK1	No hazard	No harmful hazard of flora and/or mould growth	
AK2	Hazard	Harmful hazard of flora and/or mould growth	The hazard depends on local conditions and the nature of flora. Distinction should be made between harmful growth of vegetation or conditions for promotion of mould growth
	Presence of fauna		
AL1	No hazard	No harmful hazard from fauna	
AL2	Hazard	Harmful hazard from fauna (insects, birds, small animals)	The hazard depends on the nature of the fauna. Distinction should be made between: – presence of insects in harmful quantity or of an aggressive nature – presence of small animals or birds in harmful quantity or of an aggressive nature

Code	Class designation	Characteristics	Applications and examples
Electromagnetic, electrostatic or ionizing influences			
AM1	Negligible	No harmful effects from stray currents, electromagnetic radiation, electrostatic fields, ionizing radiation or induction	
AM2	Stray currents	Harmful hazards of stray currents	
AM3	Electro-magnetics	Harmful presence of electro-magnetic radiation	
AM4	Ionization	Harmful presence of ionizing radiation	
AM5	Electrostatics	Harmful presence of electrostatic fields	
AM6	Induction	Harmful presence of induced currents	
Solar radiation			
AN1	Negligible	–	
AN2	Significant	Solar radiation of harmful intensity and/or duration	
Seismic effects			
AP1	Negligible	≤ 30 Gal	$1\ \text{Gal} = 1\ \text{cm/s}^2$
AP2	Low severity	$30 < \text{Gal} \leq 300$	
AP3	Medium severity	$300 < \text{Gal} \leq 600$	
AP4	High severity	> 600 Gal	
			Vibration which may cause the destruction of the building is outside the classification
			Frequency is not taken into account in the classification; however, the seismic wave resonates with the building, seismic effects must be specially considered. In general the frequency of seismic acceleration is between 0 and 10 Hz

Code	Class designation	Characteristics	Applications and examples
	Lightning		
AQ1	Negligible	–	
AQ2	Indirect exposure	Hazard from supply arrangements	Installations supplied by overhead lines
AQ3	Direct exposure	Hazard from exposure of equipment	Parts of installations located outside buildings
			The risks AQ2 and AQ3 relate to regions with a particularly high level of thunderstorm activity
	Wind		
AR-	(Under consideration)		
	Capability of persons		
BA1	Ordinary	Uninstructed persons	
BA2	Children	Children in locations intended for their occupation	Nurseries
		Note: This class does not necessarily apply to family dwellings.	
BA3	Handicapped	Persons not in command of all their physical and intellectual abilities (sick persons, old persons)	Hospitals
BA4	Instructed	Persons adequately advised or supervised by skilled persons to enable them to avoid dangers which electricity may create (operating and maintenance staff)	Electrical operating areas
BA5	Skilled	Persons with technical knowledge or sufficient experience to enable them to avoid dangers which electricity may create (engineers and technicians)	Closed electrical operating areas

Code	Class designation	Characteristics	Applications and examples
		Electrical resistance of the human body	
BB	Classification under consideration		
		Contact of persons with earth potential	
BC1	None	Persons in non-conducting situations	Non-conducting locations
BC2	Low	Persons do not in usual conditions make contact with extraneous conductive parts or stand on conducting surfaces	
BC3	Frequent	Persons are frequently in touch with extraneous conductive parts or stand on conducting surfaces	Locations with extraneous conductive parts, either numerous or of large area
BC4	Continuous	Persons are in permanent contact with metallic surroundings and for whom the possibility of interrupting contact is limited	Metallic surroundings such as boilers and tanks
		Conditions of evacuation in an emergency	
BD1		Low density occupation, easy conditions of evacuation	Buildings of normal or low height used for habitation
BD2		Low density occupation, difficult conditions of evacuation	High-rise buildings
BD3		High density occupation, easy conditions of evacuation	Locations open to the public (theatres, cinemas, department stores, etc.)
BD4		High density occupation, difficult conditions of evacuation	High-rise buildings open to the public (hotels, hospitals, etc.)
		Nature of processed or stored materials	
BE1	No significant risks	–	–
BE2	Fire risks	Manufacture, processing or storage of flammable materials including presence of dust	Barns, wood-working shops, paper factories

Code	Class designation	Characteristics	Applications and examples
BE3	Explosion risks	Processing or storage of explosive or low-flashpoint materials including presence of explosive dusts	Oil refineries, hydrocarbon stores
BE4	Contamination risks	Presence of unprotected foodstuffs, pharmaceutics, and similar products without protection	Foodstuff industries, kitchens
	Constructional materials		
CA1	Non-combustible	–	–
CA2	Combustible	Buildings mainly constructed of combustible materials	Wooden buildings
	Building design		
CB1	Negligible risks	–	–
CB2	Propagation of fire	Buildings of which the shape and dimensions facilitate the spread of fire (e.g. chimney effects)	High-rise buildings. Forced ventilation systems
CB3	Movement	Risks due to structural movement (e.g. displacement between different parts of a building or between a building and the ground, or settlement of ground or building foundations)	Buldings of considerable length or erected on unstable ground
CB4	Flexible or unstable	Structures which are weak or subject to movement (e.g. oscillation)	Tents, air-support structures, false ceilings, removable partitions

Practice 2

Protection against electric shock

Regulations for protective measures for safety can be applied to a complete installation, a section of an installation, or to a piece of equipment. No relative merit of any one measure can be implied from the order in which they appear in this section.

The application of protection against electric shock shall be by one of the following:

Direct and indirect contact. A measure specified herein which combines protection in day to day service (direct contact) and protection in the event of a fault (indirect contact); or

Direct contact. A measure specified herein for protection against direct contact; and/or

Indirect contact. A measure specified herein for protection against indirect contact.

The chart given in Figure 2.1 sets out these three main methods and their subdivisions. The chart also indicates the special provisions and exemptions which are applicable, shows the reduced voltage system which is an alternative to safety extra low voltage and the special measures required for particular locations which are covered in Practice 2A.

(1) Protection against both direct and indirect contact

One (or more) of the following measures must be used to provide protection against direct and indirect contact:
(1A)   Safety extra low voltage (SELV)
(1B)   Functional extra low voltage
(1C)   Limitation of discharge of energy

(1A)   Protection by safety extra low voltage (*Regulations 411-2 to 411-10 and 471-2 and 471-3*)

To achieve protection by safety extra low voltage the circuit nominal voltage must not exceed 50V a.c. or 120V d.c. between conductors or from conductors to earth. In circumstances where live parts can be uninsulated (or accessible) this voltage must not exceed 25V rms a.c. or 60V d.c. This applies only to normal body resistance. See Figure 2.2.

In humid and/or hot environments where body resistance can be expected to be low the nominal voltage should be reduced. In addition, the requirements set out in Schedules 2.2 and 2.3 (Safety sources), Schedule 2.1 (circuits) and Schedule 2.4 (plugs and sockets) have to be met.

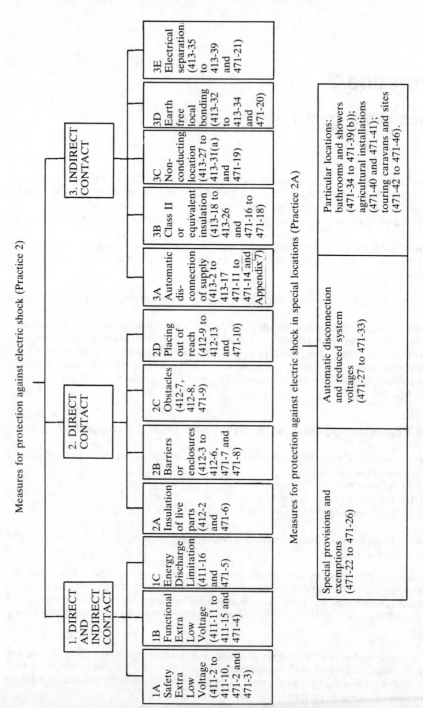

Figure 2.1 The several measures which can be applied for protection against electric shock (direct and indirect contact).

Measures for protection against electric shock (Practice 2)

1. DIRECT AND INDIRECT CONTACT

1A Safety Extra Low Voltage (411-2 to 411-10, 471-2 and 471-3)

1B Functional Extra Low Voltage (411-11 to 411-15 and 471-4)

1C Energy Discharge Limitation (411-16 and 471-5)

2. DIRECT CONTACT

2A Insulation of live parts (412-2 and 471-6)

2B Barriers or enclosures (412-3 to 412-6, 471-7 and 471-8)

2C Obstacles (412-7, 412-8, 471-9)

2D Placing out of reach (412-9 to 412-13 and 471-10)

3. INDIRECT CONTACT

3A Automatic disconnection of supply (413-2 to 413-17 471-11 to 471-14 and Appendix 7)

3B Class II or equivalent insulation (413-18 to 413-26 and 471-16 to 471-18)

3C Non-conducting location (413-27 to 413-31(a) and 471-19)

3D Earth free local bonding (413-32 to 413-34 and 471-20)

3E Electrical separation (413-35 to 413-39 and 471-21)

Measures for protection against electric shock in special locations (Practice 2A)

Special provisions and exemptions (471-22 to 471-26)

Automatic disconnection and reduced system voltages (471-27 to 471-33)

Particular locations: bathrooms and showers (471-34 to 471-39(b)); agricultural installations (471-40 and 471-41); touring caravans and sites (471-42 to 471-46).

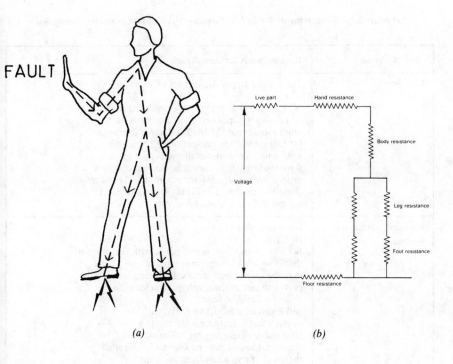

FAULT

(a) *(b)*

Figure 2.2 *(a)* *Normal body resistance is that between one hand and both feet with skin moist but not wet* *(b)* *Equivalent circuit showing earth path.*

Schedule 2.1 – Requirements for SELV circuits – circuit arrangements

Part of circuit	Requirements for compliance
Safety source	(i) If nominal voltage is greater or equal to 25V rms a.c. or 60V d.c. ripple free – protection against direct contact should be provided by IP2X barriers or enclosures or by insulation to withstand a 500V test for 1 minute. (ii) If the nominal voltage is less than 25V rms a.c. protection against direct contact is not required (iii) The limit of 25V rms a.c. (60V d.c.) is to be reduced where body resistance is below normal in damp or confined conductive situations for instance, or where animals are present (iv) Various sources of safety extra low voltage are shown in Schedules 2.2 and 2.3

(continued)

Part of circuit	Requirements for compliance
Live Parts	There must be no connection to: (i) Earth (ii) Live parts or protective conductors must be physically separated from live parts of other circuits, or, SELV conductors insulated for highest voltage present or SELV circuit conductors are non-metallic sheathed or separated by earthed metallic screen or sheath or in a multicore cable etc when SELV conductors should be insulated individually or collectively for the highest voltage present.
Exposed conductive parts	No connection to: (i) Earth (ii) Extraneous conductive parts, with the proviso that if such a connection is inherent, it must be established that such extraneous parts can not attain a voltage greater than that of a SELV circuit. (iii) Exposed conductive parts, with the proviso that if fortuitous contact is at all possible, measures for the protection should no longer depend on SELV and shall therefore, be in accordance with the measures applicable to the exposed conductive parts of the other circuit.
Electrical separation	Extra low voltage cables must have insulation adequate for these circuits. If necessary further protection to prevent danger should be provided. Separation must be equal to that between input and output winding of a safety isolating transformer. The requirements for a maximum volt drop 2½% do not apply to these circuits but the current carrying capacity of the ELV cables to be equal to or greater than that required by the load supplied. The associated volt drop must be within limits which ensure satisfactory operation of the appliance etc. connected to the SELV circuit.

Schedule 2.2 – Safety sources for SELV circuits
Primary supply at a voltage greater than extra low voltage

Equipment	Installation	Requirement
Class II safety isolating transformer to BS 3535		Secondary winding to be earth free and voltage less than or equal to 25V rms a.c. (60V d.c.) for protection against direct contact, unless live parts in IP2X enclosure or insulated for 500V test. See Schedule 2.1
Motor generator set or other source	 M Motor G Generator a.c. or d.c.	Giving isolation between output and input equal to BS 3535 transformer
Electronic device	 Electronic device Circuit output less than ELV	Protection ensures that output voltage cannot exceed ELV in event of internal faults

Schedule 2.3 – Safety sources for SELV circuits
Supply from source of energy independent of any higher voltage circuit

Equipment	Installation	Requirement
Electrochemical source	 + – BATTERY	For example battery or a solar cell etc.
Source driven by prime mover	 AC or DC DIESEL G	For example a diesel generator or air motor generator 25V rms a.c. (60V d.c.) or less.

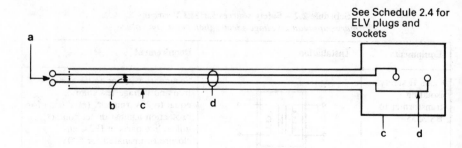

See Schedule 2.4 for ELV plugs and sockets

*Figure 2.3   Requirements for safety extra low voltage circuits (SELV) – also see FELV below –
(a) Safety source (b) live parts (c) exposed conductive parts (d) separated electrically.*

(1B) Functional extra-low voltage systems (FELV) *(Regulations 411-11 to 411-15 and 471-4)*

If for operational reasons it is not possible to meet all the requirements of safety extra low voltage systems (SELV), for instance if the secondary winding of the extra low voltage transformer to BS 3535 is earthed or if metal conduit is used to provide mechanical protection for the conductors, the system becomes a functional extra low voltage system (FELV).

Additional protection against direct contact will need to be provided by enclosures which protect at least to IP2X or insulation capable of withstanding the minimum test voltage of the primary circuit (500V rms ac). This system will also be deemed to protect against indirect contact.

The same limitations on voltage (50V rms ac 120 V dc) apply to the secondary circuit systems; 25V rms ac where other than dry conditions prevail.

Functional extra low voltage is chosen when it is necessary to meet the requirements of the equipment being used, such as exposed conductive parts, or the insulation of transformers etc. which have insulation insufficient to meet the requirements of SELV circuits, for example door bell installations. Factory built equipment can be installed in a FELV circuit provided that all accessible insulation of the equipment which is below the standard required is reinforced during erection to withstand 1500V rms ac for one minute.

If the primary circuit of a FELV source is protected by automatic disconnection (fuse or circuit breaker) then exposed conductive parts of the equipment in the FELV circuit should be connected to the protective conductor (earth bond) of the primary circuit, i.e. where the FELV source is not a safety source and there is a possibility of the primary source voltage affecting the functional extra low voltage circuit.

The requirement that socket outlets on FELV circuits must not accept plugs to be used on circuits of a different voltage in the same building also applies (see Schedule 2.4).

Schedule 2.4 – Plugs and sockets for ELV circuits

Equipment	Installation	Requirement
Sockets		Plugs from other voltage systems in use in the same premises shall be excluded from use in SELV socket Protective conductors shall not be provided except as detailed below
Plugs		Shall not be able to enter socket outlets of other voltage systems in use in the same premises.
Sockets and plugs for particular compliance	Where protective conductor required	Two pin plugs and sockets must be connected to equipment having Class II insulation with double or reinforced insulation or a factory built assembly having total insulation to BS5486 or supplementary or reinforced insulation as a process of its erection. Where Class II insulation is not provided a protective conductor is required. Such socket must not receive a plug from another voltage system and such a plug must be excluded from socket outlets of other voltage systems.

(1C) Protection by limitation of discharge of energy *(Regulations 411-16 and 471-5)*

Protection against electric shock can also be achieved by using equipment complying with appropriate British Standard specification which incorporates a means of limiting the current which can pass through a person (or livestock) to a value lower than the shock current (e.g. electric fences supplied from a controller complying with BS 2632. (If such equipment serves an external installation, this is covered also if provided for by the British Standard). Circuits relying on this measure shall be electrically separated from other circuits in a manner similar to the separation required for SELV circuits.

Safety measures shall be applied to British Standard equipment which limits shock current to a safe value by incorporating a suitable safety device. (See Figure 2.4).

(2) Protection against direct contact *(Regulations 412-1 to 412-13 and 471-6 to 471-10)*

There are four methods by which protection against direct contact can be provided. It is unlikely that in any installation, only one of these methods will be sufficient. Provision of at least two of the forms of protection will be necessary. One of the methods used must, however, give full protection irrespective of that given by any other method. Partial protection by two methods will not be deemed to comply with the requirements of the Regulations. The four methods are detailed in 2A, 2B, 2C, and 2D which follow.

(2A) Protection by insulation of live parts

The live parts of an installation must be protected by durable and irremovable insulation which is able to withstand any stresses to which it may be subjected in service e.g.: electrical, mechanical, thermal or chemical. Electric cables are an example. As in the case of FELV circuits (see earlier text) where insulation must be tested by the same methods applied to factory built assemblies to BS5486, Part 1. Paints, varnishes and lacquers are not, in themselves, considered to provide the degree of insulation required for this type of protection.

(2B) Protection by barriers or enclosures

This protection is provided by means of insulated boxes, conduit, switchgear enclosure, etc., see Figure 2.5 (a). Where a fuseboard is not of the fully protected type to BS5486 Part 2, it may be necessary to put a barrier internally to prevent accidental contact with live parts. In all these instances access to the enclosure, or removal of a barrier, must depend upon the use of a key or tool such as a screwdriver. In the case of the fuseboard with an additional barrier internally, the use of a tool or key to open the enclosure is unnecessary.

Where livestock is present enclosures or barriers must be provided to prevent their contact with live parts. (See requirements for SELV circuits). The protection provided for protection by barriers or enclosures should be IP2X unless there are substantial reasons (e.g. access to equipment for proper function) for apertures to be larger. Schedule 2.5 show the degrees of protection (IP Code) specified by British Standard BS5490 *"Specification for degrees of protection provided by enclosures"*.

Where access to an enclosure or barrier is from the top face, additional protection to IP4X will be necessary. All barriers and enclosures must be firmly fixed in position so that they continue to provide the protection required under normal conditions of service.

Where the Electricity (Factories Act) Special Regulations 1908 and 1944 are applicable to an installation, the requirements for this protection may be more stringent. Ceiling roses (BS67), ceiling switches (BS3676) and lampholders are exempt from this requirement.

(2C) Protection by means of obstacles

Protection of live parts in normal use can be provided by obstacles, such as a handrail around an open switchboard. These have to be firmly fixed and prevent accidental or unintentional bodily contact with live parts. The obstacle may be removable without the use of a tool or key, because this protection is provided only in areas where skilled or instructed persons under direct supervision have access. See Figure 2.5 (b)

Schedule 2.5 – Index of Protection (IP) Code

(First numeral represents degree of protection (a) of persons against live or moving parts inside enclosure and (b) of equipment against ingress of solid bodies. Second numeral represents degree of protection against ingress of liquid).

First or second number	Degree of protection issued by first number	Degree of protection indicated by second number
0	(a) No protection (b) no protection	No protection
1	(a) Protection against accidental or inadvertent contact by a large surface of the body, e.g. hand, but not against deliberate access (b) protection against ingress of large solid objects 50mm dia.	Protection against drops of water falling on enclosure shall have no harmful effect
2	(a) Protection against contact by standard finger (b) protection against ingress of medium size bodies <12mm dia. <80mm length	Drip proof: protection against drops of liquid. Drops of falling liquid shall have no harmful effect when the enclosure is tilted at any angle up to 15° from the vertical
3	(a) Protection against contact by tools, wires or such like more than 2.5mm thick (b) protection against ingress of small solid bodies	Rain proof; water falling as rain at any angle up to 60° from vertical shall have no harmful effect
4	(a) As 3 above but against contact by tools, wires or the like, more than 1.0mm thick (b) Protection against ingress of small foreign bodies	Splashproof: liquid splashed from any direction shall have no harmful effect
5	(a) Complete protection against contact (b) Dustproof: protection against harmful deposits of dust, dust may enter but not in amount sufficient to interfere with satisfactory operation	Jet proof; water projected by a nozzle from any direction (under stated conditions) shall have no harmful effect
6	(a) Complete protection against contact (b) dust-tight: protection against ingress of dust	Watertight equipment; protection against conditions on ship's decks etc. water from heavy seas or power jets shall not enter the enclosures under prescribed conditions.

(continued)

Schedule 2.5 – Index of Protection (IP) Code — *continued*

(Second number represents degree of protection against ingress of liquid.)

Second number only	Degree of protection	Notes
7	Protection against immersion in water: it shall not be possible for water to enter the enclosure under stated conditions of pressure and time	– Degree of protection is stated in form IPXX – Protection against contact or ingress of water respectively is specified by replacing first or second X by digit number tabled eg – IP2X defines an enclosure giving protection against finger contact but without any specific protection against ingress of water or liquid
8	Protection against indefinite immersion in water under specified pressure: it shall not be possible for water to enter the enclosure	

Note: Refer to BS5490 for full information on degrees of protection offered by enclosures

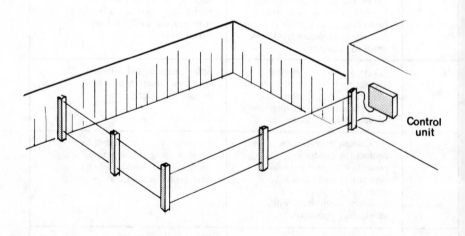

Control unit

Figure 2.4   An electric fence installation must be served from a battery operated, or mains operated control unit built to BS2632. The pulse generator must limit each pulse to a safe level of magnitude, duration and frequency in order to restrict the current and energy at each pulse.

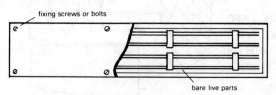

fixing screws or bolts

bare live parts

Figure 2.5(a)   Barrier or enclosure. Busbar chamber with part of the lid removed, showing protection by barrier or enclosure, lid removed by spanner or screwdriver.

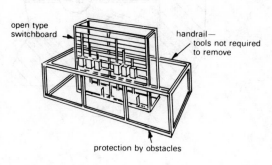

open type switchboard

handrail — tools not required to remove

protection by obstacles

Figure 2.5(b)   Obstacles. Open type switchboard with handrail firmly fixed.

(2D) Protection by placing out of reach

This type of protection is limited to areas accessible to a skilled or instructed person only. It applies to overhead lines for distribution between buildings and structures and to bare live parts other than overhead lines. The latter must be out of "arm's reach", a zone of accessibility to touch which is shown in Figure 2.6.

Where large objects constructed of conducting material, such as metal ladders or scaffold poles are used in the vicinity of live parts, the "arm's reach" limits must be adjusted accordingly.

Where bare live parts, other than overhead lines are accessible, even though they are out of arm's reach they must not be installed within 2.5m of any (a) exposed conductive part, (b) extraneous conductive part or (c) the bare live parts of other circuits.

Figure 2.7 illustrates some examples of placing installations "out of reach".

NOTES.

1. NO BARE CONDUCTORS IN THE SHADED AREA (ARM'S REACH)

2. WHERE LONG TOOLS ARE USED THE AREA MUST BE EXTENDED TO PREVENT CONTACT WITH LIVE CONDUCTORS OR PARTS WHEN USING TOOLS.

3. FOR SKILLED OR SUPERVISED PERSONS ONLY.

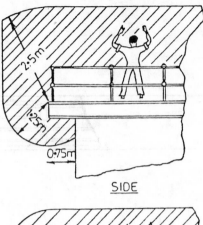

SIDE

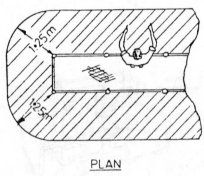

PLAN

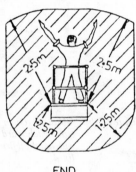

END

Figure 2.6   Protection by placing out of reach.

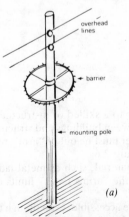

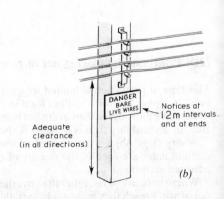

Figure 2.7   Overhead lines. Protected by placing 'out of reach' with   (a) barrier on pole supplementing the protection given.   (b) by providing adequate clearance in all directions.

(3) Protection against indirect contact *(Regulations 413-1 to 413-39, 471-11 to 471-14 and 471-16 to 471-21)*

There are five recognised methods of complying with the requirements of the Regulations for protection against indirect contact. These can be used singly or more than one method can be used in each installation. Schedule 2.6 shows the approved methods.

Schedule 2.6 – Basic protective measures for protection against indirect contact

(Regulation 413-1)

Method	Notes, ASEE comment and related Regulations
Automatic disconnection of supply and Earthing and Bonding	See sub-section 3A of text (Regulations 413-2 to 413-17 and 471-11 to 471-14)
Class II or equivalent insulation	See sub-section 3B of text (Regulations 413-18 to 413-26 and 471-16 to 471-18)
Non-conducting locations	See sub-section 3C of text (Regulations 413-27 to 413-31 and 471-19)
Earth free local bonding	See sub-section 3D of text (Regulations 413-32 to 413-34 and 471-20)
Electrical separation	See sub-section 3E of text (Regulations 413-35 to 413-39 and 471-21)

The provisions mentioned below and those of the Regulations in respect of overcurrent (see Practice 6) and the Regulations in respect of isolating and switching (see Practice 8) apply to the whole of, or parts of, an installation or the equipment to ensure protection against electric shock. The various protective devices or measures for safety employed in any installation should not interact and thereby reduce overall safety.

(3A) Protection by earthed equipotential bonding and automatic disconnection of supply

The Regulations call for the creation of an earthed equipotential zone in order to minimise any voltage between exposed and extraneous conductive parts. The main equipotential bonding conductors are required to be connected to the main earthing terminal of the installation. In domestic premises this would normally include the dwelling. On larger sites or where several buildings are involved on one site, each building would be considered to be an equipotential zone with the equipotential bonding terminating at the point of intake (see Practice 7). Reference to the Regulations of other Authorities will be necessary, with regard to P.M.E. Approval 1974 (Department of Energy) and to the telephone system earth wires (British Telecom). In the former case compliance with the Regulations will normally satisfy the Department of Energy's requirements, and in the latter case connection to British Telecom earth wires should, if possible, be avoided unless permission has been obtained. For other incoming piped services reference to the appropriate Code of Practice is recommended i.e. piped medical gases – Health Technical Memorandum: Butane or Propane – LPG Code of Practice (published by Department of Health and Social Security).

Figure 2.8 to 2.10 shows the services which should be bonded to meet these requirements. Figure 2.11 shows the effect of bonding.

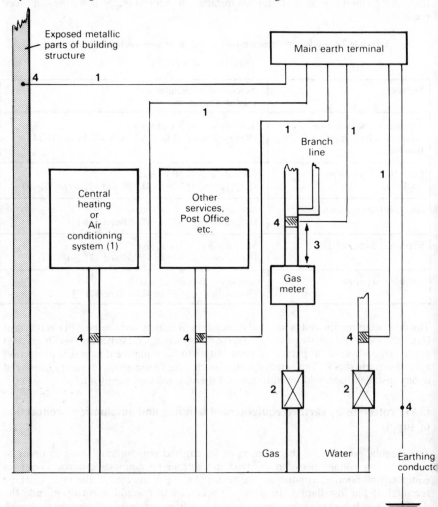

Figure 2.8   The equipotential bonding of extraneous conductive parts and other services.
(1)   Main equipotential bonds
(2)   Insulating or non-conducting section where fitted – all bonding connections to be consumers' side of incoming supplies
(3)   Maximum distance 600mm (CP331)
(4)   Connection must be accessible and have a warning notice – (see Practice 10). Disconnection by means of tool only.

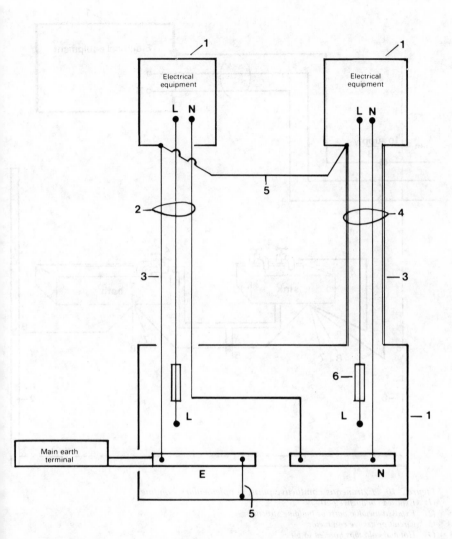

Figure 2.9   The bonding of exposed conductive parts.
(1)   Exposed conductive parts
(2)   Composite cable – protective conductor included
(3)   Protective conductor
(4)   Conduit, duct, trunking
(5)   Supplementary bond
(6)   Protective device characteristics and the earth fault loop impedance of the circuits to be co-ordinated so that:
(a) socket outlet circuits are disconnected in 0.4 secs. or less
(b) fixed equipment circuits are disconnected in 5.0 secs. or less
(c) for residual current devices the earth fault loop impedance x the residual operating current is equal to or less than
50 in TT or TN systems

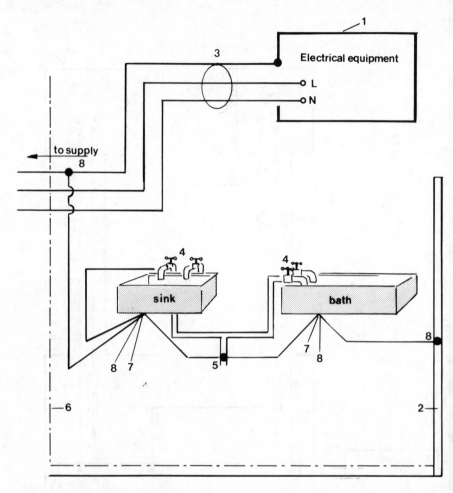

Figure 2.10   Extraneous conductive parts, supplementary bonding.
(1)   Exposed conductive parts
(2)   Exposed metallic parts of building structure
(3)   Circuit protective conductor
(4)   Hot and cold taps bonded to pipe
(5)   Water pipe bonded
(6)   Local equipotential zone
(7)   Waste pipe, metal bath or sink bonded
(8)   Accessible connection with warning notice, tool required to disconnect.

It is a principal requirement of the Regulations concerned with the automatic disconnection of supply that protective devices, earthing arrangements and circuit impedances must be coordinated so that in the event of an earth fault any voltage above earth potential between exposed and extraneous conductive parts shall be so restricted as to offer no danger. Within the main equipotential zone this requirement is satisfied if socket outlets are disconnected within 0.4 seconds and fixed equipment within 5 seconds, in the event of an earth fault.

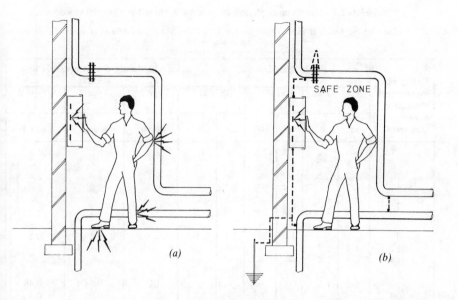

Figure 2.11 (a) Shock under fault conditions by indirect contact when exposed conducting parts of other systems are not bonded to earth. (b) Safety under fault conditions where all exposed conductive parts are connected by equipotential bonding to earth.

If the overcurrent device cannot meet the specified disconnection times (0.4 seconds or 5 seconds) the Regulations permit the use of a residual current device of up to 30mA rating where it's operating time does not exceed 40ms.

Where equipment connected within the main equipotential bonding zone is to be used outside that zone, e.g. in domestic premises where a gardening appliance is connected to a socket outlet of 32A rating or less within the house, protection must be provided by a residual current device rated up to 30mA, disconnecting within 40ms at a residual operating current of 150mA, fixed equipment outside the zone must disconnect within 0.4 seconds (400ms).

Appendix 7 of the IEE Regulations provides another method of meeting the requirements of the Regulations in respect of socket-outlet circuits, and that Appendix is summarised at the conclusion of this section.

If an overcurrent protective device is utilised in 240V (rms) a.c. nominal voltage circuits the earth fault loop impedance must not exceed the appropriate value tabulated in Schedule 2.7. For situations not covered in Schedule 2.7 it is necessary to refer to time/current characteristics for particular overcurrent protective devices which are published by the manufacturers. Appendix 8 of the IEE Regulations also contains time/current characteristics for various protective devices (see also Practice 7 – "Limitations of earth fault loop impedance").

If conditions involve conventionally normal body resistance, the earth fault loop impedances given in Schedule 2.7 may be used in selecting the protective device. A much lower impedance value or an alternative method of protection should be used if a lower than normal body resistance is anticipated (see Figure 2.2).

Schedule 2.7 – Maximum earth fault impedance (Z$_s$ ohms) for 5A to 800A circuits

Column (a) – socket outlet circuits (Z$_s$ for fuses to BS1362, in 13A plugs is 2.5 ohms). Column (b) – fixed equipment circuits.

Rating of overcurrent Protective device (Amperes)	Fuses to						Miniature circuit breakers to BS3871		
	BS88 Pt.2		BS1361		BS3036		Type 1	Type 2	Type 3
	a	b	a	b	a	b	a or b	a or b	a or b
5	–	–	11.4	17	9.6	20	12	6.8	4.8
6	8.7	13	–	–	–	–	–	–	–
10	5.3	7.7	–	–	–	–	6	3.4	2.4
15	–	–	3.4	5.3	2.7	5.6	4	2.3	1.6
16	2.8	4.4	–	–	–	–	–	–	–
20	1.8	3	1.8	2.9	1.8	4.0	3	1.7	1.2
25	1.5	2.4	–	–	–	–	–	–	–
30	–	–	1.2	2.0	1.1	2.8	2	1.1	0.8
32	1.1	1.8	–	–	–	–	–	–	–
40	0.8	1.4	–	–	–	–	–	–	–
45	–	–	0.6	1.0	0.6	1.6	–	–	–
50	0.6	1.1	–	–	–	–	1.2	0.68	0.48
60	–	–	–	0.6	–	1.2	1.0	0.56	0.4
63	–	0.86	–	–	–	–	0.95	0.53	0.38
80	–	0.6	–	0.48	–	–	0.75	0.42	0.3
100	–	0.45	–	0.28	–	0.55	0.6	0.34	0.24
125	–	0.34	–	–	–	–	–	–	–
160	–	0.27	–	–	–	–	–	–	–
200	–	0.19	–	–	–	–	–	–	–
250	–	0.16	–	–	–	–	–	–	–
315	–	0.11	–	–	–	–	–	–	–
400	–	0.096	–	–	–	–	–	–	–
500	–	0.065	–	–	–	–	–	–	–
630	–	0.054	–	–	–	–	–	–	–
800	–	0.034	–	–	–	–	–	–	–

Local supplementary equipotential bonding connections are to be made between extraneous conductive parts and also between exposed conductive parts and other extraneous conductive parts, for example metal tanks, sinks, baths, pipes, taps, radiators and accessible structural steelwork. Figure 2.12 illustrates the general principle of protective earthing and incorporates an example of local equipotential bonding.

Example

From Schedules 2.8A to 2.14 which give R1 and R2 impedances in series and the maximum impedances for overcurrent protective devices given in Schedule 2.7 and using the cables shown in the provisional design depicted in Figure 3.18 (repeated in this section as Figure 2.13 and described in the related text in Practice 3) the total earth fault loop impedance of the circuits and maximum impedances of the overcurrent protective devices can be compared.

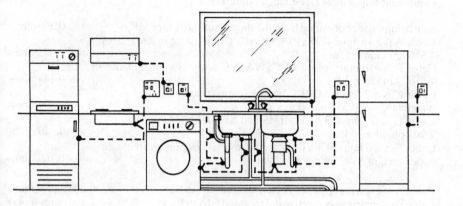

Figure 2.12 Supplementary bonding where simultaneous contact can be made between exposed conductive parts of electrical equipment and extraneous conductive parts which may convey a potential under fault conditions.

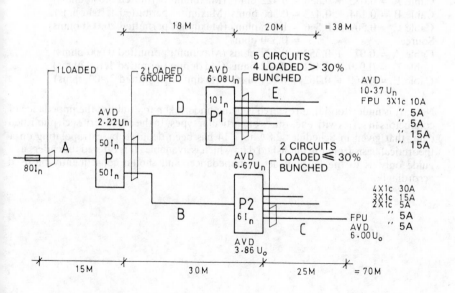

Figure 2.13 Provisional design approach for cable installation.

Component impedances (fault temperature 115°C)

Source impedance obtained from the supply authority for PME	=	0.350 ohms
Cable A is a 16 mm² 4 core PVCSWAPVC and has an impedance of 4.816 ohm/km x 15m	=	0.072 ohms
Cable B is a 16mm² 4 core PVCSWAPVC and has an impedance of 4.816 ohm/km x 30m	=	0.144 ohms
Cable C is a 2.5mm² SCPVC in HG 20mm conduit and has an impedance of 20.354 ohm/km x 25m	=	0.509 ohms
Cable D is a 16mm² 3 core MIMS and has an impedance of 2.202 ohm/km x 18m	=	0.040 ohms
Cable E is a 6 mm² SCPVC in 50 x 50 mm HG trunking and has an impedance of 8.462 ohm/km x 20m	=	0.169 ohms

Cable A overcurrent protective device rated 80A to BS88	=	0.600 ohms (max)
Cable B overcurrent protective device rated 50A to BS88	=	1.100 ohms (max)
Cable C overcurrent protective device rated 6A to BS3036	=	20.000 ohms (max)
Cable D overcurrent protective device rated 50A to BS88	=	1.100 ohms (max)
Cable E overcurrent protective device rated 10A to BS3871 Type 3	=	2.400 ohms (max)

Total impedances of circuits
Source   = 0.350 ohms
Cable A = 0.072 + 0.350 = 0.422 ohms (Maximum permitted 0.600 ohms)
Cable B = 0.144 + 0.422 = 0.566 ohms (Maximum permitted 1.100 ohms)
Cable C = 0.509 + 0.566 = 1.075 ohms (Maximum permitted 20.000 ohms)
Source   = 0.350 ohms
Cable A = 0.072 + 0.350 = 0.422 ohms (Maximum permitted 0.600 ohms)
Cable D = 0.040 + 0.422 = 0.462 ohms (Maximum permitted 1.100 ohms)
Cable E = 0.169 + 0.462 = 0.631 ohms (Maximum permitted 2.400 ohms)

Note: It is understood that research is being undertaken to establish the impedance of conductors in series with enclosures of particular types. In the absence of such published data, that given in Schedules 2.8A to 2.14 has been deduced by extrapolating on a theoretical basis from the published data which is available. It is offered to readers as a guide only as to the level of actual impedances and should consequently be used accordingly.

Schedule 2.8A – Impedance of Single Core PVCSWAPVC BS6346 Copper conductors and armour in series (Ohm/km). Fault temperature 115°C

Copper Conductor mm²	2 Single Core Cables Touching				3 Single Core Cables Touching				4 Single Core Cables Touching			
	(a) R1	(b) R1 R2	(c) R1 R2	SWA CSA	(a) R1	(b) R1 R2	(c) R1 R2	SWA CSA	(a) R1	(b) R1 R2	(c) R1 R2	SWA CSA
50	0·542	1·084	1·130	2 x 40	0·542	—	0·934	3 x 40	0·542	1·084	0·836	4 x 40
70	0·382	0·764	0·914	2 x 45	0·382	—	0·736	3 x 45	0·382	0·764	0·648	4 x 45
95	0·283	0·566	0·744	2 x 51	0·283	—	0·590	3 x 51	0·283	0·566	0·513	4 x 51
120	0·232	0·464	0·558	2 x 73	0·232	—	0·449	3 x 73	0·232	0·464	0·395	4 x 73
150	0·196	0·392	0·493	2 x 80	0·196	—	0·394	3 x 80	0·196	0·392	0·345	4 x 80
185	0·166	0·332	0·435	2 x 88	0·166	—	0·345	3 x 88	0·166	0·332	0·300	4 x 88
240	0·140	0·280	0·381	2 x 99	0·140	—	0·300	3 x 99	0·140	0·280	0·260	4 x 99
300	0·122	0·244	0·349	2 x 109	0·122	—	0·273	3 x 109	0·122	0·244	0·235	4 x 109
400	0·113	0·226	0·284	2 x 155	0·113	—	0·228	3 x 155	0·113	0·226	0·199	4 x 155
500	0·103	0·206	0·247	2 x 170	0·103	—	0·199	3 x 170	0·103	0·206	0·175	4 x 170
630	0·094	0·188	0·225	2 x 187	0·094	—	0·181	3 x 187	0·094	0·188	0·159	4 x 187
800	0·091	0·182	0·189	2 x 262	0·091	—	0·156	3 x 262	0·091	0·182	0·140	4 x 262
1000	0·089	0·178	0·182	2 x 289	0·089	—	0·151	3 x 289	0·089	0·178	0·136	4 x 289

Column (a) Line impedance; Column (b) Line plus neutral impedance; Column (c) Line plus aluminium wire armour impedance.

Schedule 2.8B – Impedance of Multi Core PVCSWAPVC BS6346 Copper conductors and armour in series (Ohm/km). Fault temperature 115°C

Copper Conductor mm²	2 Core Cable				3 Core Cable				4 Core Cable			
	(a) R1	(b) R1 R2	(c) R1 R2	SWA CSA	(a) R1	(b) R1 R2	(c) R1 R2	SWA CSA	(a) R1	(b) R1 R2	(c) R1 R2	SWA CSA
1.5	16.613	33.226	32.342	16	16.613	—	31.607	17	16.613	33.226	30.578	19
2.5	9.996	19.992	23.373	19	9.996	—	22.932	20	9.996	19.992	21.609	21
4	6.330	12.660	17.355	22	6.331	—	16.621	23	6.331	12.662	13.093	36
6	4.230	8.460	14.226	24	4.230	—	10.992	37	4.230	8.460	10.257	40
10	2.514	5.028	8.247	42	2.515	—	7.954	45	2.515	5.030	7.513	49
16	1.581	3.162	6.580	47	1.581	—	6.139	50	1.581	3.162	4.816	72
25	1.002	2.004	4.825	61	1.002	—	4.531	67	1.002	2.004	4.090	76
35	0.724	1.448	4.253	66	0.724	—	3.812	75	0.724	1.448	3.518	85
50	0.537	1.074	3.625	76	0.537	—	3.331	85	0.537	1.074	2.450	123
70	0.376	0.752	3.170	85	0.376	—	2.289	122	0.376	0.752	2.142	139
95	0.277	0.554	2.190	123	0.276	—	2.042	140	0.276	0.552	1.719	160
120	0.223	0.446	1.989	133	0.223	—	1.842	151	0.223	0.446	1.270	221
150	0.186	0.372	1.805	146	0.186	—	1.277	190	0.186	0.372	1.145	243
185	0.156	0.312	1.305	205	0.156	—	1.159	234	0.156	0.312	1.026	269
240	0.127	0.254	1.143	230	0.128	—	1.013	262	0.128	0.256	0.896	308
300	0.111	0.222	1.040	254	0.111	—	0.849	289	0.111	0.222	0.806	335
400	0.098	0.196	0.924	281	0.099	—	0.823	322	0.099	0.198	0.605	474

Column (a) Line impedance; Column (b) Line plus neutral impedance; Column (c) Line plus steel wire armour impedance.

Schedule 2.8C – Impedance of PVCSWAPVC BS6346 Copper conductors and armour in series (ohm/km)
Fault temperature 115°C

Copper Conductors mm²	Reduced Neutral 4 Core Cable			
	(a) R1	(b) R1 R2	(c) R1 R2	SWA CSA
25/16	1·001	2·581	4·100	76
35/16	0·724	2·304	3·518	85
50/25	0·537	1·534	3·037	123
70/35	0·376	1·100	2·142	139
95/50	0·276	0·813	1·748	160
120/70	0·223	0·599	1·284	221
150/70	0·186	0·562	1·159	243
185/95	0·156	0·432	1·041	269
240/120	0·127	0·350	0·925	308
300/150	0·111	0·297	0·821	335
400/185	0·099	0·255	0·619	474

Column (a) Line impedance; Column (b) Line plus neutral impedance; Column (c) Line plus steel wire armour impedance.

Schedule 2.9 – Impedance of Multicore Light Duty MIMS Cable 600V BS6207 Exposed to touch or PVC sheathed (ohm/km).
Fault temperature 115°C

mm² Cores	1.0 (a) R1	1.0 (b) R1 R2	1.0 (c) R1 R2	1.5 (a) R1	1.5 (b) R1 R2	1.5 (c) R1 R2	2.5 (a) R1	2.5 (b) R1 R2	2.5 (c) R1 R2	4.0 (a) R1	4.0 (b) R1 R2	4.0 (c) R1 R2
2	23·672	47·344	28·159	15·781	31·562	19·603	9·468	18·936	12·395	5·918	11·836	8·167
3	23·672	–	27·286	15·781	–	18·859	9·468	–	12·000	–	–	–
4	23·672	47·344	26·804	15·781	31·562	18·437	9·468	18·936	11·714	–	–	–
7	23·672	47·344	26·025	15·781	31·562	17·829	9·468	18·936	11·003	–	–	–

Column (a) Line impedance; Column (b) Line plus neutral impedance; Column (c) Line plus sheath impedance.

Schedule 2.10A – Impedance of Single Core Heavy Duty MIMS Cable 1000V BS6207 Exposed to touch or PVC sheathed, cables touching (ohm/km). Fault temperature 115°C

mm² Cables	6			10			16			25			35			50		
	(a) R1	(b) R1 R2	(c) R1 R2	(a) R1	(b) R1 R2	(c) R1 R2	(a) R1	(b) R1 R2	(c) R1 R2	(a) R1	(b) R1 R2	(c) R1 R2	(a) R1	(b) R1 R2	(c) R1 R2	(a) R1	(b) R1 R2	(c) R1 R2
2	3·948	7·896	5·488	2·370	4·740	3·639	1·484	2·968	2·522	0·952	1·904	1·754	0·682	1·364	1·468	0·480	0·960	1·031
3	3·948	–	4·974	2·370	–	3·216	1·484	–	2·172	0·952	–	1·487	0·682	–	1·206	0·480	–	0·847
4	3·948	7·896	4·717	2·370	4·740	3·004	1·484	2·968	2·003	0·952	1·904	1·353	0·682	1·364	1·075	0·480	0·960	0·755

mm² Cables	70			95			120			150			185			240		
	(a) R1	(b) R1 R2	(c) R1 R2	(a) R1	(b) R1 R2	(c) R1 R2	(a) R1	(b) R1 R2	(c) R1 R2	(a) R1	(b) R1 R2	(c) R1 R2	(a) R1	(b) R1 R2	(c) R1 R2	(a) R1	(b) R1 R2	(c) R1 R2
2	0·348	0·696	0·794	0·262	0·524	0·636	0·211	0·422	0·559	0·176	0·352	0·455	0·149	0·298	0·377	0·133	0·266	0·304
3	0·348	–	0·645	0·262	–	0·511	0·211	–	0·443	0·176	–	0·362	0·149	–	0·301	0·133	–	0·247
4	0·348	0·696	0·571	0·262	0·524	0·449	0·211	0·422	0·385	0·176	0·352	0·315	0·149	0·298	0·263	0·133	0·266	0·218

Column (a) Line impedance; Column (b) Line plus neutral impedance; Column (c) Line plus sheaths impedance.

Schedule 2.10B – Impedance of Multi Core Heavy Duty MIMS Cable 1000V BS6207 Exposed to touch or PVC sheathed (ohm/km).
Fault temperature 115°C

mm² / Cores	1.5 (a) R1	1.5 (b) R1 R2	1.5 (c) R1 R2	2.5 (a) R1	2.5 (b) R1 R2	2.5 (c) R1 R2	4.0 (a) R1	4.0 (b) R1 R2	4.0 (c) R1 R2	6.0 (a) R1	6.0 (b) R1 R2	6.0 (c) R1 R2
2	15·781	31·562	17·968	9·468	18·936	11·217	5·919	11·838	7·465	3·947	7·894	5·256
3	15·781	–	17·792	9·468	–	11·149	5·919	–	7·331	3·947	–	5·137
4	15·781	31·562	17·562	9·468	18·936	10·945	5·919	11·838	7·120	3·947	7·894	4·967
7	15·781	31·562	17·103	9·468	18·936	10·568	–	–	–	–	–	–
12	–	–	–	9·468	18·936	10·182	–	–	–	–	–	–
19	15·781	31·562	16·474	–	–	–	–	–	–	–	–	–

mm² / Cores	10.0 (a) R1	10.0 (b) R1 R2	10.0 (c) R1 R2	16.0 (a) R1	16.0 (b) R1 R2	16.0 (c) R1 R2	25.0 (a) R1	25.0 (b) R1 R2	25.0 (c) R1 R2
2	2·369	4·738	3·389	1·483	2·966	2·282	0·950	1·900	1·585
3	2·369	–	3·276	1·483	–	2·202	0·950	–	1·527
4	2·369	4·738	3·161	1·483	2·966	2·097	0·950	1·900	1·442
7	–	–	–	–	–	–	–	–	–
12	–	–	–	–	–	–	–	–	–
19	–	–	–	–	–	–	–	–	–

Column (a) Line impedance; Column (b) Line plus neutral impedance; Column (c) Line plus sheath impedance.

Schedule 2.11 – Impedance of copper conductors and steel conduit in series (ohm/km) for fault levels less or equal to 100A.
Fault temperature 115°C

LG Steel Conduit Metric BS4568 Part 1 1970

Cable CSA mm²	Tube DIA mm	Tube CSA mm²	(a) R1	(b) R1 R2	(c) R1 R2
1·5	16	47·13	16·618	33·236	25·585
2·5	"	"	10·177	20·354	19·144
4	"	"	6·332	12·664	15·299
6	"	"	4·231	8·462	13·198
1·5	20	59·64	16·618	33·236	23·821
2·5	"	"	10·177	20·354	17·380
4	"	"	6·332	12·664	13·535
6	"	"	4·231	8·462	11·434
10	"	"	2·515	5·030	9·718
1·5	25	89·73	16·618	33·236	20·440
2·5	"	"	10·177	20·354	13·999
4	"	"	6·332	12·664	10·154
6	"	"	4·231	8·462	8·053
10	"	"	2·515	5·030	6·337
1·5	32	116·11	16·618	33·236	19·411
2·5	"	"	10·177	20·354	12·790
4	"	"	6·332	12·664	9·125
6	"	"	4·231	8·462	7·024
10	"	"	2·515	5·030	5·308
16	"	"	1·582	3·164	4·375

HG Steel Conduit Metric BS4568 Part 1 1970

Cable CSA mm²	Tube DIA mm	Tube CSA mm²	(a) R1	(b) R1 R2	(c) R1 R2
1·5	16	64	16·618	33·236	22·934
2·5	"	"	10·177	20·354	16·318
4	"	"	6·332	12·664	12·653
6	"	"	4·231	8·462	10·552
1·5	20	92·4	16·618	33·236	21·023
2·5	"	"	10·177	20·354	14·587
4	"	"	6·332	12·664	10·742
6	"	"	4·231	8·462	8·641
10	"	"	2·515	5·030	6·925
1·5	25	117·6	16·618	33·236	19·852
2·5	"	"	10·177	20·354	13·411
4	"	"	6·332	12·664	9·566
6	"	"	4·231	8·462	7·465
10	"	"	2·515	5·030	5·749
1·5	32	152·8	16·618	33·236	18·529
2·5	"	"	10·177	20·354	12·088
4	"	"	6·332	12·664	8·243
6	"	"	4·231	8·462	6·142
10	"	"	2·515	5·030	4·426
16	"	"	1·582	3·164	3·493

HG Steel Conduit Imperial BS31 1940

Cable CSA mm²	Tube DIA inch	Tube CSA mm²	(a) R1	(b) R1 R2	(c) R1 R2
1·5	1¼	205·28	16·618	33·236	18·043
2·5	"	"	10·177	20·354	11·602
4	"	"	6·332	12·664	7·757
6	"	"	4·231	8·462	5·656
10	"	"	2·515	5·030	3·940
16	"	"	1·582	3·164	3·007
25	"	"	1·003	2·006	2·428
35	"	"	0·724	1·448	2·149
50	"	"	0·538	1·076	1·963
70	"	"	0·377	0·754	1·802
1·5	2	301·59	16·618	33·236	17·588
2·5	"	"	10·177	20·354	11·147
4	"	"	6·332	12·664	7·302
6	"	"	4·231	8·462	5·201
10	"	"	2·515	5·030	3·485
16	"	"	1·582	3·164	2·552
25	"	"	1·003	2·006	1·973
35	"	"	0·724	1·448	1·694
50	"	"	0·538	1·076	1·508
70	"	"	0·377	0·754	1·347
95	"	"	0·277	0·554	1·247
120	"	"	0·225	0·450	1·195

Column (a) Line impedance; Column (b) Line plus neutral impedance; Column (c) Line plus conduit impedance.

Schedule 2.12 – Impedance of copper conductors and steel conduit in series (ohm/km) for fault levels greater than 100A.
Fault temperature 115°C

LG Steel Conduit Metric BS4568 Part 1 1970

Cable CSA mm²	Size Tube DIA mm	Tube CSA mm²	Impedance (a) R1	(b) R1 R2	(c) R1 R2
1·5	16	47·13	16·618	33·236	30·583
2·5	"	"	10·177	20·354	24·142
4	"	"	6·332	12·664	20·297
6	"	"	4·231	8·462	12·693
1·5	20	59·64	16·618	33·236	25·732
2·5	"	"	10·177	20·354	19·291
4	"	"	6·332	12·664	15·446
6	"	"	4·231	8·462	13·345
10	"	"	2·515	5·030	11·629
1·5	25	89·73	16·618	33·236	22·792
2·5	"	"	10·177	20·354	16·351
4	"	"	6·332	12·664	12·506
6	"	"	4·231	8·462	10·405
10	"	"	2·515	5·030	8·689
1·5	32	116·11	16·618	33·236	21·175
2·5	"	"	10·177	20·354	14·734
4	"	"	6·332	12·664	10·889
6	"	"	4·231	8·462	8·788
10	"	"	2·515	5·030	7·072
16	"	"	1·582	3·164	6·139

HG Steel Conduit Metric BS4568 Part 1 1970

Cable CSA mm²	Size Tube DIA mm	Tube CSA mm²	Impedance (a) R1	(b) R1 R2	(c) R1 R2
1·5	16	64	16·618	33·236	29·407
2·5	"	"	10·177	20·354	22·966
4	"	"	6·332	12·664	19·121
6	"	"	4·231	8·462	17·020
1·5	20	92·4	16·618	33·236	24·997
2·5	"	"	10·177	20·354	18·556
4	"	"	6·332	12·664	14·711
6	"	"	4·231	8·462	12·610
10	"	"	2·515	5·030	10·894
1·5	25	117·6	16·618	33·236	22·645
2·5	"	"	10·177	20·354	16·204
4	"	"	6·332	12·664	12·359
6	"	"	4·231	8·462	10·258
10	"	"	2·515	5·030	8·542
1·5	32	152·8	16·618	33·236	20·146
2·5	"	"	10·177	20·354	13·705
4	"	"	6·332	12·664	9·860
6	"	"	4·231	8·462	7·759
10	"	"	2·515	5·030	6·043
16	"	"	1·582	3·164	5·110

HG Steel Conduit Imperial BS31 1940

Cable CSA mm²	Size Tube DIA inch	Tube CSA mm²	Impedance (a) R1	(b) R1 R2	(c) R1 R2
1·5	1½	205·28	16·618	33·236	19·244
2·5	"	"	10·177	20·354	12·803
4	"	"	6·332	12·664	8·958
6	"	"	4·231	8·462	6·857
10	"	"	2·515	5·030	5·141
16	"	"	1·582	3·164	4·208
25	"	"	1·003	2·006	3·629
35	"	"	0·724	1·448	3·350
50	"	"	0·538	1·076	3·164
70	"	"	0·377	0·754	3·003
1·5	2	301·59	16·618	33·236	18·407
2·5	"	"	10·177	20·354	11·966
4	"	"	6·332	12·664	8·121
6	"	"	4·231	8·462	6·020
10	"	"	2·515	5·030	4·304
16	"	"	1·582	3·164	3·371
25	"	"	1·003	2·006	2·792
35	"	"	0·724	1·448	2·513
50	"	"	0·538	1·076	2·327
70	"	"	0·377	0·754	2·166
95	"	"	0·277	0·554	2·066
120	"	"	0·225	0·450	2·014

Column (a) Line impedance; Column (b) Line plus neutral impedance; Column (c) Line plus conduit impedance.

Schedule 2.13 – Impedance of copper conductors and steel trunking in series (ohm/km). Fault temperature 115°C

			Trunking size												
Width mm			50	75	100	75	150	100	150	100	150	200	150	225	300
Depth mm			50	50	50	75	50	75	75	100	100	100	150	150	150
Gauge mm			1·2	1·2	1·2	1·2	1·2	1·2	1·6	1·6	1·6	1·6	1·6	1·6	1·6
CSA mm²			180	210	240	270	300	300	464	480	560	640	720	840	960
	Cable impedance						Line plus steel trunking impedance								
CSA mm²	(a) R1	(b) R1 R2	(c) R1 R2	(c) R1 R2	(c) R1 R2	(c) R1 R2	(c) R1 R2	(c) R1 R2	(c) R1 R2	(c) R1 R2	(c) R1 R2	(c) R1 R2	(c) R1 R2	(c) R1 R2	(c) R1 R2
1·5	16·618	33·236	18·970	18·634	18·382	18·187	18·029	18·029	17·531	17·500	17·374	17·280	17·206	17·122	17·059
2·5	10·177	20·354	14·881	12·193	11·941	11·746	11·588	11·588	11·090	11·059	10·933	10·839	10·765	10·681	10·618
4	6·332	12·664	8·684	8·348	8·096	7·901	7·743	7·743	7·245	7·214	7·088	6·994	6·920	6·836	6·773
6	4·231	8·462	6·583	6·247	5·995	5·800	5·642	5·642	5·144	5·113	4·987	4·893	4·819	4·735	4·672
10	2·515	5·030	4·867	4·531	4·279	4·084	3·926	3·926	3·428	3·397	3·271	3·177	3·103	3·019	2·956
16	1·582	3·164	3·934	3·598	3·346	3·151	2·993	2·993	2·495	2·464	2·338	2·244	2·170	2·086	2·023
25	1·003	2·006	3·355	3·019	2·767	2·572	2·414	2·414	1·916	1·885	1·759	1·665	1·591	1·507	1·444
35	0·724	1·448	3·076	2·740	2·488	2·293	2·135	2·135	1·637	1·606	1·480	1·386	1·312	1·228	1·165
50	0·538	1·076	2·890	2·554	2·302	2·107	1·949	1·949	1·451	1·420	1·294	1·200	1·126	1·042	0·979
70	0·377	0·754	2·729	2·393	2·141	1·946	1·788	1·788	1·290	1·259	1·133	1·039	0·965	0·881	0·818
95	0·277	0·554	2·629	2·293	2·041	1·846	1·688	1·688	1·190	1·159	1·033	0·939	0·865	0·781	0·718
120	0·225	0·450	2·577	2·241	1·989	1·794	1·636	1·636	1·138	1·107	0·981	0·887	0·813	0·729	0·666

Column (a) Line impedance; Column (b) Line plus neutral impedance; Column (c) Line plus trunking impedance.

Left portion

Unvented Al	Unvented Cupo	Unvented Cu	Vented Al	Vented Cupo	Vented Cu	(a) R1	(b) R1 R2	(c) R1 R2
		40				1·476	2·952	1·624
		80				0·742	1·484	0·878
		160				0·569	1·138	0·646
		225				0·493	0·986	0·570
		300				0·238	0·476	0·315
		400				0·208	0·416	0·285
400						0·237	0·474	0·346
	450		500			0·216	0·432	0·325
		500		550	600	0·183	0·366	0·292
500						0·175	0·350	0·282
	600		630			0·165	0·330	0·272
		650		700	800	0·147	0·294	0·254
650						0·141	0·282	0·244
	700		800	900		0·134	0·268	0·237
		800			1000	0·122	0·244	0·225

Right portion

Unvented Al	Unvented Cupo	Unvented Cu	Vented Al	Vented Cupo	Vented Cu	(a) R1	(b) R1 R2	(c) R1 R2
890						0·112	0·224	0·187
	950		1050			0·108	0·216	0·183
		1050		1150	1250	0·102	0·204	0·177
1050						0·096	0·192	0·167
	1150		1250			0·093	0·186	0·164
		1250		1400	1500	0·088	0·176	0·159
1250						0·084	0·168	0·152
	1350		1450			0·082	0·164	0·150
		1450		1600	1750	0·077	0·154	0·145
1600						0·065	0·130	0·213
		1800				0·061	0·122	0·209
1800						0·051	0·102	0·199
		2250				0·048	0·096	0·196

Column (a) Line impedance; Column (b) Line plus neutral impedance; Column (c) Line plus enclosure impedance.
Al = Aluminium conductor. Cupo = Cuponal copper on aluminium conductor. Cu = Copper conductor.

Design fault level
Regulation 434–2 Requires the prospective short circuit current at relevant points in the system distribution to be determined by calculation or measurement, this is usually assessed at the points of distribution where equipment is connected. All items of equipment selected should have a fault rating equal to or greater than the prospective fault level at the point of connection.

Taking Figure 2.13 as the installation under consideration and disregarding the fault limiting characteristics of fuses and circuit breakers for clarity the prospective fault levels at the main fuse, switchboard 'P' distribution boards 'P1' and 'P2' and points of utilisation can be assessed from the supply characteristics and the installation conductor impedances.

Schedules 2.8–2.14 give the impedance of conductors at an average temperature reached during symetrical fault in ohm/km arranged for convenience in three groups.

(a) R1 — line impedance used to assess a fault between phases.

$$\frac{240v}{R1} = Ip$$

(b) R1 R2 — line impedance plus neutral impedance used to assess a fault between phase and neutral.

$$\frac{240v}{R1+R2} = Ip$$

(c) R1 R2 — line impedance plus protective conductor impedance used to assess a fault between phase and protective conductor.

$$\frac{240v}{R1+R2} = Ip$$

Note
Because of the many configurations found in cable systems and where a choice of conductor impedances presents itself the aim should be to select the lower impedances for establishing the fault level with respect to selecting equipment with an adequate fault rating and to select the higher impedances to calculate the fault level with respect to proving the protective device will operate within the prescribed time period.

An example of system fault levels to determine the minimum fault rating for selected equipment

Supply authority Ip for single phase 240V at point of connection of their service cable to their LV distributing main is 16kA and they estimate a 10 metres run of 25 mm² aluminium or 16 mm² copper service cable would reduce this prospective short circuit current to 7.8 kA. Therefore external impedance Z_E = 240/7800 = 0.030 ohm.

SYSTEM IMPEDANCES 115°C	OHM
Z_E installation origin as above	= 0.030
Cable 'A' — 15 metres 16 mm² 4 core PVCSWAPVC	
15 × 1.581 ohm/km (R1)	= 0.023
15 × 3.162 ohm/km (R1 R2)	= 0.047
Cable 'B' — 30 metres 16mm² 4 core PVCSWAPVC	
30 × 1.581 ohm/km (R1)	= 0.047
30 × 3.162 ohm/km (R1 R2)	= 0.094
Cable 'C' — 25 metres 1.5 mm² SCPVC 20 mm HG conduit	
25 × 33.236 ohm/km (R1 R2)	= 0.830
Cable 'D' — 18 metres 16mm² 3 core HD MIMSPVC Cable	
18 × 1.483 ohm/km (R1)	= 0.026

Cable 'E' — 20 metres 6 mm^2 SCPVC 50 × 50 mm Trunking
20×4.231 ohm/km (R1)   = 0.084

Fault Levels (R1)

kA

Z_E Installation origin = 0.030 ohm   240/0.030 = 8.00
Switchboard 'P' (Cable 'A') 0.023 + 0.030 = 0.053   240/0.053 = 4.53
Distribution Board 'P1' (Cable 'D') 0.026 + 0.053 = 0.079   240/0.079 = 3.04
FPU (Cable 'E') 0.084 + 0.079 = 0.163   240/0.163 = 1.47

Fault Levels (R1 R2)

kA

Z_E Installation origin = 0.030 ohm   240/0.030 = 8.00
Switchboard 'P' (Cable 'A') 0.047 + 0.030 = 0.077   240/0.077 = 3.11
Distribution Board 'P2' (Cable 'B') 0.094 + 0.077 = 0.171   240/0.171 = 1.40
FPU (Cable 'C') 0.830 + 0.171 = 1.001   240/1.001 = 0.24

Schedule 2.15 – Automatic disconnection of supply – requirements of Regulations peculiar to TN and TT systems

Item	Requirement TN systems	Requirement TT system
Exposed conductive parts	To be connected by protective conductor to the installation main earthing terminal which in turn is connected to earth point of supply point	Overcurrent or residual current protective device: exposed conductive parts connected by protective conductors to earth electrode(s). Fault voltage operated protective device:* exposed conductive parts and related extraneous conductive parts connected by protective conductors through device voltage sensitive element to earth electrode
Protective device	May be of overcurrent or residual current type but the latter cannot be used if neutral and protective functions are combined in a PEN conductor. If fault-voltage operated, total earth loop impedance should not exceed 500 ohms	Preference should be given to the use of residual current devices. If in house or similar premises. rcd rated at 30mA (maximum) must be used
Disconnection times	If achieved through a residual current device, the following must be met: rated residual operating current times the earth loop impedance must not exceed 50	Same as for TN system

*The January 1985 amendments discontinued the provisions for fault voltage operated protective devices, with effect from 1 January 1986 but reference to them has been retained in the Guide to assist those who may find such devices still in use in installations completed before 1 January 1986.

Schedule 2.16 – Automatic disconnection of supply – requirements of Regulations peculiar to IT systems

Item	Requirement
Earth connections	No live conductor (phase or neutral) should be connected directly to Earth. It may be necessary to earth through impedances or artificial neutral points to reduce over voltage
Exposed conductive parts	Common earth electrode to be used to connect exposed conductive parts which are accessible at the same time, and the related extraneous conductive parts
Protective device	Only residual current device or fault-voltage operated device * to be employed as protective device. If fault-voltage operated, total earth loop impedance must not exceed 500 ohms A first fault between a live part and an exposed conductive part or to Earth to be indicated through use of an insulation monitoring device which should automatically disconnect the supply or give an audible or visual warning. See also Practice 7 (systems of supply). An IT system behaves as a TN or TT system after first fault occurs (see Practice 6); therefore the conditions for a TN or TT system will then apply.

*See note to Schedule 2.15.

Automatic disconnection

Some special points to bear in mind regarding automatic disconnection of the supply for particular systems of supply are shown in Schedules 2.15 and 2.16.

Alternative method of complying with the Regulations covering disconnection times for socket-outlet circuits.

The method described in Appendix 7 of the IEE Regulations will allow a disconnection time of 5 seconds (the same as for fixed equipment) for those socket outlets that are located within the zone created by the main equipotential bonding. This alternative method limits the impedance of the protective conductor (earthing conductor) to the main earthing terminal.

Schedule 2.17 gives limiting values of protective conductor impedance for various types and ratings of overcurrent protective devices.

The Schedule is based on conductor temperatures of 30°C and (apart from semi-enclosed fuses to BS3036 which are based on voltages not exceeding 240V above Earth) apply for all values of nominal voltage above Earth.

For radial circuits the impedance of the protective conductor is calculated from the most distant socket or place of utilization on a radial circuit. This value must not exceed the figures given in Schedule 2.17.

Also the total earth fault loop impedance for protective conductors must not exceed the figures given in Schedule 7.6 or those obtained by calculations by the method set out in Practice 7 (see text "Limitation of earth fault loop impedance") or the fixed equipment section of Schedule 2.7, whichever is the smaller.

For ring circuits the impedance of the protective conductor is calculated between its

Schedule 2.17 – Maximum impedance of protective conductor *(IEE Tables 7A)*

Rating of overcurrent protective device (Amperes)	Fuses to				Miniature circuit breakers to BS3871		
	BS88 Pt.2 (ohms)	BS1361 (ohms)	BS3036 (ohms)	BS1362 (ohms)	Type 1 (ohms)	Type 2 (ohms)	Type 3 (ohms)
5	–	3.57	2.0	–	2.5	1.42	1.06
6	2.78	–	–	–	2.08	1.18	0.88
10	1.61	–	–	–	1.25	0.71	0.53
13	–	–	–	0.83	-	-	-
15	–	1.08	0.55	–	0.83	0.47	0.35
16	0.92	–	–	–	0.78	0.44	0.33
20	0.65	0.63	0.38	–	0.63	0.35	0.26
25	0.5	–	–	–	-	-	-
30	–	0.42	0.24	–	0.41	0.24	0.17
32	0.39	–	–	–	0.39	0.22	0.16
40	0.29	–	–	–	0.31	0.18	0.13
45	–	0.21	0.125	–	-	-	-
50	0.24	–	–	–	0.25	0.14	0.1

two ends before final connection is made and shall not exceed four times the value given in Schedule 2.17.

With a spured ring circuit, the value obtained from Schedule 2.17 shall not be exceeded at any point of utilization on a spur.

When a spur is fed from a fused connection box and 13A fuses to BS1362 are used the value to be used is also shown in Schedule 2.17.

Also the total earth fault loop impedance must not exceed the value given in Schedule 2.7 or be in accord with Practice 7 (see text "Limitation of earth fault loop impedance"). The lowest figure should be taken.

(3B) Protection by use of Class II equipment

BS2754 1976 Memorandum – Construction of Electrical Equipment for Protection Against Electric Shock – contains information on the classification of equipment with regard to protection provided against electric shock.

Class II equipment is usually double insulated and is not provided with an earth terminal as this is considered unnecessary. The British Standard covering factory built assemblies BS5486 outlines the requirements for these assemblies to comply with the standard for Class II protection – sometimes referred to as total insulation. A factory built assembly can be given the equivalent of Class II protection by means of supplementary insulation during the course of erection provided that it meets the requirements of Class II and only when it is impractical to provide double insulation. Enclosures must have a minimum of IP2X protection and reliance on paint, varnish or similar products will not fulfil the requirements.

The foregoing requirements need to be observed regarding the opening of lids and doors of enclosures. Adequate insulation must be provided for all other circuits which pass through the enclosure. When installing cables or equipment that has double or re-inforced insulation or total insulation the standard of safety of the manufactured equipment must be preserved. Only circuit conductors are allowed to pierce the insulating enclosure.

Non conducting screws must not be used to satisfy Class II requirements as these could subsequently be substituted by conducting screws. The operation of handles or screws must in no way impair the supplementary insulation.

A protective conductor must not be connected to conductive parts inside an insulated enclosure, but connections may be provided for a protective conductor associated with a circuit passing through an enclosure, and the equipment it serves must be fully protected. The completely insulated enclosure must not prevent the equipment operating in the way it was designed to do.

Figure 2.14 illustrates the effect of using Class II equipment in relation to bonded extraneous conductive parts. Where Class II equipment is likely to be replaced by equipment which needs a connection to a protective conductor, such a means should be provided for future use.

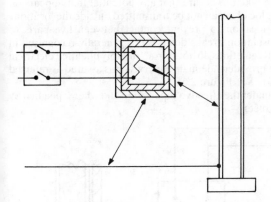

Figure 2.14   Class II equipment is double insulated and this prevents transmission of earth faults to exposed or extraneous conductive parts.

(3C) Protection by non-conducting location *(Regulations 413-27 to 413-31a and 471-19)*

This is an optional way of affording protection against indirect contact, such a space in a building used to be referred to as an "Earth-free" location.

Usually the electrical designer was tempted to take advantage of the building finishes (wooden floors, non-conducting walls, absence of piped services etc) to reduce cost in such spaces.

The main problem with such a course of action is that changes in the incomes (norms and living standards) of the population can bring about changes not envisaged by the designer (i.e. central heating installations in domestic premises that would not have been thought of even twenty years ago). If this method of protection is used it *must be permanent*.

Therefore for such locations the resistance of insulating floors and walls should be tested as specified in Practice 11, not just on completion, but regularly throughout the life of the installation. It may be necessary to ensure that humidity does not affect the resistance.

The minimum acceptable reading of resistance for a supply voltage below 500V is 50,000 ohms, or 100,000 ohms if supply voltage exceeds 500V.

Within the space protective conductors (earth wires – bonding conductors) are not permitted. Any socket outlets installed within the space must not have an earthing contact.

If failure of the basic insulation of live parts of equipment would lead to exposed conductive parts being at different potentials, the latter must be so arranged that (under ordinary circumstances) a person cannot come into contact with more than one exposed conductive part or with such a part and an extraneous conductive part. However, this requirement is met if more than 2 metres (or 1.25 metres out of the arm's reach zone) exists between conductive parts in a location having insulating floors and walls. It is also met in such a location if effective insulated obstacles are placed between conductive parts, provided that the relative spacing of 2 metres (1.25m out of 'arm's reach' zone) is maintained. Finally, the requirement will be met if the extraneous conductive parts are themselves adequately insulated.

Permanent precautions must be taken to ensure that any potential that appears on extraneous conductive parts in the location can not be transmitted outside the location.

The use of a non-conducting location to prevent contact between live parts of different potentials if the basic insulation breaks down is not generally recognised in these Regulations. However, the Regulations do not stop a "suitably qualified electrical engineer" specifying this measure provided adequate supervision is assured as referred to in Regulations 413-27 to 413-31. See Figure 2.15.

The use of this method must be under the effective supervision and where specified by a suitably qualified electrical engineer.

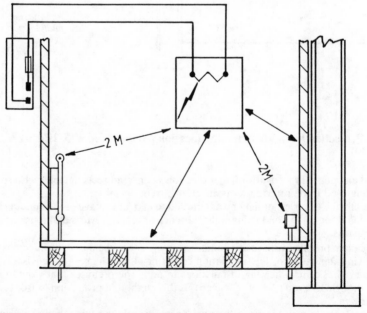

Figure 2.15   Requirements in a non-conducting location.
Special precaution shall be taken to prevent portable tools or hand-held leads from being used in this area if they are served from socket outlets outside the non-conducting location and have normal earthing facilities. Portable tools and hand-held leads served from socket outlets in the zone must not be used beyond the Non-Conducting Zone.

(3D) Protection by earth free local equipotential bonding *(Regulations 413-32 to 413-34 and 471-20*

To achieve this situation it is necessary to bond together all exposed conductive parts and all extraneous conductive parts that are simultaneously accessible. The local equipotential bonding conductors must not be in direct electrical contact with earth. Nor must there be a direct electrical path to earth through any of the exposed conductive parts or extraneous conductive parts. Precautions must be taken to prevent persons moving to or from the equipotential location being exposed to a dangerous potential difference at the point of entry, in particular where a conductive floor is insulated from earth and connected to the equipotential bonding conductors.

The use of earth free locations using earth free bonding must only be used where specified by a suitably qualified electrical engineer. See Regulations 413-32 to 413-34. This measure is used to avoid dangerous voltage differences between simultaneous accessible parts if basic insulation fails. See Figure 2.16

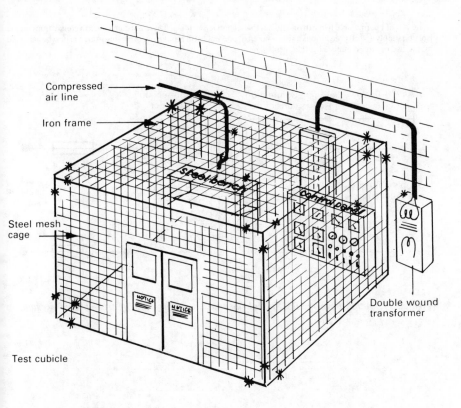

Figure 2.16   Earth free bonding in a Test Cubicle.
Items marked * must be bonded to an equipotential bonding tape so that a common voltage will appear within the steel cage in the event of a breakdown of insulation and simultaneous accessible parts becoming live. Note Notice on door must warn users of the dangers of making connections to services outside the zone.

(3E) Protection by electrical separation *(Regulation 413-35 to 413-39 and 471-21)*

When using this method of protection, the source of supply shall be a BS3535 double wound transformer, a motor generator set providing the same degree of protection, or a mobile source with double or reinforced insulation. Normally only one circuit should be supplied and under no circumstances should that circuit be earthed. (One example of this protection in domestic and hotel installations is the use of BS3052 shaver sockets). See also Figure 2.17.

No connection between a live part of a separated circuit and any part of another circuit is permitted. Where there is a possible danger from mechanical damage to a flexible cord it must be visible over its full length.

Protection by electrical separation is a method which may be applied only in situations under effective supervision and where specified by a suitably qualified electrical engineer.

Note: It is not permissible to earth one side of the secondary winding. There must be no earth connections on the isolated supply and all precautions must be taken to prevent earth faults from occurring – this can best be achieved by the use on non metallic sheathed cables.

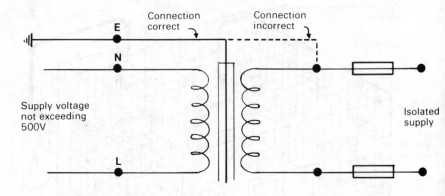

Figure 2.17   A transformer to BS3535 with unearthed secondary winding to comply with Regulation 471-21.

Practice 2A

Protection against electric shock in special locations

Special provisions and exemptions *(Regulations 471-22 to 471-26)*

The provisions of these Regulations allow for considerable relaxation where certain locations are restricted to skilled persons, or instructed persons under direct supervision. In such cases it is permitted to place live parts out of reach or to use obstacles to prevent unintentional contact with live parts out of reach or to use obstacles to prevent unintentional contact with live parts. In such areas compliance with Regulation 17 of the Electricity (Factories Act) is necessary concerning the dimensions of access ways and platforms for equipment having exposed live parts. In these areas relaxation of the measures for protection against electric shock referred to in Practice 2 may be dispensed with if allowed by the Electricity (Factories Act) Special Regulations. An example of such areas must have suitable warning notices to restrict all but skilled or instructed persons. See Practice 10 and Figure 2.18.

Automatic disconnection and reduced voltage systems *(Regulations 471-27 to 471-33)*

These Regulations acknowledge that the Health and Safety Executive recognise voltages of 65V to earth (three-phase) and 55V to earth (single phase) to be safe in most locations covered by the Factories Act. The use of these low voltages is preferred for hand held portable electric motor driven tools on construction sites. The term reduced low voltage is one covering the major areas where the Health and Safety at Work Act applies. It is important to realise however that there are circumstances (i.e. working inside metal enclosure in a damp atmosphere) where the reduced low voltage would be too high and SELV would be required. If in doubt consult the Health and Safety Inspectorate.

Double wound transformers to BS3535, motor generators having windings with isolation equivalent to BS3535 and diesel generators or other prime movers comply with these Regulations. Such equipment must not exceed 110V ac between phases, and 65V to earth three-phase, or, 55V to earth single-phase. The star point of any three-phase system must be connected to earth to comply with these Regulations.

All exposed conductive parts must be effectively earthed. Automatic disconnection shall be provided by the use of fuses or circuit breakers in each phase conductor or by using residual current devices (see Figure 2.19). The impedance of the circuit must be restricted to ensure the maximum disconnection time of 5 seconds is never exceeded.

Information on the safe use of portable electrical apparatus is given in Guidance Note PM 32 published by the Health and Safety Executive and available from Her Majesty's Stationery Office.

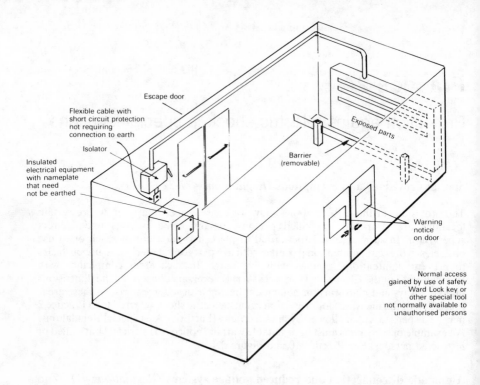

Figure 2.18 An example of a location restricted to skilled or instructed persons under direct supervision.

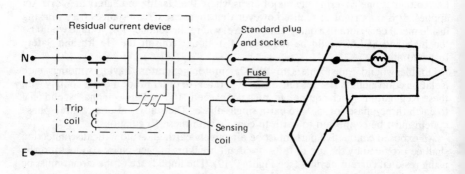

Figure 2.19 Portable apparatus may be protected by a residual current device.

Protective measures for particular locations *(Regulations 471-34 to 471-47)*

Bathrooms

Rooms containing a fixed bath and/or shower and other rooms containing a shower cubicle are referred to in Regulations 471-34 to 471-39(b). Bathrooms containing a bath and/or shower shall not have any mains sockets or make provision for mains portable equipment. However it is permissible to install in bathrooms a shaver supply unit or shaver light unit to BS3052, instantaneous shower heater to BS3456, insulated BC lampholder with shield to BS5042 or totally enclosed luminaire and to have normal access to the insulated cord of a cord switch all within reach of a person using a bath or shower, all other mains switches, controls or equipment must be out of normal reach. Metal work and other conductive parts in bathrooms must be bonded to prevent dangerous fault voltages existing during an earth fault. Circuit protective devices and earthing/bonding conductors must clear any line to earth fault with in 0.4 seconds. See Schedule 2.18.

Room with a shower cubicle

Bedrooms and other rooms with a shower cubicle (not a bathroom) may contain mains sockets and mains portable equipment if sited more than 2.5m from the shower cubicle. See Schedule 2.18.

SELV circuits in bathrooms

SELV sockets, controls and luminaires not exceeding 12V RMS ac or 12V dc may be sited in close proximity to a person using a bath or shower in a bathroom or a shower in other rooms. See Schedule 2.18.

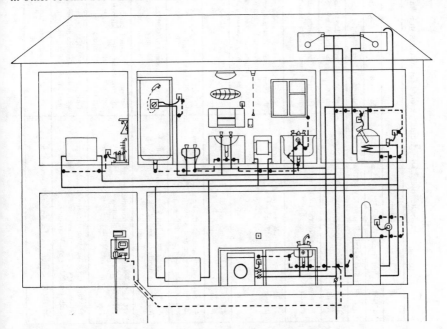

Figure 2.20   Protection against electric shock in a bath/shower room.

Schedule 2.18 – Requirements for circuits in a bathroom and in other rooms having a shower cubicle

Regulation	Bathroom	Other room with shower
471-34. Sockets (mains or over 12V RMS ac or 12V dc)	Means to connect portable equipment excluded	Exclude within 2.5M from shower.
471-34(a). Sockets (SELV up to 12V RMS ac or 12V dc)	Non-earth 2 pin insulated sockets permitted	As for bathroom.
471-38. Luminaires (mains or over 12V RMS ac or 12Vdc)	Insulated BC lampholders with shield to BS5042 or totally enclosed luminaires permitted within 2.5M of a bath or shower cubicle	As for bathroom. No luminaires inside the shower cubicle.
No regulation. Luminaires (SELV up to 12V RMS ac or 12V dc)	Insulated BC lampholders with shield to BS5042 or totally enclosed luminaires IP44 recommended. Metallic lampholder or luminaire not permitted	As for bathroom.
471-39. Switches, controls or stationary appliances (mains or over 12V RMS ac or 12V dc)	Normal access to insulated cord of a cordswitch or controls of a shower heater to BS3456 is permitted within reach of a person in a bath or shower. It is not permitted to have normal access to other switches, controls or radiant heater elements within 2.5M of a bath or a shower cubicle	As for bathroom.
471-39. Switches and controls (SELV up to 12V RMS ac or 12V dc)	Insulated switches or controls without an earth connection are permitted	As for bathroom.
471-34(a). Safety source such as a class II transformer, battery, driven generator or electronic unit (SELV up to 12V RMS ac or 12V dc)	The safety source to be out of reach or 2.5M from a person in a bath or shower cubicle	As for bathroom.
471-37. Shaver outlet, shaver light or a shaver supply unit (mains supply or over 12V RMS ac or 12V dc)	Shaver supply unit to BS3052 or shaver light to BS3052 is permitted if the unit transformer is connected to the circuit protective conductor. Mains 2 pin sockets for shavers not permitted	Shaver supply unit or shaver light to BS3052 permitted as for bathroom, other outlets or shaver adaptors must be 2.5M or more from shower cubicle.
471-35. Supplementary equipotential bonding (excluding SELV circuits) for safety of persons	Between (1) exposed conductive parts of all equipment. (2) equipment and extraneous parts. (3) various extraneous conductive parts such as taps, overflows, wastes, pipes, bath, towel rail, radiator etc.	As for bathroom if within 2.5M of a shower cubicle, or where appropriate
471-36. Limitation of the duration of fault voltages between exposed conductive parts during line to earth faults (excluding SELV circuits)	Circuits over 12V RMS ac or 12V dc must disconnect a fault within 0.4s, the characteristics of protective devices and bonding must satisfy this requirement	Protection as for bathroom if within 2.5M of the shower cubicle.
471-39. Siting of electrical equipment for safety of persons	No electrical equipment allowed inside a bath tub or shower tray	No electrical equipment inside a shower cubicle except shower water heater to BS3456.

Agricultural installations

In agricultural installations all electrical equipment shall be to Class II standards or be suitably insulated. Where livestock is intended to be present, care shall be taken to ensure dangerous voltages do not exist. The very low body resistance of some animals puts them at extreme risk at shock voltages below 25V ac (see Figure 2.21) and require an appropriate reduction in the earth loop impedance. Similarly where SELV is used for protection in such situations, the limit of 50V ac should be reduced appropriately.

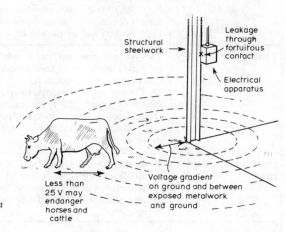

Figure 2.21   Showing danger to livestock of earth-leakage currents even at levels below 25V.

Socket for equipment used outdoors

Regulation 471-47 requires at least one socket (with a durable label marked *"for equipment outdoors"*) to be conveniently positioned for the connection of outdoor portable equipment. The circuit shall be protected by an RCD having a rated residual current of 30mA or less designed to trip within 40mS when the residual current rises to 150mA as a result of an earth fault in the lead or in the equipment. This does not apply where protection against indirect contact is by SELV (411-2 to 411-10), or electrical separation (413-35 to 413-39) or reduced system voltage with automatic disconnection (471-2 to 471-33).

Caravans

The protective measures to be adopted for touring caravans and their associated installations are set out in Schedule 2.19.

Schedule 2.19 – Requirement for touring (mobile) caravans* and their site

Subject	Requirement
Maximum demand	Must not exceed 16A
Protection	Site installation to allow for indirect contact protection by automatic disconnection of supply (see Practice 2 Item 3A). Class II equipment may be used.
Supply	For site socket outlet (see Figure 2.22 and Practice 9) in groups of one to six associated with 30mA residual current device and connected to earth. Plugs, sockets and couplers to be splash proof to BS6343.
Earth	TNS system – main earthing terminal connected to protective conductor in underground cable or overhead system protective conductor. TN-C-S system – connection to system main earthing terminal, subject to consent of Department of Energy. Other supply systems – independent earth electrode associated with residual current device protecting one or more site socket-outlets.
Extraneous conductive parts	To be connected by 4mm² (minimum) bonding conductor to installation protective conductor (continuity ensured by multiple bonding if necessary). Not applicable to isolated metal parts of insulated caravans unlikely to become live.
Warning notices	See Practice 10.

*For transported caravans the Regulations generally are applicable. Other caravans, e.g. mobile workshops, may be covered by Electricity (Factories Act) Special Regulations 1908 and 1944.

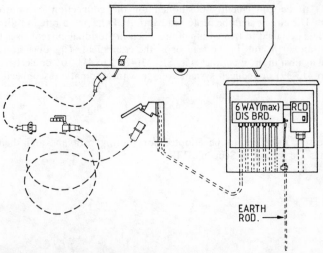

Figure 2.22   Supply to caravans from site socket-outlets.

Practice 3

Conductors and cables

This section covers the selection of and methods of installation for conductors and cables. It also deals with the requirements of the Regulations in respect of the operational and environmental conditions which apply to conductors and cables.

Cables specified under Regulation 12 of the Electricity Supply Regulations are also permitted.

Information on the following subjects is given in the Practice section indicated:
1. Heating cables and conductors (Practice 9 – Regulations 554-31 to 554-34)
2. Earth concentric wiring systems (Practice 7 – Regulations 541-1 to 547-7)
3. Cables operating at a voltage in excess of low voltage (discharge lighting) – (Practice 9 – Regulation 554-3)

Selection of low voltage non-flexible cables and conductors *(Regulations 521-1 to 521-4)*

Schedule 3.1 gives details of the types of approved low voltage non-flexible cables and conductors and the relevant British Standard. These are illustrated in Schedule 3.2 where their construction and application are described.

Up to and including 10mm^2 cross sectional area conductors must be of copper or copperclad aluminium construction. Aluminium conductors can be used when the cross sectional area of the conductor is 16mm^2 or greater.

A catenary wire may be included in a cable for overhead installations if the sheath is pvc, o.r.f.r. or h.o.f.r.

Mineral insulated cables are not suitable for discharge lighting unless dangerous voltage surges can be suppressed.

Surge suppression may also be necessary when this type of cable is used for a supply to a rotating machine (BICC Information Sheet No. 402 "Surge generation and control").

When using 'wet' cables drainage of oil can occur if the rise or fall of the cable on the route is as little as 1m in 1.5 metres. Where such draining is likely to occur cables to BS6480 (non draining type) must be used.

Reference must be made to BS5486 (Part 1) factory built assemblies for busbar and associated connections.

Low voltage overhead line conductors (not cables) must be selected in accordance with the Schedule 3.3.

Schedule 3.1 — Approved non-flexible cables and conductors (conductors*)

BS Number	Title	See Schedule 3.2 Illustration Number
BS6480	Impregnated paper-insulated cables lead sheathed	1
BS6007, BS6883	Rubber insulated cables	2
BS6004 or BS6346	Non-armoured pvc insulated cables	3 & 4
BS6346	Armoured pvc insulated cables	5
BS4553	Split-concentric copper conductors pvc insulated cables	6
BS6207 Part 1 or 2	Mineral insulated cables	7
BS6231	Type B non-armoured pvc insulated cables	8
BS5593	Consac cables	9
BS5467	Armoured cables with thermo setting insulation	10
BS6081	Fittings for mineral insulated cables	11

*See Schedule 5, page 6 regarding BASEC cable assessment.

Schedule 3.2 – Configuration construction and application of non-flexible cable referred to in Schedule 3.1

Cable type	Construction and application
1. BS6480 Impregnated paper-insulated cables a b c d e f g h j k	Shaped stranded or solid copper or aluminium conductor (a) with a carbon paper screen (b) impregnated paper insulation (c) screen of metal paper (d) with filler (e) copper woven fabric tape (f) lead or lead alloy sheathed (g) with bedding (h) galvanised wire armour (j) and pvc sheathed overall (k) Application. Mains distribution in ground, duct or air.
2. BS6007 Rubber-insulated cables a b c	Stranded tinned copper conductor (a) 85°C elastomer insulation (b) with impregnated textile braid finish (c) Application. Surface mounting or embedded conduits for hot situations.
3. BS6004 Non armoured pvc-insulated cables a b (i) a b c (ii)	(i) Ref 6491X solid or stranded plain copper conductor (a) pvc insulated (b) (ii) Ref 6181Y solid or stranded plain copper conductor (a) pvc insulated (b) pvc sheathed (c) Application. (i) Cables for drawing into trunking or conduit. (ii) Suitable for use surface wiring where there is little risk of mechanical damage. Single core used in conduit and trunking where conditions are arduous.
4. BS6004 Non armoured pvc cables d a b c	Two or three core flat cables pvc insulated (b) pvc sheathed overall (c) copper conductors solid or stranded (a) Ref 6242Y with uninsulated earth continuity conductor (d) between cores of twin cable and between yellow and blue cores of three core cable Application. Domestic and industrial wiring, suitable for surface wiring where there is little risk of mechanical damage.

	Construction and application
5. BS6346 Armoured pvc insulated cables a b c d e	Ref 6943X: 2 or 3 or 4 core solid or stranded copper conductors (a) pvc insulated (b) cross laid up, pvc bedded (c) galvanised steel wire armoured (d) pvc sheathed overall (e) Application. Mains distribution, industry and elsewhere, suitable for installation in ground, ducts and air.
6. BS6346 Armoured pvc insulated cables. Split concentric a b c d e f g	Ref 6945X Solid plain copper conductors (a) pvc insulated, cross laid up pvc bedded (b) earth continuity conductor (c) neutral conductor black covered pvc conductors (d) pvc strings (e) binder (f) pvc sheathed overall (g) Application. Mains distribution as in item 5
7. BS6207 Mineral insulated copper sheathed cables a b c d	Copper conductors (a) with magnesium oxide insulation (b) and copper sheathed (c) with pvc oversheath (d) Application. Industry, where high temperatures, mechanical strength, fire resistance etc are required.
8. BS6231 Type B Non-armoured cable b a	Plain annealed copper wire bunched or stranded (b), plasticised pvc insulation (a) for up to a max 600V between conductor and earth for use up to 105°C for heat resisting purposes Application. Designed for use in switch control, relay and instrument panels etc.

Cable type	Construction and application
9. BS5593 Consac cables a b c d e f	Solid aluminium conductors (a) paper core insulation (b) paper belt insulation (c) extruded smooth aluminium sheath (d) thin layer of bitumen containing a corrosion inhibitor (e) covered with extruded pvc or polythene oversheath (f)
10. BS5467 Armoured cables with thermosetting insulation a b c d e	Solid aluminium conductor (a) insulated with XPLE (b) with taped bedding (c) and galvanised steel wire armour (d) overall sheath of pvc (e)
11. BS6081 M.I.M.S. fittings a b c d a b c	Seal with earth tail Application. For use at lighting points, switch positions, socket outlets and in earth concentric wiring systems where protective conductor needs to be continued Seal (a) pvc sleeves to insulate conductor tails (b) disc to close mouth of pot (c) compound (d) brass pot. Application. To exclude moisture from micc cable Gland (a) gland body (b) compresson ring (c) gland nut Application. To connect or anchor mims cable at a box

Note: See also the second Annex to Practice 3. *(With acknowledgements to Delta Enfield Cables Ltd).*

Schedule 3.3 – Type of conductors permitted by Regulations for low voltage overhead lines

BS Number	Type
BS125	Hard drawn copper or cadium copper conductors
BS215	Hard drawn aluminium and steel re-inforced aluminum conductors
BS3242	Aluminium alloy conductors
BS6485 Type 8	Conductors covered with pvc for overhead lines

Schedule 3.3 does not apply to cable installed overhead.

Selection of flexible cords and cable for low voltage *(Regulations 521-5 to 521-6)*

Flexible cables and cords must be selected from those shown in Schedule 3.4 and may have steel or phosphor bronze armour or tinned copper braid screening incorporated in their construction.

Schedule 3.4 – Flexible cords and cables permitted by Regulations

BS Number	Title	Illustration see Schedule 3.6
BS6004	Pvc insulated flexible cords (non armoured)	
BS6007	Rubber insulated flexible cables	
BS6116	Rubber insulated flexible trailing cables for quarries and mines	
BS6500	Insulated flexible cords	(13, 14, 15, 16, 17, 18, 19, 20)
BS6977	Braided travelling cables for lifts	

Flexible cords associated with a portable appliance, or luminaire, the whole of which is covered by a British Standard are excluded from the Regulation, as are specific cords and cables for combined power and telecommunications (see Practice 5 – Segregation requirements) for instance flexible cords used between bed head units and the patient's handset in hospitals. Only the types of flexible cable and cord shown in Schedule 3.5 are permitted by the Regulations. Some of these are illustrated in Schedule 3.6 where their construction and applications are described.

Schedule 3.5 – Permitted types of flexible cord and cable

Type	Illustration see Schedule 3.6
Braided circular	20
Unkinkable	14
Circular sheathed	15, 16
Flat twin sheathed	17
Parallel twin, only for the wiring of luminaires (where permitted by BS4533)	
Twisted twin non-sheathed, only for the wiring of luminaires (where permitted by BS4533)	18, 19
Braided circular twin and three-core, insulated with glass fibre (where permitted by Regulation 523-2)	
Single-core pvc-insulated non-sheathed flexible cables complying with BS6004 (installed in accordance with Regulation 523-29)	

Reference needs to be made to BS3456 for flexible cords for use with certain appliances and BS4533 for flexible cords for use with luminaires. The Electrical Equipment (Safety) Regulations 1975 with 1976 amendment is also pertinent to this matter. Reference to Annex 2 hereto will supply details of the most suitable types of flexible cable and cord to be used.

Selection of cables for extra low voltage *(Regulation 521-7)*
Cables for extra low voltage must be suitably insulated and provided with additional protection if necessary to prevent danger. Note must be taken of the environmental conditions. See text headed 'Environmental conditions' which follows.

Cable type	Construction and application
13. BS6500 Insulated flexible cords a b c d e	Ref 3802Y. Two, three or four core flexible cords are formed from plain flexible copper conductor (a) pvc insulated (b) cores laid up, pvc sheathed (c) plain copper wirebraided (d) and pvc sheathed overall Application. General purpose screened flexible cords used for temporary wiring on building sites, portable hand lamps and in flameproof installations.
14. BS6500 Insulated flexible cord, unkinkable a b c	Ref 2213. Two or three tinned copper conductors (a) insulated with 60°C elastomer (b) twisted together with textile fillings, covered with a layer of elastomer (rubber) and textile braiding (c) to form a circular unkinkable cord Application. For supplying hand appliances which are subject to low mechanical stresses in dry situations in domestic premises. *Unsuitable* for use out-doors in industrial buildings or agricultural buildings or for supplying portable hand tools.
15. BS6500 Circular sheathed flexible cord a b c	Ref 3183Y. Two or three plain copper conductors laid up pvc insulated (b) pvc sheathed (c) Application. General purpose indoors or outdoors in damp or dry conditions, portable tools, washing machines, vacuum cleaners, lawn mowers. Should not be used where sheath can come into contact with hot surfaces and not suitable for temperatures below 0°C
16. BS6500 Circular sheathed flexible cord a b c	Ref 3183. Two, three, four or five flexible tinned copper conductors (a) 60°C elastomer (rubber) insulated cores (b) and elastomer sheathed overall (c) Application. In domestic premises, kitchens and offices for supplying portable or light mobile appliances which are subject to low mechanical stresses (eg vacuum cleaners, electric irons and cooking appliances)

Schedule 3.6 – Configuration, construction and application of some flexible cable and cords
– *continued*

Cable type	Construction and application
17. BS6500 Flat twin sheathed flexible cord a b c	Ref 2192Y. Flexible plain copper conductors (a) pvc insulated (b) two cores laid parallel and pvc sheathed overall (c) Application. Sometimes known as pendant flexibles, used for lighting fittings, push switches and other light domestic applications
18. BS6500 Twin non-sheathed flexible cord a b	Ref 2491X. Flexible plain copper conductors (a) pvc insulated and laid parallel (b) Application. Intended for internal use in appliances where it can be adequately protected
19. BS6500 Twin twisted non-sheathed a b c	Ref 2492X. One or two flexible plain copper conductor (a) cores laid up 60°C elastomer (rubber) insulated (b) individually textile braided (c) Application. Light duty flexible cords for fixed protected installations inside appliances and in or on luminaires
20. BS6500 Braided circular insulated with glass fibre a b c	Ref 3183TQ. Stranded copper conductors (a) silicone rubber insulated (b) glass braiding overall Application. For use with heating appliances such as immersion heaters, night storage heaters etc.

Note: See also second Annex to Practice 3. *(With acknowledgements to Delta Enfield Cables Ltd).*

Selection of cables for a.c. circuits *(Regulations 521-8)*

Because of the electromagnetic effects of alternating current in single core cables the use of ferrous materials in the form of tape and armour is prohibited. Where single core cables are installed in conduit and trunking manufactured out of ferrous material each circuit shall be arranged to cancel out the electromagnetic effects and be contained in the same ferrous enclosure.

Figure 3.1 shows a gland plate for four single core cables of a 3 phase and neutral circuit. The slot between the holes prevents the circulation of eddy currents in the ferrous gland plate. The Regulations require that there is no ferrous metal between cables or conductors; this meets that requirement. Non-ferrous (i.e. brass or aluminium, paxolin or laminated hardwood) gland plates are, however, to be preferred.

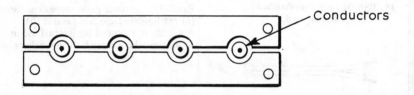

Figure 3.1   Means of preventing appreciable eddy currents in ferrous gland plate.

Operating conditions

Current-carrying capacity – *(Regulations 522-1 to 522-7)*

Cables and conductors should be chosen so that their current carrying capacity and hence their cross sectional area is not less than the full load (design) current.

The temperature appropriate to the insulation used on the cable shall not be exceeded by the limiting temperature to which the current carrying capacity relates. Conductors in switchboards designed to BS5486, Part 1 are not subject to this requirement. Reference must be made to the Annex 1 to Practice 3 for the limiting temperatures and for the method for determining the cross sectional area of a cable or conductor complying with this requirement.

Reference to BS5486, Part 1 must be made when considering busbars, busbar connections and bare conductors forming part of a factory built assembly (switchboard) with regard to their current carrying capacity and temperature limitations.

The requirements for conductors connected in parallel are shown in Figure 3.2. As bare conductors are subject to expansion and contraction account should be taken of the physical limitations of the metal used and the effect on any joints. The maximum temperature permissible for bare conductors is 90°C.

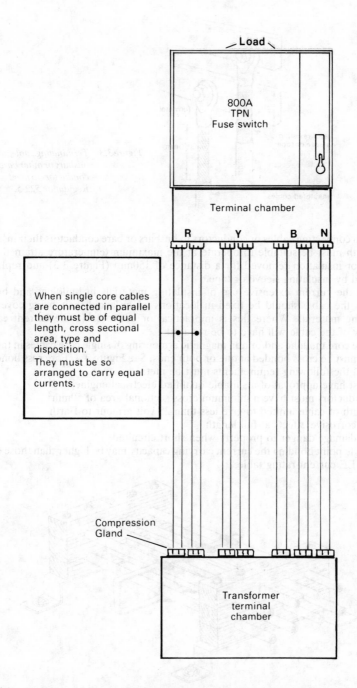

Figure 3.2 Arrangements for conductors in parallel to meet Regulation 522-3.

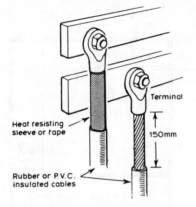

Figure 3.3 Terminating cables at busbars or other bare conductors to meet Regulation 522-5.

When connecting cables or conductors to busbars or bare conductors their insulation or sheath must be suitable to operate at the maximum temperature attained or the sheath or insulation removed for a distance of 150mm (Figure 3.3) and replaced if required by insulating sleeve or tape.

With the current extensive use of insulating materials in buildings and building services the cable should be fixed in locations which avoid their being covered by insulating material. Where this is impractical or unavoidable the current carrying capacity of the cable will have to be reduced.

Single core metallic and/or non magnetic armouring of single core cables in the same circuit must be cross bonded at one or both ends. See Figure 3.4. For cross bonding at one end the following requirements must be met:

(a) must have approval of a suitable qualified electrical engineer
(b) conductors must have a minimum cross sectional area of 50mm^2
(c) length of cable limited to give less than 25 volt armour to Earth
(d) no corrosive effects at full length
(e) no damage/danger to property when short circuited.

For single point bonding the current carrying capacity may be higher than those quoted in the IEE current rating table.

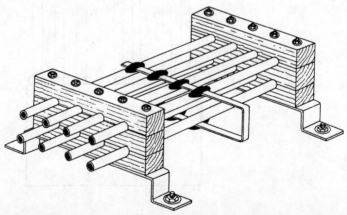

Figure 3.4 Sheathed single core cables in same circuit to be bonded (Regulation 522-7)

Voltage drop *(Regulation 522-8)*

Engineers responsible for design or installation must ensure by calculation the volts dropped between a source and any equipment or device does not exceed the requirements of Regulation 522-8 (see page 116 and Figure 3.5). Voltage drop tables in Appendix 9 of the Regulations contain resistive (mVr), reactive (mVx) and inductive (mVz) values of voltage drop in milli-volts (mV) per ampere (I_b) per metre (m) for cables and cords. The method of calculation will depend on size of conductor, loading and load power factor applied to tabulated values.

Cables fully loaded

dc or for ac 16mm² or less CSA $V = \left(\dfrac{mVr}{1000} \right) \times I_b \times M.$

ac over 16mm², PF of load and cable the same $V = \left(\dfrac{mVz}{1000} \right) \times I_b \times M.$

Cables partially loaded

dc or for ac 16mm² or less CSA $V = \left(\dfrac{(ct.mVr)}{1000} \right) \times I_b \times M.$

ac under 16mm² CSA $V = \left(\dfrac{\sqrt{(ct.mVr)^2 + (mVx)^2}}{1000} \right) \times I_b \times M.$

Correction factor (Ct). For lower conductor temperature in partially loaded cable

$$Ct = \dfrac{230 + t_p - \left(C_a^2 \times C_g^2 - \dfrac{I_b^2}{I_t^2} \right) \times (t_p\text{-}30)}{230 + t_p}$$

t_p = maximum permitted conductor operating temperature, °C.
C_a = correction factor for ambient temperature, °C.
C_g = correction factor for cable grouping.
I_b = circuit design current.
I_t = tabulated current carrying capacity of cable.
Note:- equation does not apply to circuits with rewirable fuses or ambient temperatures over 30°C.

Correction for load power factor. Cables fully loaded

ac 16mm² or less CSA $V \simeq \left(\dfrac{\cos\phi.mVr}{1000} \right) \times I_b \times M.$

ac over 16mm² CSA $V \simeq \left(\dfrac{\sqrt{(\cos\phi.mVr)^2 + (\sin\phi.mVx)^2}}{1000} \right) \times I_b \times M.$

Cables partially loaded

ac 16mm² or less CSA $V \simeq \left(\dfrac{Ct.\cos\phi.mVr}{1000} \right) \times I_b \times M.$

ac over 16mm² CSA $V \simeq \left(\dfrac{\sqrt{(Ct.\cos\phi.mVr)^2 + (\sin\phi.mVx)^2}}{1000} \right) \times I_b \times M.$

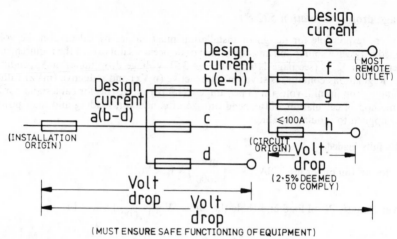

Figure 3.5   Illustrating the measurement of voltage drop referred to by Regulation 522-8.

Minimum cross sectional area of conductors *(Regulation 522-9)*

When an installation using a multicore cable is made up of several individual single-phase loads it is sometimes difficult to balance these loads over a three-phase supply causing an out-of-balance current to flow in the neutral conductor. If this out-of-balance is likely to be small in magnitude a neutral conductor with a reduced cross sectional area can be used. This also applies where single-core cables are used, but where there are significant harmonic currents present the neutral must be capable of carrying the current likely to flow.

Where a significant amount of discharge lighting is installed a full sized neutral is required.

Electromechanical stresses *(Regulation 522-10)*

Cables are subject to electromechanical stresses that can be caused by the current flowing in them during their service, including short-circuit currents. They must so be constructed and fixed as to withstand these stresses.

Environmental conditions *(Regulations 523-1 to 523-13 and 523-19 to 523-35)*

Ambient temperature

All current-carrying parts and the insulation part of a circuit must be selected for the maximum operating temperature they are likely to reach in normal operation; including heat transferred from any accessory, appliance or luminaire to which they are connected.

The relevant ambient temperature when selecting fixed wiring cables for installation in a heated floor, ceiling or structure is the temperature of those parts, BS Code of Practice CP1018 details information on floor temperatures in "off-peak" floor warming slabs. Floor heating and other heating cables are not included in this requirement.

It is permitted to use suitable supplementary heat resisting electrical insulation over the separate cable cores to relieve the normal insulation from protection against short circuit or earth faults.

Plastic insulation at high temperature:

(1) will migrate under pressure or by gravity, even after a short time
(2) will harden or crack, over a long period
(3) above 115°C may be corrosive to conductors and metalwork

There is no need under normal conditions to take the likely minimum ambient temperature into consideration. Cables liable to mechanical damage in low temperatures should either be suitably protected or run on routes which avoid the low temperature area, where this is possible.

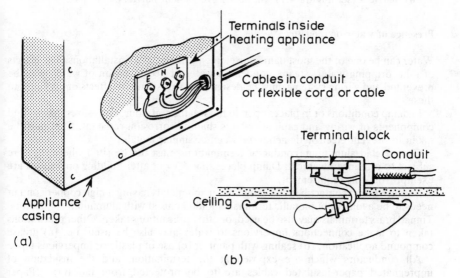

Figure 3.6   Precautions to be taken for cables and flexible cords entering appliances, accessories and luminaires: (a) terminations in appliance (b) terminations in typical tungsten luminaire – high temperature tails required between lampholder and terminals – porcelain terminals in a 'cool' conduit box. The insulation and sheath of cables entering into an accessory or appliance must be suitable for the maximum working temperature, or be fitted with supplementary insulating sleeves or beads suitable for such temperature. The circuit wiring to a luminaire should be connected to suitable terminals in an outlet box with heat resisting 150°C rubber – or 185°C glass fibre – insulated leads between the terminals and the lampholder. (85°C pvc for pendant flexibles). Also applies to batten holders.

Precautions should be taken when cables or flexible cords enter appliances, accessories and luminaires (see Figure 3.6) as follows:

(a) The insulation and sheath of cables entering into the accessory or appliance must be suitable for the maximum working temperature, or be fitted with supplementary insulating sleeves or beads suitable for such temperature.
(b) The circuit wiring should be connected to suitable terminals in an outlet box with heat resisting 150°C rubber – or 185°C glass fibre – insulated leads between the terminals and the lampholder. (85°C pvc for pendant flexibles). Also applies to batten holders.

Conduits, trunking and all cable enclosures must be suitable for the extremes of ambient temperatures that will be met in normal use. Where a pvc or similar thermoplastic box is used to support a luminaire or is in contact with it, the box temperature must not exceed 60°C and the load on the box not be greater than 3kg as the box will become distorted or deformed. Box distortion can sometimes be overcome by utilising a metal insert. The normal maximum temperature of the cables enclosed must not be overlooked when determining the box temperature. (See Figure 3.6)

As warm air rises the air temperature at the top of a rising duct system may increase to a high level due to heat generated by conductors. Heat barriers shall be fitted at intervals not exceeding 5 metres or at each floor level, which ever distance is less.

Fire barriers (see Figure 4.7) will also serve as heat barriers.

Presence of water or moisture

Water can be one of the most damaging elements in electrical installations. The effects of rain, dripping water, steam, condensed water or accumulation of water must be prevented and wiring systems must be designed to withstand the affects of exposure to these.

In damp conditions or in places open to the weather, armour, enclosures, fixings and components of wiring and cabling systems shall be corrosion resistant. Care must be taken to prevent electrolytic action between dissimilar metals.

Copper clad aluminium conductor terminations must not be sited where they are subject to prolonged wetness. Damp places that dry out after building operations are exempt from this requirement.

Because direct contact between aluminium and metals having a high copper content needs to be avoided, bi-metallic terminals should be used with aluminium conductors. Tinned brass terminals may also be used, or other precautions taken. Other precautions taken to make connections impervious to water may also be used: i.e. (a) grease compound application; (b) sealing with paint or (c) use of plastic or impervious tape.

All conductors which are exposed at the termination, and the insulation of impregnated paper-insulated cables are to be protected from moisture. (Paper insulation is normally hygroscopic) – see also Practice 3 (joints and terminations).

The ends of mineral-insulated cables (see Figure 3.7) must be protected from moisture in the following manner:
(a) ensure that the cable insulation is thoroughly dry
(b) fit watertight gland and seal with compound having adequate insulating and moisture proofing properties.
(c) install protective sleeve to the conductors where they emerge from the seal. The type of sleeve used must be suitable for operating under the full range of temperature to which it will be subjected in service.

Reference will need to be made to text on "Identification of cables" in this Section regarding the use of tapes, sleeves and discs for colour identification of conductor cores.

Installations in damp situations should meet the following requirements.
(a)   Single core non-sheathed cables or sheathed cables from which the sheath has been removed must be installed in damp/corrosion proof enclosures.
(b)   Any cable forming part of an installation in a damp situation must be protected from the effects of moisture and corrosion.

Typical examples of damp situations are: (1) Building services plant rooms (2) Boiler houses. See also Practice 3 (Joints and Terminations) and Annex 3 to Practice 1 which deals with the classification of external influences.

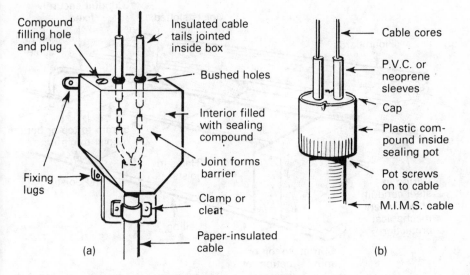

Figure 3.7   (a) Typical sealing chamber for paper-insulated cable
             (b) Mineral-insulated cable seal (Regulation 523-12).

Damage by fauna

Where livestock is kept, fixed wiring shall be inaccessible to them. Where vermin can attack cables, such cables should be of a suitable type or be adequately protected against the vermin.

Solar radiation

Even in the UK exposure to solar radiation can have an adverse effect on some cable sheaths. In the event of such exposure care must be taken when selecting cables for use in such conditions.

C.S.P, P.C.P and polyethylene sheath compounds formulated with weather resistance in mind have probably the best performance, but black pvc has equally good performance. Alternatively the cables must be screened from the sun. Sunlight passing through ordinary window glass is not considered to be direct sunlight.

Mechanical stresses

Where there is a risk to conductors and cables in normal use, they must be protected from mechanical damage by use of metal, or pvc trunking, conduit or sheathing. Figure 3.8 illustrates the requirements of the Regulations when cables are installed under floors or above ceilings and when concealed in walls or partitions.

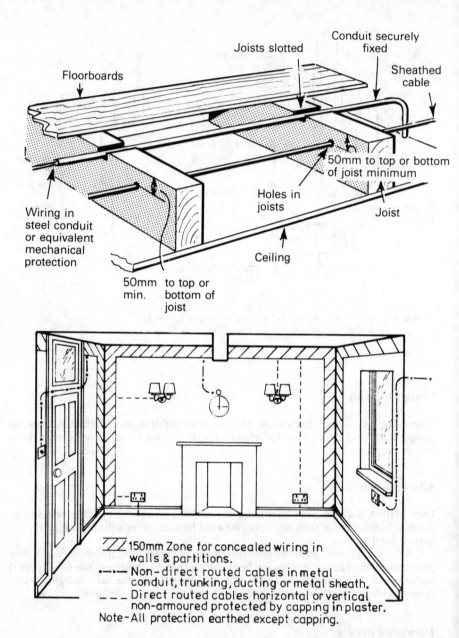

Figure 3.8 Illustrating mechanical protection for cables under floors, above ceilings and concealed in walls or partitions. Regulations 523-20(a)-(d).

Figure 3.9 illustrates the requirements of the Regulations in respect of cables passing through holes in metalwork.

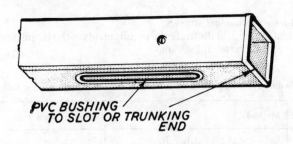

PVC BUSHING
TO SLOT OR TRUNKING END

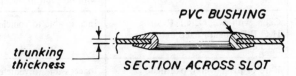

PVC BUSHING

trunking thickness

SECTION ACROSS SLOT

Figure 3.9   Pvc or similar bushing applied to prevent damage from sharp edges of holes in metal work as required in Regulation 523-21.

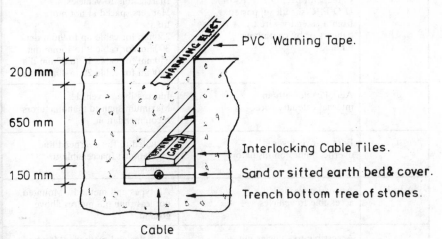

PVC Warning Tape.

200 mm

650 mm

150 mm

WARNING ELECT

CABLE

Interlocking Cable Tiles.

Sand or sifted earth bed & cover.

Trench bottom free of stones.

Cable

Figure 3-10   Mechanical protection of a cable buried in the ground. Regulation 523-23.

Cables without a sheath are liable to mechanical damage or damage from stress and should be enclosed in a conduit, duct, ducting or turnking but where such duct or ducting is formed insitu by concrete or screed the cables shall be sheathed. See Figure 3.13.

Armoured cables with an overall sheathing may be buried underground or be pulled into an underground pipe or duct. Cables buried directly in the ground must be protected by interlocking cable tiles and/or be marked by an underground PVC warning tape.

Underground cable routes should be marked at the surface by flush concrete blocks or posts at 20 metre intervals and at every change of direction and entry into a building. See Figures 4.2 and 4.3 page 161 and 162.

Overhead cables – mechanical stresses
Schedule 3.7 and Figure 3.11 illustrate the requirements of the Regulations in respect of cables used overhead between buildings.

Schedule 3.7 – Requirements for cables used overhead between buildings

Figure 3.11	Method	Requirements
A	Cables with pvc, O.R.F.R. or H.O.F.R. sheath in conduit	Inaccessible to vehicles. Heavy gauge steel conduit with no joint in the span.
B	Cable with pvc, O.R.F.R. or H.O.F.R. sheath fixed at each end only	Inaccessible to vehicles.
C	Bare or pvc covered overhead lines on insulators at each end only	Inaccessible to vehicles.
D	Cable with pvc, O.R.F.R. or H.O.F.R. sheath supported from a catenary wire by hangers or by continuous binding	Inaccessible to vehicles. Hangers spaced at not more than:– 250mm for cable up to 9mm dia 300mm for cable 9 to 15mm dia 350mm for cable 15 to 20mm dia 400mm for cable 20 to 40mm dia
E	Aerial cable with an internal catenary wire	Inaccessible to vehicles. Maximum span to manufacturers recommendation.
F	Bare or pvc covered overhead lines on insulators	Installed to the overhead line regulations. Inaccessible to vehicles.
A to F	At road crossings, accessible to vehicles	All types and methods. Mounted not less than 5.8 metres above ground.
A to F	Accessible to vehicles but not a road crossing	All types and methods. Mounted not less than 5.2 metres above ground.

Note: *A to F are not applicable to agricultural installations*

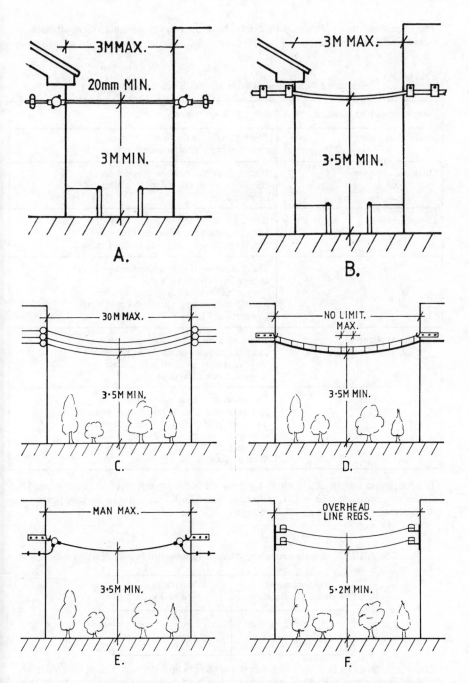

Figure 3.11 Distribution between buildings (see Schedule 3.7 for details of requirements).

The requirements applicable to flexible cords in respect of mechanical stresses are shown in Schedule 3.8.

Schedule 3.8 – Mechanical stresses on flexible cords – requirements

Usage/condition/application	Requirements
Mechanical damage	To be sheathed with rubber or pvc and, if necessary, armoured
Domestic situations	Where minimum bending or wear occur, BS6500 cords of the unkinkable kind are permitted
Luminaires	Braided circular flexible cords with glass fibre insulation are to be used provided that they are not subject to undue flexing
Fixing Wiring	These cords must not be used except in the case of final connections. They must then have protection from mechanical damage. (See also item "Final Connections" below)
Portable appliances	To be used for connecting such equipment, including cookers under 3kW, provided that the length involved is insufficient to incur mechanical damage.
Final connections	Can be used as final connection to fixed appliances but must be as short as possible and connected to fixed wiring using a suitable accessory, ie spur, socket outlet and plug etc. (See also item "Fixing Wiring" above).

The maximum weight of a luminaire supported or partly supported shall not exceed the values given in Schedule 3.9. (from Regulation 523-32, reproduced by kind permission of the Institution of Electrical Engineers).

Schedule 3.9 – Maximum weight of luminaire supported by twin flexible cord

Nominal csa of conductor (mm²)	Maximum Weight (kg)
0.5	2
0.75	3
1.00 to 4.00	5

Account needs to be taken of mechanical strains and stresses placed on cables and flexibles during the normal process of erection, and care must be taken to see that no damage is done.

Identification of cores of cables and cords *(Regulations 524-1 to 524-5)*

The identification colour reserved for the protective conductor is green and yellow and must not be used for other purposes. One of the colours shall cover a minimum of 30% and not more than 70% of the surface, while the other colour covers the remainder.

For non-flexible cables and conductors the following methods of identification (see Figure 3.12) shall be used:

(i)   at every termination conductors shall be identified by either colour (as shown in Schedule 3.10) or by using numbered cores

(ii) it is preferable that cable cores should be identified throughout their length, but this is not always practical (ie for M.I.M.S. cables)

(iii) bare conductors shall be made identifiable by using coloured sleeves to comply with Schedule 3.10. This also applies to busbars although painting the appropriate colour is considered satisfactory identification.

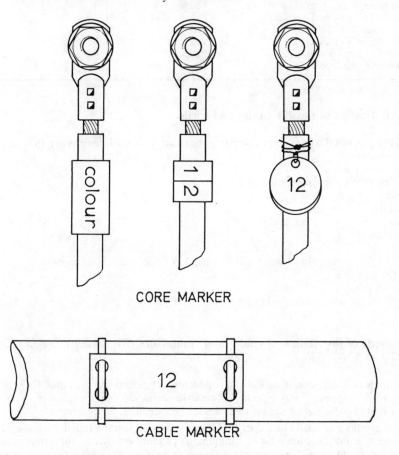

CORE MARKER

CABLE MARKER

Figure 3.12   Identification of non-flexible cables and conductors.

Function of conductor	Colour of core or sleeve or disc etc.	Alternative: core number for PILC cables etc.
Protective or earthing	green and yellow	sheath (or 0 for PME)
Phase of single-phase a.c.	red (or yellow or blue)	1 (or 2 or 3)
Neutral of a.c.	black	0
Phase R of 3-phase a.c.	red	1
Phase Y or 3-phase a.c.	yellow	2
Phase B or 3-phase a.c.	blue	3
Positive of d.c. 2 wire	red	1
Negative of d.c. 2 wire	black	0
Outer (+ or −) of d.c. 2 wire derived from 3 wire system	red	1
Positive of 3 wire d.c.	red	1
Middle wire of 3 wire d.c.	black	0
Negative of 3 wire d.c.	blue	2

Identification of flexible cables and cords

Every core of a flexible cable or cord must be clearly coloured along its length to indicate its function.

The colours recommended are:
Phase   – Brown
Neutral   – Blue
Protective   – Green and yellow
(earthing)

The following colours must *NOT* be used in flexible cables or cords:
Yellow (alone)
Green (alone)
Any colour combination other than green and yellow

Methods of installation of cables and conductors *(Regulations 521-13, 526-1, 527-1 to 527-9, 528-1, 529-1, 529-3, 529-7)*

Methods of installation of cables and conductors are referred to in Annex 1. Qualified electrical engineers may specify alternative methods but compliance with the Regulations which are relevant to cables and conductors, is necessary.

Where floor trunking or a duct is cast in concrete in situ the radial thickness of the concrete in any direction must be a minimum of 15mm, whether or not formers are left in place. Resident civil or structural engineers or builders representatives must be made aware of this requirement at an early stage of construction. See Figure 3.13.

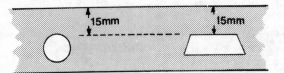

Figure 3.13   Ducts cast in situ:
                      thickness of concrete.

Accessibility

It must always remain possible to inspect joints in cables and cords. This requirement does not apply to joints: (1) in underground cables, or (2) encased by building material with the ignitibility characteristic 'P' as given in BS476 Part 5, or (3) by welding, soldering, brazing or compression and put in an enclosure having the ignitability characteristics 'P' as given in BS476 Part 5. In (2) the joints if inaccessible must not be made with mechanical clamps.

Joints and terminations

Connection of all cable terminations or joints must be mechanically and electrically reliable, and if vibration or mechanical damage is possible then protection must be given and must not cause any mechanical damage to the cable conductor. Non-flexible cable which has joints; these must be made by soldering or brazing, or welding or be mechanical or compression type clamps. These clamps must accommodate all the strands of the conductor.

Terminations and joints must be appropriate for the size and type of conductor used, and they shall be suitably insulated for the circuit voltage.

Terminations, other than those of the protective conductor, shall be enclosed in material having the ignitability characteristic 'P' as specified in BS476 Part 5. Alternatively, terminations may be in an accessory or luminaire which complies with the appropriate British Standard. Non-sheathed cables, and cores of sheathed cables when the sheath has been removed must also be enclosed by one of these methods.

Compression joints must be of a type certified to BS4579. For joint connectors, tools specified by the manufacturers should be used.

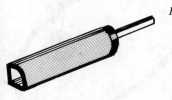

Figure 3.14   A typical shaped compression connector for copper and aluminium cables.
These can be obtained in various configurations and stud hole sizes. The aluminium connectors are chemically cleaned, dried and then packed in heat sealed plastic pouches. This protects them, prevents oxidation of the aluminium and ensures good electrical conductivity when the connectors are installed.

Sleeves provided for mineral-insulated cable terminations shall be a similar temperature rating to that of the seals.

Cable outer sheath or armour must be secure and firmly held without damage from cable glands. See Figure 3.15.

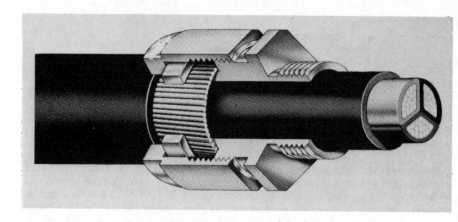

Figure 3.15 Compression type gland, for plastic insulated, plastic-sheathed single-wire armoured cables (suitable for dry indoor conditons) (Regulation 527-8).

Coupling together lengths or flexible cable is not generally seen as good practice. However if it is unavoidable, couplers complying with BS196, BS1778 or BS4343 should be used. Apart from safety extra low voltage circuits, couplers shall be non-reversible with an earthing connection. The coupler shall be connected such that the "plug" is on the load side of the coupler.

Note only BS4343 couplers are permissible on construction sites. See Figure 3.16.

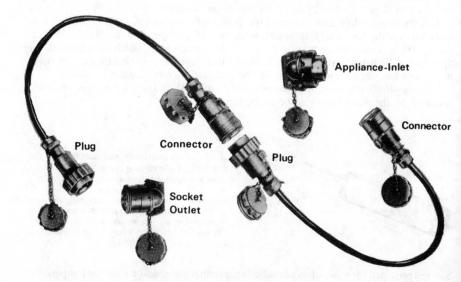

Figure 3.16 Joints in flexible cords or flexible cables to be made only with couplers.

Fire barriers

Where cables are routed through floors or walls the opening through which they pass should be made good to the necessary degree of fire resistance. Internal fire resistance: internal fire resistant barriers are required where cables are installed in shafts or trunking (or channels, ducts or ducting) which pass through such floors or walls, so as to provide a barrier to the spread of fire.

Supports

Fixed wiring cable and conductors must be supported so there is no unjustifiable mechanical strain and no measureable strain at the terminations of the conductors, consideration is to be given to any mechanical strain due to the supported mass of the cable or conductor itself. See Figure 3.17.

Note. For guidance on methods of support see Annex 3 hereto.

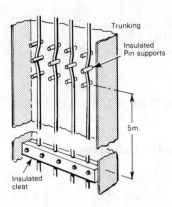

Figure 3.17 Supports for vertical cables in trunking (Regulation 529-1).

Bends

Bends in non-flexible cables must have a larger internal radius than the minimum shown in Annex 3.

Space Factors

An enclosure of a wiring system must be such that when a number of cables are installed into it, no damage can occur either to the cables or the enclosure.

Practice 4 gives cable capacities for conduit and trunking. A simple calculation overleaf shows how this can be utilised. Not all the sizes and types of cable and sizes of trunking are given, therefore any other calculation should ensure that a space factor of 45% is not exceeded.

Example 1. It is proposed to install 2 lighting circuits 2 x 2-1.5mm^2 single-core pvc insulated cables, and a power circuit requiring 4-6 mm^2 single-core pvc insulated cables. The conduit length is 6 metres and incorporates 2-bends.

∴from Practice 4, the cable factors are

1-5 mm^2 = 22 x 4 cables = 88
6.0 mm^2 = 58 x 4 cables = 232
                                        320   Total

and a 6 metre run with 2 bends shows a 25 mm conduit has a factor of 333, therefore a 25 mm conduit would be required.

Example 2. It is proposed to install 8 single-phase circuits each taking 16 amperes, these cables being installed in trunking where there is an ambient temperature of 35°C.

The overcurrent protection devices to be used are BS88 fuses rated 16A.

There are also protective conductors for each single-phase circuit. "Correction Factor" for temperature as given in the first Annex to this Practice Section

$$\frac{16}{0.94} = 17.0A.$$

Correction Factor for grouping = 8 single phase circuits plus 8 protective conductors = 8 loaded circuits and therefore correction factor = 0.52.

$$\therefore \frac{17}{0.52} = 32.69A.$$

The cable to be chosen is 6 mm^2 rated 41A.

From Practice 4 it can be seen that the cable factor for 6 mm is 22.9 and therefore

Number of cables   x   Cable Factor
      =   24   x   22.9
      =   549.6

This gives a minimum size of trunking of 50 mm x 37.5 mm or 75 mm x 25 mm.

ABBREVIATIONS used in the example which follows

FPU	Furthest point of utilisation
AVD	Anticipated voltage drop
V	Voltage drop
U_n	Nominal voltage line to line
U_o	Nominal voltage phase to neutral
A	Amperes
I_n	Nominal rating of overload protection device, Amperes
I_b	Circuit design current. Amperes
I_2	Current effecting operation of the overload protective device, Amperes
I_Z	Current carrying capacity of a cable, Amperes
mV	Millivolts drop in cables representing a value mV/A/m
mV/A/M	Millivolts drop per ampere of load per metre of route length
CSA	Cross sectional area of a conductor
mm^2	Cross sectional area of a conductor expressed in millimetres squared.
M	Metres
C_a	Correction factor for ambient temperature
C_g	Correction factor for cable grouping
0.725	Correction factor for semi-enclosed fuses
C_i	Correction factor for thermal insulation (0.5 cables embedded in)

Example of calculation of voltage drop and the minimum cross sectional area of conductors

Assuming the siting of the supply authority fuse or private generator circuit breaker has been agreed and the points of utilisation located from the schedule of installed loads, the first consideration should be to site correctly all points of distribution for final circuits, the design should ensure these circuits are kept as short as possible.

Where it is found the proposed final circuits require unusually large conductors to compensate for the effects of (1) voltage drop, (2) high ambient temperature, (3) high cable grouping, (4) characteristics of semi-enclosed fuses or (5) reduced heat loss in cables attached to or surrounded by thermal insulation, then the provisional design should be improved. Where a change of design is not possible the alternatives are (i) to reduce the circuit loadings, (ii) to reroute cables to avoid high ambient temperatures, (iii) to reduce the numbers of cables grouped or bunched, (iv) to use other types of overload protection devices where semi-enclosed fuses were proposed, (v) to reroute cables to avoid contact with large areas of thermal insulation. Before implementing alternatives (i) to (v), consider first that to implement (i) the number of final circuits would be increased; to implement (ii) and (v) the length of circuits may be increased, to implement (iii) the number of parallel runs of conduit, trunkings, ducts, cable tray or ladders may be increased; and to implement (iv) the use of more precise overload protection devices may substantially increase the cost of the devices but may enable a smaller cable to be used.

When all points of distribution for final circuits have been located, determine the number and practical location of points of sub-distribution then select and measure the most economical or practical cable routes using standard methods of installation only.

Having established provisionally all the points of distribution, points of utilisation and cable routes, adopt a design approach that will (a) confirm early in the design work if the cross sectional area of the longest final circuit cables are too large for practical purposes and (b) avoid the problem of calculating voltage drops shared by the meter tails, main cable, sub-main cables and final circuit cables, see the provisional design method shown in Figure 3.18.

The method proposed in Figure 3.18 declares a provisional anticipated voltage drop (AVD) at each point of distribution when the voltage drop at the furthest points of utilisation (FPU) are at the maximum allowed by Regulation 522-8.

See **Design volt drop in cables** (page 116).

The maximum voltage drop for each cable route (V) can then be deduced from the provisional voltage drops, any cable with an equal or lower voltage drop at design load will meet the requirements for voltage drop in that part of the distribution.

Taking as an example the provisional design in Figure 3.18 make an early check on the validity of the design approach by sampling the minimum cross sectional area of the final circuit conductors to the furthest points of utilisation, in this case circuit C from distribution board P2 and cable E from P1. If the resulting conductor sizes can be connected satisfactorily or terminated in standard accessories, etc, the design of the shorter final circuits can proceed.

When the cross sectional area of all final circuits has been determined the cross sectional areas of the sub-main cables and main cables can be determined to accommodate voltage drop and the nominal current rating of fuses or circuit breakers for overload protection and discrimination when operating under fault conditions.

For each circuit under consideration select a cable type appropriate for the methods of installation and environmental conditions envisaged in service, from the appropriate cable table covering the type of cable and method of installation, obtain the basic data for current carrying capacity, voltage drop and correction for ambient temperature. In the example the cables specified for circuits C and E are single core pvc-insulated bunched in conduit trunking. Therefore Table 9D1 should be used: Method 3 column 4 for cable C and method 3 column 5 for cable E.

The minimum conductor size used shall have a cross sectional area large enough to satisfy Regulation 522-8 for voltage drop, have a current carrying capacity (I_z) not less than the nominal rating or setting of the overload protection device (I_n) and satisfy the other requirements of Regulation 433-2 to coordinate conductors and devices for overload protection.

i) The design current must not exceed the current setting of the device $I_b \leqslant I_n$.

ii) The current setting of the device must not exceed lowest conductor rating $I_n \leqslant I_z$.

iii) The current effecting operation of the device must not exceed 1.45 times the lowest conductor rating $I_2 \leqslant 1.45\ I_z$.

$\therefore I_b \leqslant I_n \leqslant I_z$

$\therefore I_2 \leqslant 1.45\ I_z$

Where the cables are protected by HBC fuses or circuit breakers and the basic cable installation design data applicable to the IEE current rating tables is relevant then compliance with (ii) is also deemed to comply with (iii); this also applies when correction factors have been applied to compensate for the effects of ambient temperature, cable grouping, rewirable fuses and thermal insulation.

Where the cables are protected by (re-wirable) semi-enclosed fuses, the requirements of Regulation 433-2 are also deemed to be met if I_n does not exceed $0.725\ I_z$ eg.for a re-wirable fuse having a nominal current rating of 10A the minimum cable current carrying capacity would be $\frac{10}{0.725}$ = 13.793 A to satisfy co-ordination of conductors and devices for overload protection due to the higher fusing factor of $I_z = 2I_n$. To comply with (iii) $2I_n \leqslant 1.45I_z$ $\therefore In \leqslant 0.725\ I_z$.

Design voltage drop in cables

When all conductors of an installation are loaded to their design current I_b, Regulation 522-8 limits the total voltage drop between a source such as the Electricity Board fuses and any point of utilisation such as a socket outlet, luminaire, motor, etc, to a value that is appropriate to the safe functioning of the equipment in normal service.

Supplementary to the above requirement a relaxation is permitted for final circuits where the overcurrent device nominal rating does not exceed 100A.

In this case the voltage drop requirement is deemed to be met if the drop in voltage between the origin of the final circuit and any point on that circuit does not exceed 2½% of the nominal supply voltage, disregarding starting conditions.

Diversity may be applied as Section 311 and Appendix 4 of the regulations to determine the design current.

Selected equipment will operate safely within + or − 10% of the nominal supply voltage therefore the volt drop in the installation should not exceed this limit and should for preference operate with a margin for safety.

Where the supply is from a supply authority it may be necessary to limit the total volt drop in the installation to 2½% or less to accommodate starting conditions and to provide a reasonable margin for safe operation under normal conditions as prescribed by Regulation 522-8.

The indiscriminate application of the volt drop relaxation for final circuits up to 100A nominal current rating may not meet the requirements of Regulation 522-8 for the following possible operating considerations.

	Voltage drop as a % nominal supply voltage
(1) Maximum variation of voltage at the terminals of selected equipment.	± 10.0
(2) Supply authority statutory allowed voltage variation.	± 6.0
(3) Volt drop in main & submain cables, say	1.5
(4) Relaxation to volt drop requirements.	2.5
	10.0
(5) Margin to ensure safe operation has not been achieved in this case and does not meet the requrement of Regulation 522.8	00.0

For the purpose of the following example assume the supply is obtained from a supply authority and it has been determined the maximum design volt drop from the source of the installation shall not exceed 2½% of the nominal supply voltage.

For a three phase supply 415 x 2.5% = 10.375 volt drop (maximum) measured line to line. For a single phase and neutral supply 415/1.732 = 239.6 = 240 x 2.5% = 6.00 volt drop (maximum) measured Phase to Neutral.

Two methods of distribution for larger alternating current installations are common.
(1) Three phase mains and submains with three-phase final circuits to points of utilisation.
(2) Three phase and neutral mains and submains with single phase and neutral, three phase and three phase and neutral final circuits to points of utilisation, or combinations of (1) and (2).

When employing IEE Appendix 9 to determine cable size, the voltage drop across fuse links, protective devices, switchgear etc and voltage drop due to normal starting current is ignored. Where a heavy starting current is permitted, the effect on other parts of the installation or supply network should be assessed and conductor sizes increased if necessary to prevent voltage fluctuations in the installation and to reduce interference with other users connected to the same supply network. Because heavy starting currents may create problems for other users the Supply Authority should always be consulted. For single phase and neutral, three phase and three phase and neutral supplies where the Electricity Board fuses are rated 100A to BS1361, motors started direct on line without prior consultation should not exceed the following requirements:

EB Cat.	Type of duty	Frequency of starting	Single-phase 240V kW	480V kW	Three-phase 415V kW
1	Lift, Hoists etc.	Less than 2 hours	0.373	1.492	2.238
2	General	Not less than 2 hours	0.746	1.492	4.476

In general terms the smallest conductor cross sectional area is one that satisfies Regulation 522-8 for voltage drop. If Regulation 522-8 is satisfied other considerations requiring an increase in conductors cross sectional area are usually also met but require to be checked;

These are:– (1) Nominal current rating or setting of the overcurrent protective devices – Regulation 433-2. (2) Ambient temperature above 30°C – Annex 1. (3) Cable grouping – Annex 1. (4) Semi-enclosed fuse – Annex 1. (5) Thermal insulation to cables – Regulation 522-6.

Cable installation provisional design approach

If equipment selected will operate satisfactorily at plus or minus 10% of the supply voltage and because by statute the supply voltage may vary between plus or minus 6%, then the voltage drop in installation cables when operating at the design current should not exceed 4% of the nominal voltage. The following design is based on a maximum voltage drop from installation origin to any point of utilisation of 2½% of the nominal voltage.

In Figure 3.18 anticipated voltage drop (AVD) at points of distribution when voltage drop at the furthest points of utilisation (FPU) is at the maximum allowed by Regulation 522-8.

AVD at FPU cable C, 415 2.5% = $10.37U_n$ $\frac{10.37}{1.73}$ = $6.00U_o$

AVD at P2, 10.37 x $\frac{15 + 30}{70}$ = $6.67U_n$, $\frac{6.67}{1.73}$ = $3.86U_o$

AVD at P, 10.37 x $\frac{15}{70}$ = $2.22U_n$

AVD at FPU cable E, 415 2.5% = $10.37U_n$
AVD at P1, (10.37-2.22) x $\frac{18}{38}$ + 2.22 = $6.08U_n$

Voltage drop allocated to cable routes A to E

Volts drop (V) Route   A   = $2.22U_n$
                    B (P2-P)   6.67-2.22 = $4.45U_n$
                    C (FPU-P2) 10.37-6.67 = $3.70U_n$, $\frac{3.70}{1.73}$ = $2.14U_o$

                    D(P1-P)   6.08-2.22 = $3.86U_n$
                    E (FPU-P1)10.37-6.08 = $4.29U_n$

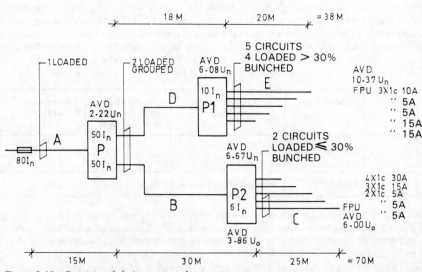

Figure 3.18   Provisional design approach.
         Notes: 1. The design does not represent an actual installation.   2. For clarity diversity has bee omitted except for main feeder.   3. The nominal rating of protective devices for discriminatio has not been considered for clarity.

Circuit details of Figure 3.18

Supply U_n *415 volts* U_o *240 volts 50hz 3 phase 4 wire*
Volt drop   *415 volts. 2.5% = 10.375V*
                 240 volts. 2.5% = 6.000V

Circuit	Description / Installation method		Cable Table	Method Column	C_a	C_g	C_f	C_i
C	2 No. SCPVC 6491X cables bunched in conduit with another circuit, 35°C, to thermal insulation, wire fuse.	4	9D1 9C2 9B	4/2 — —	35°C — 0.97	2	Wire — —	Fixed — —
E	3 No. SCPVC 6491X cables bunched in trunking with 4 No. circuits, 35°C in thermal insulation, MCB.	8	9D1 9C1 9B	3/5 — —	35°C — 0.94	4 0.60	MCB — —	EMBED 0.50
B	1 No. multicore PVCSWA PVC cable grouped with another cable on cable tray, 30°C, HBC Fuse.	11	9D4 9B	11/5 —	30°C —	2 0.86	HBC —	— —
D	1 No. multicore mineral cable PVC sheathed grouped with another cable 30°, also run singly at 50°C. HBC Fuse.	1	9J1 9J6 9C1 9B	1/3 1/11 — —	50°C — 0.67 —	2 0.85	HBC	—
A	1 No. multicore AL PVCSWA PVC cable run in enclosed trench, 25°C, HBC Fuse.	18	9K4 9C3 9C1	13/5 18/2 —	25°C — 1.02	—	HBC	—

Calculation of minimum cross sectional area to satisfy Regulations 433-2 and 522-8

Circuit	$V \times 1000 \div I_b \div M$ = Approximate mV/A/M				$I_n \div C_a \div C_g \div C_f \div C_i = I_z$						mV_1 / mV_2	mV	A	mm²
C	$2.14U_o$ —	1000 —	5 —	25 —	— 6	— 0.97	— —	— 0.725	— —	— 8.53	17.12 44.00	18.00 44.00	19.50 11.00	2.5* 1.0
E	$4.29U_n$ —	1000 —	10 —	20 —	— 10	— 0.94	— 0.60	— —	— 0.50	— 35.46	21.45 7.30	18.00 7.30	21.00 36.00	2.5 6*
B	$4.45U_n$ —	1000 —	50 —	30 —	— 50	— —	— 0.86	— —	— —	— 58.13	2.96 3.80	2.40 3.80	83.00 62.00	16* 10
D	$3.86U_n$ —	1000 —	50 —	18 —	— 50	— 0.67	— (0.85)	— —	— —	— 74.62	4.29 2.30	3.60 2.30	65.00 86.00	10 16*
A	$2.22U_n$ —	1000 —	80 —	15 —	— 80	— 1.02	— —	— —	— —	— 78.43	1.85 1.80	1.80 1.80	8.11† 88.11†	35* 35*

Regulation 522-8 volt drop   *Regulation 433-2 overload*   * *Selected cable*
                                                              † *Corrected 9C3*
                                                              (99 × 0.89 = 88.11A)

To select the smallest conductor that will satisfy the requirements for voltage drop and overload, compare as above the approximate mV/A/M for volt drop with the IEE tabulated mV/A/M for overload, select the lowest mV/A/M and find a cable with an equal or lower mV/A/M value in the IEE cable tables

Table	Cable correction factors
9B	More than one single core circuit or multicore cable
9C1	Ambient temperature protected by HBC fuse or MCB
9C2	Ambient temperature protected by semi-enclosed fuse
9C3	Cables installed in enclosed trench

Figure 3.19   Source of correction factors for cable grouping, ambient temperature and enclosed trenches.

Total voltage drop in selected cables

Circuit	$I_b \times M \times mV \div 1000 = U_n \div 1.732 = U_o$							Remarks
A	80	15	1.80	1000	2.16	1.732	1.24	Volt drop single-phase
B	50	30	2.40	1000	3.60	1.732	2.07	Volt drop single-phase
C	5	25	18.00	1000	—	—	2.25	Volt drop single-phase
Total							5.56	= Volt drop at FPU cable C. (max 6.00)
A	80	15	1.80	1000	2.16			Volt drop three-phase 4 wire
D	50	18	2.30	1000	2.07			Volt drop three-phase 3 wire
E	10	20	7.30	1000	1.46			Volt drop three-phase 3 wire
Total					5.69			= Volt drop at FPU cable E (max 10.375)

The provisional design does not represent an actual installation but represents a variety of possibilities.

Cable C is protected by a semi-enclosed fuse and although subject to the application of correction factors for ambient temperature and semi-enclosed fuse a larger conductor of 2.5mm^2 is necessary to satisfy the voltage drop allocated to that part of the distribution. A cable of this size for a 5A load would not be unusual at the furthest point of utilisation and would be capable of connection to standard accessories etc. Re-allocation of voltage drop in the provisional design is not necessary.

Cable E is protected by a miniature circuit breaker and is subject to correction for ambient temperature, cable grouping and thermal insulation, a conductor of 6mm^2 is necessary mainly to satisfy cable grouping and thermal insulation. A cable of this size for a 10A load would be unusual and may not be capable of connection in standard accessories, etc. Re-allocation of voltage drop in the provisional design would serve no purpose because the cable current carrying capacity is determined by $\dfrac{I_n}{C_a \times C_g \times C_i} = I_z$.

A change of design to this part of the distribution would be necessary.

Cable B is protected by HBC fuses, the considerations in respect of voltage drop or co-ordination of cable and protective device for overload protection are similar the former having a slight edge if compared on mV/A/M basis, a conductor of 16mm^2 satisfies both requirements.

Cable D is protected by HBC fuses and is subject to correction for ambient temperature or cable grouping, as these considerations occur in different areas the correction factor for ambient temperature satisfies both. As for Cable E the re-allocation of voltage drop in the provisional design would serve no purpose as the conductor size is determined by $\dfrac{I_n}{C_a} = I_z$.

A change of design may not be possible in a hazardous industrial area.

Cable A is protected by an HBC fuse and could be reduced to 16mm² if copper conductors were used, this would increase the voltage drop in Cable A $\dfrac{80 \times 15 \times 2.4}{1000 \times 1.732} =$ $1.66 - 1.24 = 0.42$V. This could be acommodated in cables A, B and C without exceeding the 6 volts maximum at the FPU. The increase in voltage drop would have no significance to the volt drop in A, D and E where the total voltage drop at the FPU is very much less than the provisional design due to the large conductors used for cables D and E necessary to satisfy co-ordination for overload protection.

Annex 1 to Practice 3 – Current carrying capacities and voltage drop *(IEE Appendix 9)*

Appendix 9 of the IEE Wiring Regulations deals exclusively with the sizing of cables. To calculate the most economical conductor size for a given load within the limitations imposed by conductor temperature and voltage drop, determine the cable route length, method of installation, cable type, highest cable grouping, highest ambient temperature, circuit design current and nominal current rating of the overcurrent protection device. Determine also the maximum acceptable cable route volt drop for convenience of calculation.

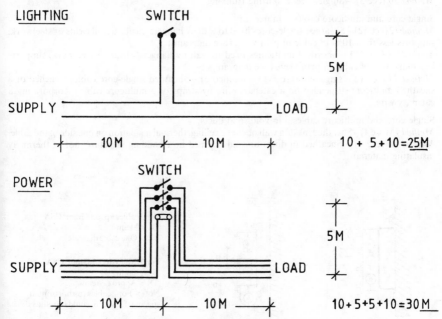

Figure 3.20   Cable route length in single- and multiphase circuits.

Methods of installation

In Table 9A of the Regulations twenty methods of cable installation are identified by number, current carrying capacity is also numbered. Cable current carrying capacity (ccc) and voltdrop (mV) can be located in a table for each cable type under the method of installation.

Standard methods 1 to 20

Single-core and multicore cables – open and clipped direct;
Method I (ccc I) – Sheathed clipped to or lying on a non-metallic surface.
Method II (ccc II) – Sheathed clipped to or lying on a horizontal or vertical cable tray or ladder.

Single-core and multicore cables – directly embedded;
Method 2 (ccc 2) – Sheathed cable in masonry, concrete, screed, plaster etc., not in thermally insulating materials.

Single-core and multicore cables – in conduit;
Method 3 (ccc 3) – Single-core non-sheathed in metal or plastic conduit on a wall or ceiling.
Method 4 (ccc 4) – Single-core non-sheathed in metal or plastic conduit inside a wall or over a ceiling, thermal insulation on one side of the conduit.
Method 5 (ccc 3) – Multi-core with non-metallic sheath in metal or plastic conduit on a wall or ceiling.
Method 6 (ccc 4) – Sheathed in metal or plastic conduit inside a wall or over a ceiling, thermal insulation on one side of the conduit.
Method 7 (ccc 3) – In metal or plastic conduit in masonry, concrete, screed, plaster etc., not in thermally insulating materials.

Single-core and multicore cables – in trunking;
Method 8 (ccc 3) – In cable trunking fixed to a wall or suspended in air.
Method 9 (ccc 3) – In flush floor and underfloor trunking.
Method 10 (ccc 3) – Single-core in skirting trunking.

Single-core and multicore cables – in free air;
Method 12 (ccc 12) – Sheathed single-cores fixed to wall by hangers, cleats, trefoil cleats or steelwork, supports less than 10% of cable in plan view. (See diagram.)
Method 13 (ccc 13) – Sheathed multicores fixed to wall by hangers, cleats or steelwork, supports less than 10% of cable in plan view. (See diagram.)
Method 14 (ccc 12 – single-core) (ccc 13 – multicore) – Sheathed single-core cables bunched or a sheathed multicore suspended on a catenary wire by straps or a multicore cable incorporating a catenary wire.

Single-core and multicore cables – in voids and ducts;
Method 15 (ccc 4) – Sheathed inside a wall or over a ceiling, thermal insulation on one side of the cable.
Method 16 (ccc 4) – Sheathed in ducts or voids formed in a building structure, not in thermally insulating materials.

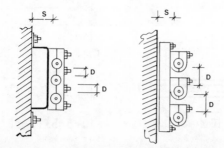

For 3 cables up to 185mm² CSA
'S' = 20mm
'D' = One cable diameter.

For 3 cables over 185mm² CSA
'S' = 20mm
'D' = Approx. 90mm
Note:– For 2 cables run horizontally spacing 'D' and 'S' could be reduced.

Single-core or multicore cables – in trenches;
Method 17 (ccc 12 – single-core) (ccc 13 – multicore) – Sheathed fixed to a wall of an open or ventilated trench. (See diagram.)
Method 18 (ccc 12 – single-core) (ccc 13 – multicore) (correction 9C3) – Sheathed in enclosed trench. (See diagram.)
Method 19 (ccc 12 – single-core) (ccc 13 – multicore) (correction 9C3) – Sheathed fixed to a wall of an enclosed trench. (See diagram.)
Method 20 (ccc 12 – single-core) (ccc 13 – multicore) (correction 9C3) – Sheathed fixed to a wall of an enclosed trench. (See diagram.)

Minimum spacings

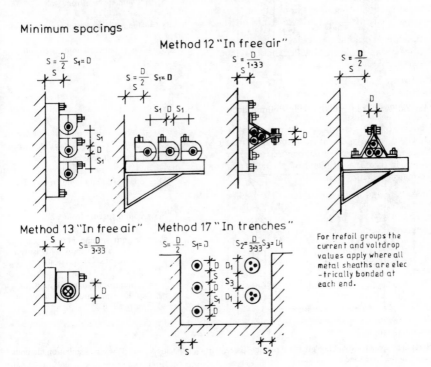

Method 12 "In free air"

Method 13 "In free air" Method 17 "In trenches"

For trefoil groups the current and voltdrop values apply where all metal sheaths are electrically bonded at each end.

Method 18 "In enclosed trenches"

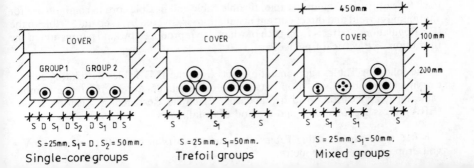

Single-core groups — $S = 25mm$, $S_1 = D$, $S_2 = 50mm$.

Trefoil groups — $S = 25 mm$, $S_1 = 50mm$.

Mixed groups — $S = 25mm$, $S_1 = 50mm$.

Method 19 – Trench 450mm, wide, 600mm deep.

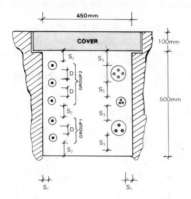

Spacings for groups of two of three single core cables and multicore cables.

'D' = Spacing equal to one group cable diameter.

'S₁' = 25mm spacing from wall.

'S₂' = 50mm between single core groups

'S₃' = 75mm between multicore cables.

Method 20 – Trench 600m wide, 760mm deep.

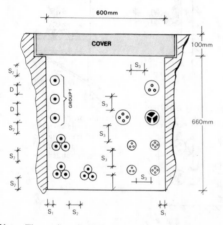

Spacings for groups of single core Trefoil and multicore cables.

'D' = Spacing equal to one group cable diameter.

'S₁' = 25mm spacing from wall.

'S₂' = 50mm spacing between single core cable groups. (Measured horizontally or vertically)

'S₃' = 75mm spacing between multicore cables. (measured horizontally or vertically).

Note: The spacings should be greater if possible particularly for spacing S₂ and S₃ where installation methods 19 and 20 are used.

Cable type

Each type of British Standard cable, flexible cable and flexible cord in common use for alternating current and direct current installations is covered by a separate Table in the IEE Regulations, extracts from each of which are reproduced by kind permission of the Institution of Electrical Engineers.

The following Tables supplement extracts from the IEE Tables by relating current carrying capacity and volt drop data to the cable manufacturer's reference number, cable type, application, British Standards, Electrical Research Association Report (ERA), cross sectional area and method of installation.

Note: In the current rating Tables: A = current carrying capacity (amperes); mV = volt drop per ampere per metre.

Copper conductor, single-core, pvc-insulated, with or without sheath (SCPVC) to BS6004 and BS6346

Manfrs. Ref.	Description	Application	BS Table No.	Voltage Grade	CSA mm²	Installation Method
6491X	SCPVC	Conduit/Trunking	1a	450/750	1 to 35	3, 4, 7, 8, 9, 10
"	"	Trunking	1a	"	50 to 1000	8, 9, 10
6181Y	SCPVC. PVC.	Tray	4	"	25 to 1000	11
"	"	Free Air	4	"	25 to 1000	12, 14
2491X	Flexible SCPVC	Flexibles	1(b)	"	1.5 to 4	Flexible conduit
6181Y	SCPVC. PVC.	Suface Wiring	4	300/500	1 to 1000	1
2491X	SCPVC	Panel Wiring	1(b)	450/750	1.5 to 4	Protected from mechanical damage.

IEE Table 9D1 (extract)

Conductor cross-sectional area	Installation methods 3 and 4				Installation method 1			
	2 cables, single-phase a.c., or d.c.		3 or 4 cables, three-phase a.c.		2 cables, single-phase a.c., or d.c.		3 or 4 cables, three-phase a.c.	
1	4	3	5	6	6	4	7	4
mm²	A	mV	A	mV	A	mV	A	mV
1.0	13.5	44	12	38	15.5	44	14	44
1.5	17.5	29	15.5	25	20	29	18	29
2.5	24	18	21	15	27	18	25	18
4	32	11	28	9.5	37	11	33	11

Copper conductors 2, 3 and 4 core, pvc insulated, pvc sheathed (pvc/pvc)
Manufacturers Reference 6192Y, 6193Y flat twin and three core to BS6004:1975 Table 4, 300/500V voltage grade, cross sectional area 1-16mm²

Application	Installation method
In conduit	5
In trunking	8
In ducts and voids	16
Surface wiring	1
On tray	11
Buried in normal plaster	2
Suspended from catenary wire	14

IEE Table 9D2 (extract)

Conductor cross-sectional area	Installation methods I				Installation methods II			
	One twin cable, with or without protective conductor, single-phase a.c., or d.c.		One three-core cable, with or without protective conductor, or one four-core cable, three-phase		One twin cable, with or without protective conductor, single-phase a.c., or d.c.		One three-core cable, with or without protective conductor, or one four-core cable, three-phase	
1	6	3	6	5	8	3	9	9
mm²	A	mV	A	mV	A	mV	A	mV
1.0	15	44	15	38	17	44	14.5	38
1.5	19.5	29	19.5	25	22	29	18.5	25
2.5	27	18	27	15	30	18	25	15
4	36	11	36	9.5	40	11	34	9.5
6	46	7.3	46	6.4	51	7.3	43	6.4
10	63	4.4	63	3.8	70	4.4	60	3.8
16	85	2.8	85	2.4	94	2.8	80	2.4

Copper conductors, pvc-insulated, pvc-sheathed, single wire armoured pvc sheathed 2, 3 and 4 core (pvc/pvc/swa pvc) cable to British Standard BS6346: 1969 Table 6, 8 and 10, voltage grade 600/1000V. Manufacturers Ref: 6942X, 6943X and 6944X.

IEE Table 9D4 (extract)

Conductor cross-sectional area	Installation method 1				Installation method 11 and 13			
	One twin cable single-phase a.c., or d.c.		One three- or four-core cable, three-phase		One twin cable single-phase a.c. or d.c.		One three- or four-core cable three-phase	
1	2	3	3	4	4	3	8	9
mm²	A	mV	A	mV	A	mV	A	mV
1.5	21	29	18	25	22	29	19	25
2.5	28	18	25	15	31	18	26	15
4	38	11	33	9.5	41	11	35	9.5
6	49	7.3	42	6.4	53	7.3	45	6.4
10	67	4.4	58	3.8	72	4.4	62	3.8
16	89	2.8	77	2.4	97	2.8	83	2.4

Application	Cross Sectional area mm²	Installation method
In ducts or voids	1.5 to 16 and 25 to 400	16
Open clipped direct	1.5 to 16 and 25 to 400	1
In free air	1.5 to 16 and 25 to 400	13
Enclosed trench	1.5 to 16 and 25 to 400	18, 19, 20
Buried direct	6 to 16 and 25 to 400	*
On trays	1.5 to 16 and 25 to 400	11
Open or ventilated trenches	1.5 to 16 and 25 to 400	17

* See ERA Report 69-30

Copper conductors, thermosetting insulation, pvc-sheathed, single-wire armoured, pvc-sheathed cable, XLP/PVC/SWA/PVC to British Standard BS5467 1977, Voltage grade 600/1000 with cross sectional areas from 16mm²–300mm².

Application	Installation method
Open clipped direct	1
On trays	11
In free air	13
Enclosed trench	18, 19, 20
In ducts, or voids	16
Open or ventilated trenches	17

IEE Table 9E2 (extract)

Conductor cross-sectional area	Installation method 1					Installation method 11 and 13				
	One twin cable, a.c. or d.c.			One three- or four-core cable, balanced three-phase a.c.		One twin cable, a.c. or d.c.			One three- or four-core cable, balanced three-phase a.c.	
1	2	2	3	3	4	4	2	3	5	4
mm²	A	mV	mV	A	mV	A	mV	mV	A	mV
16	110	2.90	2.90	94	2.50	115	2.90	2.90	99	2.50
25	146	1.85	1.90	124	1.65	152	1.85	1.90	131	1.65
35	180	1.35	1.35	154	1.15	188	1.35	1.35	162	1.15
50	219	0.98	1.00	187	0.87	228	0.98	1.00	197	0.87
70	279	0.67	0.69	238	0.60	291	0.67	0.69	251	0.60
95	338	0.49	0.52	289	0.45	354	0.49	0.52	304	0.45
120	392	0.39	0.42	335	0.37	410	0.39	0.42	353	0.37
150	451	0.31	0.35	386	0.30	472	0.31	0.35	406	0.30

Copper conductor, single core 85°C rubber insulation (SC/EPR/BC) to British Standard 6007.
Manufacturers reference 6101T (450/750V grade) or 6101V (600/1000V grade).

Application	B.S. Table No.	CSA mm^2	Installation method
In conduit trunking	1 & 6	1 to 630	3, 8
Open clipped direct	"	1 to 630	3, 8
On trays	"	25 to 630	11
In free air	"	25 to 630	12

IEE Table 9F1 (extract)

Conductor cross-sectional area	Installation methods 3 and 8				Installation method 11			
	2 cables, single-phase a.c., or d.c.		3 or 4 cables, three-phase a.c.		2 cables, single-phase a.c., or d.c.		3 or 4 cables, three-phase a.c.	
1	2	3	3	6	6	4	7	7
mm^2	A	mV	A	mV	A	mV	A	mV
1.0	17	46	15	40	—	—	—	—
1.5	22	31	19.5	26	—	—	—	—
2.5	30	18	27	16	—	—	—	—
4	40	12	36	10	—	—	—	—
6	52	7.7	46	6.7	—	—	—	—
10	72	4.6	63	4.0	—	—	—	—
16	96	2.9	85	2.5	—	—	—	—
25	127	1.9	112	1.65	153	1.85	140	1.60
35	157	1.4	138	1.20	189	1.35	174	1.15
50	190	1.05	167	0.91	229	0.99	211	0.88
70	242	0.74	213	0.65	293	0.69	269	0.62
95	293	0.58	258	0.51	356	0.52	327	0.48
120	339	0.49	298	0.43	412	0.43	379	0.41
150	372	0.42	334	0.37	475	0.36	437	0.35

Copper conductor, single-core, paper-insulated, lead-sheathed, pvc sheathed overall (PILC/PVC) to British Standard BS6480 Table 4, voltage grade 600/1000, and for sizes 50mm² – 300mm².

Application	Installation method
Open clipped direct	1,12
Underground duct or cable ducting	*
Enclosed trench	18, 19, 20
In free air	12, 17

*see ERA Report 69-30

IEE Table 9G1 (extract)

	Installation methods 1 and 12					Installation methods 12 and 17						
	2 cables, single-phase a.c., or d.c.			3 or 4 cables, three-phase a.c.		2 cables flat or vertical, single-phase a.c., or d.c.			3 or 4 cables flat or vertical, three-phase a.c.		3 cables in trefoil, three-phase a.c.	
Nominal cross-sectional area of conductor		a.c.	d.c.				a.c.	d.c.				
1	2	3	4	5	6	7	8	9	10	11	12	13
mm²	A	mV	mV	A	mV	A	mV	mV	A	mV	A	mV
50	190	0.93	0.93	180	0.82	230	0.94	0.93	220	0.84	205	0.81
70	240	0.64	0.64	230	0.61	290	0.68	0.64	280	0.61	255	0.58
95	300	0.48	0.47	285	0.48	355	0.56	0.47	345	0.47	315	0.43
120	350	0.40	0.37	340	0.39	415	0.48	0.37	405	0.41	370	0.35
150	405	0.33	0.30	390	0.35	475	0.42	0.30	460	0.38	420	0.30
185	470	0.29	0.24	450	0.31	550	0.36	0.24	535	0.35	485	0.26
240	580	0.25	0.18	575	0.28	675	0.38	0.18	670	0.33	580	0.22
300	670	0.22	0.14	660	0.26	770	0.36	0.14	760	0.32	670	0.20

Copper conductors paper insulated, twin and multicore, lead sheathed, armoured pvc-sheathed. (PILCS/SWA/PVC) mains cable to British Standard BS6480 Tables 6, 8, 10, voltage grade 600/1000, cross sectional area 50mm² – 400mm².

Application	Installation method
Open clipped direct	1, 12
In free air	12, 17
Enclosed trench	18, 19, 20
Underground duct or cable ducting	*
Buried direct underground	*

*see ERA Report 69-30

IEE Table 9G2 (extract)

Nominal cross-sectional area of conductor	Installation methods 1 and 12					Installation methods 12 and 17				
	One twin cable, single-phase a.c., or d.c.			One three- or four-core cable, three-phase		One twin cable, single-phase a.c., or d.c.			One three- or four-core cable, three-phase	
		a.c.	d.c.				a.c.	d.c.		
1	2	3	4	5	6	7	8	9	10	11
mm²	A	mV	mV	A	mV	A	mV	mV	A	mV
50	165	0.95	0.95	145	0.82	200	0.95	0.95	170	0.82
70	205	0.66	0.66	180	0.58	250	0.66	0.66	215	0.58
95	255	0.49	0.47	225	0.43	305	0.49	0.47	265	0.43
120	295	0.40	0.36	260	0.35	355	0.40	0.36	305	0.35
150	335	0.33	0.30	300	0.28	405	0.33	0.30	350	0.28
185	390	0.28	0.24	345	0.24	465	0.28	0.24	405	0.24

Tinned copper conductors, 60°C rubber insulated, PCP sheathed. (VR PCP) flexible cable to British Standard BS6007 Table 3, voltage grade 450/750

Man Ref	Description	CSA mm^2	Inst. methods applicable
6381P	SCVR. PCP	4 to 630	Maximum bunched 2 No.
6382P	2 core VR. PCP	4 to 25	Unenclosed reeling drum if derated.
6383P	3 core "	4 to 300	"
6384P	4 core "	4 to 300	"
6385P	5 core "	4 to 25	"

Note:- Cable derating factors for reeling drums.
Radial type, air on each side of cable   – Rating × 0.85
Other type drums, 1 layer of cable   – Rating × 0.85
Other type drums, 2 layers of cable   – Rating × 0.65
Other type drums, 3 layers of cable   – Rating × 0.45
Other type drums, 4 layers of cable   – Rating × 0.35

IEE Table 9H1 (extract)

Nominal cross-sectional area of conductor	Maximum diameter of wires forming conductor	d.c. or single-phase a.c. (one twin cable, with or without earth-continuity conductor, or two single-core cables bunched)	Three-phase a.c. (one three-, four- or five-core cable)	d.c.	Single-phase a.c.	Three-phase a.c.
1		2	3	2	3	4
mm^2	mm	A	A	mV	mV	mV
4	0.31	30	26	12	12	10
6	0.31	39	34	7.8	7.8	6.7
10	0.41	54	47	4.6	4.6	4.0
16	0.41	73	63	2.9	2.9	2.5
25	0.41	97	83	1.8	1.85	1.55
35	0.41	—	102	—	—	1.15
50	0.41	—	124	—	—	0.84
70	0.51	—	158	—	—	0.58
95	0.51	—	192	—	—	0.44
120	0.51	—	222	—	—	0.36
150	0.51	—	255	—	—	0.30
185	0.51	—	291	—	—	0.26

Tinned copper conductor, 85°C elastomer insulated, HORF sheath flexing cable. (VR/CSP).
Intermittent flexible cable to British Standard BS6007, Table 4, voltage grade 450/750.

Man Ref	Description	CSA mm²	Inst. methods applicable
6381TQ	SCVR. CSP. 85°C	4 to 630	Dry, humid, moist. Involving contact with oil and grease.
6382TQ	2 core CSP. 85°C	4 to 25	Unenclosed. Reeling drum if derated.
6383TQ	3 core "	4 to 50	"
6384TQ	4 core "	"	"
6385TQ	5 core "	"	"

Note:- Cable derating factors for reeling drums.
Radial type, air on each side of cable multiply rating × 0.85.
Other reeling drums.
1 layer multiply rating by 0.85
2 layers multiply rating by 0.65
3 layers multiply rating by 0.45
4 layers multiply rating by 0.35

IEE Table 9H2 (extract)

Nominal cross-sectional area of conductor	Maximum diameter of wires forming conductor	d.c. or single-phase a.c. (one twin cable, with or without earth-continuity conductor, or two single-core cables bunched)	Three-phase a.c. (one three-, four- or five-core cable)	d.c.	Single-phase a.c.	Three-phase a.c.
1		2	3	2	3	4
mm²	mm	A	A	mV	mV	mV
4	0.31	41	36	13.0	13.0	11
6	0.31	53	47	8.4	8.4	7.30
10	0.41	73	64	5.0	5.0	4.30
16	0.41	99	86	3.1	3.1	2.70
25	0.41	131	114	2.0	2.0	1.70
35	0.41	—	140	—	—	1.20
50	0.41	—	170	—	—	0.91
70	0.51	—	216	—	—	0.63
95	0.51	—	262	—	—	0.48
120	0.51	—	303	—	—	0.39
150	0.51	—	348	—	—	0.32
185	0.51	—	397	—	—	0.27

Tinned copper conductor, flexible cords to BS6500

Man Ref.	Description	Application	BS Table No.	Voltage Grade	CSA mm²	Inst. methods Applicable
2022	60°C VR braided twisted twin	Pendant cord	3	300/300	0.5 to 1	Indoor, dry. Loading = 0.5mm² 2kg, 0.75mm² 3kg, 1mm² 5kg.
2042	60°C VR braided circular twin	Flexible cord	4	"	0.5 to 1.5	"
2043	" 3 core	"	4	"	"	"
2212	60°C VR unkinkable braided CIR twin	Trailing flex	5	"	"	Indoor, dry, damp
2213	" 3 core	"	5	"	"	"
3182	60°C VR TRS circular twin	Ordinary flexible cord	6	300/500	0.5 to 2.5	Indoor, outdoor dry, wet.
3183	" 3 core	"	6	"	"	"
3184	" 4 core	"	6	"	"	"
3185	" 5 core	"	6	"	"	"
3182P	60°C VR PCP circular twin	"	6	"	0.75 to 1	"
3183P	" 3 core	"	6	"	"	"
3981	" single core	Flexible cord	8	450/750	1.5, 2.5	"
3982	" twin	"	8	"	1 to 2.5	"
3983	" 3 core	"	8	"	"	"

Code	Type	Description	No.	Voltage	Size	Situation
3984	" 4 core	"	8	"	"	Indoor, outdoor, dry, wet
3985	" 5 core	"	8	"	"	"
3182TQ	85°C EPR HOFR circular twin	HR. Flexible cord	9	300/500	0.5 to 2.5	Hot situation
3183TQ	" 3 core	"	9	"	"	"
3184TQ	" 4 core	"	9	"	0.75 to 2.5	"
2812X	PVC Parallel twin	Small flex for clock or similar	14	300/300	0.5, 0.75	Indoor, dry, cool. Not hard wearing
2491X	SCPVC	Internal wiring apparatus	17	300/500	0.5 to 1	Protected from mechanical damage
2492X	PVC twisted twin	Small flex for clock or similar	17	"	"	Indoor, dry, cool. Not hard wearing
2192Y	PVC. PVC flat twin	Light duty cord for radio, TV, lamps etc	15	300/300	0.5, 0.75	Indoor, dry, cool
2182Y	PVC PVC circular	"	15	"	"	"
2183Y	"	"	15	"	"	"
3192Y	PVC PVC flat twin	Ordinary flex for vac, fridge, wash m/c	16	300/500	0.75	"
3182Y	PVC PVC circular	"	16	"	0.5 to 2.5	Indoor, outdoor, damp, dry, cool, hard wearing
3183Y	" 3 core	"	16	"	"	"
3184Y	" 4 core	"	16	"	"	"
3185Y	" 5 core	"	16	"	"	"

Light duty, copper conductor, mineral insulated, copper sheathed with or without pvc oversheath to British Standard BS6207 Pt 1 voltage grade 600V. Exposed to touch (LD/MIMS).

Unsheathed – Generally not exposed to weather or corrosion			
Man Ref	Description	C.S.A. mm^2	Installation method
CC 2L	2 core MIMS	1 - 4	1
CC 3L	3 core MIMS	1 – 2.5	1
CC 4L	4 core MIMS	1 – 2.5	1
CC 7L	7 core MIMS	1 – 2.5	1

Sheathed – Generally exposed to weather or corrosion			
CCV 2L	2 core MIMS/PVC	1 – 4	
CCV 3L	3 core MIMS/PVC	1 – 4	1, 2, 11, 16 Underground
CCV 4L	4 core MIMS/PVC	1 – 4	
CCV 7L	7 core MIMS/PVC	1 – 4	

IEE Table 9J1 (extract)

Nominal cross sectional area of conductor	One twin cable, single-phase a.c., or d.c.		One three-core cable, three-phase a.c.		One four-core cable, three-phase a.c.		One seven-core cable, all cores fully loaded		
								1-ph. a.c., or d.c.	3-ph. a.c.
1	2	5	3	11	5	11	7	5	11
mm^2	A	mV	A	mV	A	mV	A	mV	mV
1.0	18.5	42	15	36	15	36	10	42	36
1.5	23	28	19	24	19.5	24	13	28	24
2.5	31	17	26	14	26	14	17.5	17	14
4	40	10	35	9.1	—	9.1	—	10	9.1
6	—	7	—	6.0	—	6.0	—	7	6.0
10	—	4.2	—	3.6	—	3.6	—	4.2	3.6

Light duty, copper conductors, mineral insulated, copper sheathed left bare (LD/MIMS). To British Standard BS6207 Part 1, voltage grade 600, for application in domestic premises where not exposed to weather or to corrosion. Not exposed to touch and not in contact with combustibles.

Man Ref	Description	CSA mm^2
CC-2L	2 core MIMS	1 to 4
CC-3L	3 core MIMS	1 to 2.5
CC-4L	4 core MIMS	1 to 2.5
CC-7L	7 core MIMS	1 to 2.5

Note: The sheath operating temperature should not exceed the design limits of the termination, seal or conductor sleeving.

Termination	Sealing compound	Type of sleeving	Seal temperature (max)
Increased safety protection.	Epoxy putty.	PTFE	100°C
Screw on pot seal	105°C Compound	PVC	105°C
Shrink on seal	185°C Compound	Acrylic Resin/Glass	135°C
Screw on pot, Med. temp. seal.	185°C Compound	Silicone rubber.	185°C
Screw on pot, High temp. seal	Glazing Flux	PTFE	250°C

IEE Table 9J2 (extract)

Nominal cross-sectional area of conductor	One twin cable, single-phase a.c., or d.c.		One three-core cable, three-phase a.c.		One four-core cable, three-phase a.c.		One seven-core cable, all cores fully loaded		
								Single-phase a.c. or d.c.	Three-phase a.c.
1	2	5	3	11	4	11	6	5	11
mm^2	A	mV	A	mV	A	mV	A	mV	mV
1.0	19.5	42	16.5	36	16	36	11	42	36
1.5	25	28	21	24	21	24	14	28	24
2.5	33	17	28	14	28	14	19	17	14
4	44	10	37	9.1	—	—	—	—	—

Heavy duty, copper conductors, mineral-insulated, copper-sheathed cables left bare (HD/MIMS) to BS6707, Part 1, 1000V grade for application in hazardous industrial situations Not exposed to touch and not in touch with combustibles.

Man Ref	Description	CSA mm²
CC-1H	1 core MIMS	6 to 240
CC-2H	2 core MIMS	1.5 to 25
CC-3H	3 core MIMS	1.5 to 25
CC-3H	4 core MIMS	1.5 to 25
CC-7H	7 core MIMS	1.5, 2.5

IEE Table 9J3 (extract)

Nominal cross-sectional area of conductor	Two single-core cables, single-phase a.c., or d.c.		Three or four single-core cables, three-phase a.c.		One twin cable, single-phase a.c., or d.c.		One three-core cable, three-phase a.c.		One four-core cable, three-phase a.c.		One seven-core cable, all cores fully loaded		
												1-ph a.c., or d.c.	3-ph a.c.
1	2	2	4	5	2	5	3	11	5	11	7	5	11
mm²	A	mV	A	mV	A	mV	A	mV	A	mV	A	mV	mV
1.0	24	47	24	40	24	47	20	40	20	40	14	47	40
1.5	31	31	30	27	31	31	26	27	26	27	17.5	31	27
2.5	42	19	41	16	42	19	35	16	35	16	24	19	16
4	55	12	53	10	55	12	47	10	46	10	32	12	10
6	70	7.8	67	6.8	70	7.8	59	6.8	58	6.8	—	—	—
10	96	4.7	91	4.1	96	—	81	4.1	78	4.1	—	—	—
16	127	3	119	2.6	127	—	107	2.6	103	2.6	—	—	—
25	166	1.85	154	1.65	166	—	140	1.6	134	1.6	—	—	—
35	203	1.35	187	1.20	—	—	—	—	—	—	—	—	—
50	251	1.00	230	0.91	—	—	—	—	—	—	—	—	—

Heavy duty copper conductors, mineral insulated, copper sheathed cable left bare (HD/MIMS). To British Standard BS6207 Part 1, voltage grade 1000, not exposed to touch or in contact with combustible materials

Man. ref	Description	CSA mm²	Inst. method
CC-1H	1 core MIMS	6 to 240	12
CC-2H	2 core MIMS	1.5 to 25	13
CC-3H	3 core MIMS	1.5 to 25	13
CC-4H	4 core MIMS	1.5 to 25	13
CC-7H	7 core MIMS	1.5, 2.5	13

Related current rating Table below.

IEE Table 9J4 (extract)

Nominal cross-sectional area of conductor	Two single-core cables, single-phase a.c., or d.c.		Three or four single-core cables, three-phase a.c.		One twin cable, single-phase a.c., or d.c.		One three-core cable, three-phase a.c.		One four-core cable, three-phase a.c.		One seven-core cable, all cores fully loaded		
												1-ph. a.c. or d.c.	3-ph. a.c
1	2	3	3	5	2	5	3	11	5	11	6	5	11
mm²	A	mV	A	mV	A	mV	A	mV	A	mV	A	mV	mV
1.0	26	47	22	40	26	47	22	40	19	40	15	47	40
1.5	33	31	28	27	33	31	28	27	24	27	19	31	27
2.5	45	19	38	16	45	19	38	16	32	16	26	19	16
4	60	12	50	10	60	12	50	10	43	10	34	12	10
6	76	7.8	64	6.8	76	7.8	64	6.8	54	6.8	—	—	—
10	104	4.7	87	4.1	104	4.7	87	4.1	73	4.1	—	—	—
16	137	3	115	2.6	137	3.0	115	2.6	97	2.6	—	—	—
25	179	1.85	150	1.6	179	1.85	150	1.6	126	1.6	—	—	—
35	220	1.35	184	1.15	—	—	—	—	—	—	—	—	—
50	272	1.00	228	0.88	—	—	—	—	—	—	—	—	—

Aluminium conductor, single core, pvc insulated with or without sheath. (AL SC PVC PVC) to British Standard BS6346, voltage grade 600/1000

Application	CSA mm²	Installation method
Clipped direct	50 to 1200	1
Conduit/trunking	50 to 120	3 and 8
On tray	50 to 1200	11
In free air	50 to 1200	12
Enclosed trench	50 to 1200	18
Catenary wire	50 to 600	14

IEE Table 9K1 (extract)

Cross sectional area of conductor	Installation methods 3 and 8					Installation method 11					Installation method 12					
	2 cables, single-phase a.c., or d.c.			3 or 4 cables, three-phase a.c.		2 cables, single-phase a.c., or d.c.			3 or 4 cables, three-phase a.c.		Flat or vertical (2 cables, single-phase a.c., or d.c., or 3 or 4 cables three-phase)				Trefoil (3 cables three-phase)	
		a.c.	d.c.				a.c.	d.c.				1ph.	d.c.	3ph.		
1	4	3	2	5	6	8	4	2	9	8	11	5	2	9	12	7
mm²	A	mV	mV	A	mV	A	mV	mV	A	mV	A	mV	mV	mV	A	mV
50	118	1.60	1.55	104	1.4	144	1.55	1.55	132	1.35	148	1.55	1.55	1.40	128	1.35
70	150	1.15	1.05	133	0.97	185	1.05	1.05	169	0.94	191	1.10	1.05	0.96	165	0.92
95	181	0.86	0.70	161	0.74	225	0.79	0.77	206	0.71	234	0.82	0.77	0.74	203	0.69
120	210	0.70	0.61	186	0.61	261	0.64	0.61	240	0.58	273	0.67	0.68	0.61	237	0.55
150	—	—	—	—	—	301	0.52	0.49	277	0.48	317	0.55	0.49	0.52	274	0.45

Aluminium conductor, pvc-insulated, pvc-sheathed, single-wire armoured, pvc-sheathed (AL/PVC/PVC). To British Standard BS6346, voltage grade 600/1000

Description	Application	CSA mm²	Installation method
Twin AL, PVC, PVC, SWA, PVC		16 to 95	1
3 or 4 core AL, PVC, PVC, SWA, PVC		16 to 300	1
Twin AL, PVC, PVC, SWA, PVC	Wall or tray	16 to 95	11
3 or 4 core AL, PVC, PVC, SWA, PVC	Wall or tray	16 to 300	11
Twin AL, PVC, PVC, SWA, PVC	In free air	16 to 95	13
3 or 4 core AL, PVC, PVC, SWA, PVC	In free air	16 to 300	13
Twin AL, PVC, PVC, SWA, PVC	Enclosed trench	16 to 95	18, 19, 20
3 or 4 core AL, PVC, PVC, SWA, PVC	Enclosed trench	16 to 300	18, 19, 20
Twin AL, PVC, PVC, SWA, PVC	Buried direct in the ground	16 to 95	*
3 or 4 core AL, PVC, PVC, SWA, PVC	Buried direct in the ground	16 to 300	*

* See ERA Report 69-30

IEE Table 9K4 (extract)

	Installation methods 11 and 13					Installation method 1				
Cross-sectional area of conductor	One twin cable, single-phase a.c., or d.c.			One three- or four-core cable, three-phase		One twin cable, single-phase a.c., or d.c.			One three- or four-core cable, three phase	
		a.c.	d.c.				a.c.	d.c.		
1	4	3	2	5	4	2	3	2	3	4
mm²	A	mV	mV	A	mV	A	mV	mV	A	mV
16	71	4.5	4.5	61	3.9	68	4.5	4.5	58	3.9
25	94	2.9	2.9	80	2.5	89	2.9	2.9	76	2.5
35	115	2.1	2.1	99	1.8	109	2.1	2.1	94	1.80
50	139	1.55	1.55	119	1.35	131	1.55	1.55	113	1.35
70	175	1.05	1.05	151	0.92	165	1.05	1.05	143	0.92
95	211	0.79	0.77	186	0.68	199	0.79	0.77	174	0.68
120	—	—	—	216	0.55	—	—	—	202	0.55

Aluminium conductor, thermosetting insulation, pvc-sheathed, single-wire armoured, pvc-sheathed (XLPE SWA PVC) to British Standard BS5467, voltage grade 600/1000. Manufacturers' reference XLPE

Description	Application	CSA mm²	Installation method
Twin AL, PVC, PVC, SWA, PVC	Underground duct or cable ducting	16 to 95	1
3 or 4 core AL, PVC, PVC, SWA, PVC	Underground duct or cable ducting	16 to 300	1
Twin AL, PVC, PVC, SWA, PVC	Wall or tray	16 to 95	11
3 or 4 core AL, PVC, PVC, SWA, PVC	Wall or tray	16 to 300	11
Twin AL, PVC, PVC, SWA, PVC	In free air	16 to 95	13
3 or 4 core AL, PVC, PVC, SWA, PVC	In free air	16 to 300	13
Twin AL, PVC, PVC, SWA, PVC	Enclosed trench	16 to 95	18, 19, 20
3 or 4 core AL, PVC, PVC, SWA, PVC	Enclosed trench	16 to 300	18, 19, 20
Twin AL, PVC, PVC, SWA, PVC	Buried direct in the ground	16 to 95	*
3 or 4 core AL, PVC, PVC, SWA, PVC	Buried direct in the ground	16 to 300	*

* See ERA Report 69-30

IEE Table 9L2 (extract)

	Installation methods 11 and 13					Installation method 1				
Conductor cross-sectional area	One twin cable, a.c., or d.c.			One three- or four-core cable, balanced three-phase a.c.		One twin cable, a.c., or d.c.			One three- or four-core cable, balanced three phase a.c.	
1	4	a.c. 3	d.c. 2	5	4	2	a.c. 3	d.c. 2	3	4
mm²	A	mV	mV	A	mV	A	mV	mV	A	mV
16	85	4.8	4.8	74	4.2	82	4.8	4.8	71	4.2
25	112	3.1	3.1	98	2.7	108	3.1	3.1	92	2.7
35	138	2.2	2.2	120	1.95	132	2.2	2.2	113	1.95
50	166	1.65	1.60	145	1.45	159	1.65	1.60	137	1.45
70	211	1.15	1.10	185	0.97	201	1.15	1.10	174	0.97
95	254	0.84	0.82	224	0.72	242	0.84	0.82	214	0.72
120	—	—	—	264	0.58	—	—	—	248	0.58
150	—	—	—	305	0.47	—	—	—	284	0.47

Aluminium conductor, single-core, impregnated paper-insulated, lead-sheathed, pvc-oversheathed (AL SC PILC PVC), to BS6480, voltage grade 600/1000, cross-sectional area 50 to 1000mm².

Application	Installation methods
Underground duct or cable ducting	*
Wall and tray	1 and 11
In free air	12
Enclosed trench	18, 19, 20

*See ERA Report 69-30

IEE Table 9M1 (extract)

Nominal cross-sectional area of conductor	Installation methods 1 and 11					Installation method 12						
	2 cables, single-phase a.c., or d.c.			3 or 4 cables, three-phase a.c.		2 cables, flat, or vertical, single-phase a.c., or d.c.			3 or 4 cables flat or vertical, three-phase a.c.		3 cables in trefoil, three-phase a.c.	
		a.c.	d.c.				a.c.	d.c.				
1	2	3	4	5	6	7	8	9	10	11	12	13
mm²	A	mV	mV	A	mV	A	mV	mV	A	mV	A	mV
50	145	1.6	1.6	144	1.3	175	1.6	1.6	170	1.4	155	1.3
70	185	1.1	1.1	175	0.96	225	1.1	1.1	215	1.0	200	0.92
95	225	0.8	0.77	215	0.72	275	0.82	0.77	270	0.77	245	0.68
120	265	0.64	0.61	260	0.58	325	0.68	0.61	315	0.64	285	0.55
150	300	0.52	0.51	295	0.50	370	0.58	0.51	360	0.56	325	0.46
185	355	0.44	0.40	345	0.44	430	0.50	0.40	420	0.49	380	0.38
240	435	0.36	0.33	430	0.39	530	0.47	0.33	530	0.46	455	0.32
300	495	0.30	0.24	500	0.34	610	0.41	0.24	605	0.40	525	0.27

Aluminium conductor, impregnated paper-insulated, twin and multicore, lead- or aluminium-sheathed, armoured, pvc-sheathed (AL/PILC/PVC) to British Standard BS6480 voltage grade 600/1000 and for sizes 4mm² to 400mm²

Description	Application	Installation method
Twin	On tray	11
3 or 4 core	On tray	11
Twin	Open clipped direct	1
3 or 4 core	Open clipped direct	1
Twin	In free air	13
3 or 4 core	In free air	13
Twin	Enclosed trench	18, 19, 20
3 or 4 core	Enclosed trench	18, 19, 20
Twin	Buried direct in the ground	*
3 or 4 core	Buried direct in the ground	*

* See ERA Report 69-30

IEE Table 9M2 (extract)

Nominal cross-sectional area of conductor	Installation methods 1 and 11					Installation method 13				
	One twin cable, single-phase a.c., or d.c.			One three- or four-core cable three-phase		One twin cable, single-phase a.c., or d.c.			One three- or four-core cable, three-phase	
1	2	a.c. 3	d.c. 4	5	6	7	a.c. 8	d.c. 9	10	11
mm²	A	mV	mV	A	mV	A	mV	mV	A	mV
50	125	1.6	1.6	115	1.3	145	1.6	1.6	130	1.3
70	165	1.1	1.1	140	0.95	195	1.1	1.1	160	0.95
95	205	0.81	0.79	170	0.70	240	0.81	0.79	200	0.70
120	235	0.64	0.63	200	0.55	275	0.64	0.63	230	0.55
150	265	0.53	0.53	225	0.46	315	0.53	0.51	265	0.46
185	310	0.44	0.41	245	0.38	365	0.44	0.41	305	0.38
240	370	0.36	0.31	290	0.31	435	0.36	0.31	365	0.31

Ambient temperature correction factors

Schedule 3.11 gives examples of ambient temperature correction factors (C_a) related to the cable table number, conductor insulation type and the conductor maximum permitted operating temperature or in the case of mineral cables the sheath operating temperature. The IEE tabulated current rating and voltdrop data for cables are based on an ambient temperature of 30°C, where a cable is operated in a temperature other than 30°C an appropriate correction factor is applied as a divisor to the nominal current rating of the protective device (I_n) this determines a minimum conductor size for continuous current carrying capacity (I_z). A cable selected from the tables by this method must therefore have an equal or higher current rating than the calculated value of (I_z). The above method avoids trial and error calculation, it is therefore simpler and more convenient to apply all correction factors as divisors to (I_n) to obtain the minimum size of cable required. See Figure 3.18.

The following examples relate to IEE Tables 9C1 and 9C2.

Schedule 3.11 – Correction factors for cable protected by fuse to BS88 or BS1361 or a circuit breaker to BS3871 Part 1 or BS4752 Part 1, for cables protected by semi-enclosed fuse to BS3036 the values are indicated here in *italics*

TABLE NUMBER	TYPE OF INSULATION	AMBIENT TEMPERATURE °C												°C MAX CONDUCTOR OR SHEATH
		25	30	35	40	45	50	55	60	65	70	75	80	
9D1-4, 9K1-4	General purpose PVC.	1·03	1·00	0·94	0·87	0·77	0·71	0·61	0·50	0·35	–	–	–	70
		1·03	*1·00*	*0·97*	*0·94*	*0·91*	*0·87*	*0·84*	*0·69*	*0·84*	–	–	–	
9E1-2, 9L1-2	Thermo-setting.	1·02	1·00	0·96	0·91	0·87	0·82	0·76	0·71	0·65	0·58	0·50	0·41	90
		1·03	*1·00*	*0·98*	*0·95*	*0·93*	*0·91*	*0·89*	*0·87*	*0·85*	*0·79*	*0·69*	*0·56*	
9F1-2	Rubber.	1·02	1·00	0·95	0·90	0·85	0·80	0·76	0·67	0·60	0·62	0·43	0·30	85
		1·04	*1·00*	*0·96*	*0·91*	*0·86*	*0·79*	*0·56*	–	–	–	–	–	
9G1-2, 9M1-2	Impregnated Paper.	1·02	1·00	0·95	0·89	0·84	0·77	0·71	0·63	0·55	0·45	0·32	–	80
		1·02	*1·00*	*0·97*	*0·95*	*0·92*	*0·90*	*0·82*	*0·84*	*0·76*	*0·62*	*0·43*	–	
9H1-2	Rubber Flexibles	1·04	1·00	0·92	0·82	0·71	0·58	0·41	–	–	–	–	–	60
		–	1·00	0·95	0·90	0·85	0·80	0·74	0·67	0·60	0·52	0·40	0·30	85
		1·02	*1·00*	*0·97*	*0·95*	*0·93*	*0·91*	*0·88*	*0·86*	*0·83*	*0·71*	*0·58*	*0·41*	
9H3	Rubber & PVC	–	1·00	0·92	0·82	0·71	0·58	0·41	–	–	–	–	–	60
		–	–	1·00	1·00	1·00	1·00	0·96	0·83	0·67	0·47	–	–	85
9J1-2,	Mineral	1·03	1·00	0·93	0·85	0·77	0·62	0·57	0·45	–	–	–	–	70
		1·03	*1·00*	*0·96*	*0·93*	*0·89*	*0·86*	*0·79*	*0·62*	*0·42*	–	–	–	
		1·02	1·00	0·96	0·92	0·88	0·84	0·80	0·75	0·70	0·65	0·60	0·54	105
		1·02	*1·00*	*0·98*	*0·96*	*0·93*	*0·91*	*0·89*	*0·86*	*0·84*	*0·82*	*0·79*	*0·77*	

Cables in enclosed trenches correction factors

The continuous current carrying capacity of cables in enclosed trenches can be obtained by multiplying the tabulated current rating of cables "in free air" by a correction factor from IEE Table 9C3.

(a) Single core cable "in free air" rating-reference method 12 in Table 9D1, 9D3, 9E1, 9F1, 9G1, 9J2, 9J4, 9K1, 9K3 or 9L1.

(b) Multicore cable "in free air" rating-reference method 13 in Table 9D2, 9D4, 9E2, 9F2, 9G2, 9J2, 9J4, 9K2, 9K4 or 9L2.

(c) Correction factor – table 9C3 for single or multicore cable groups installed in enclosed trenches under installation method 18, 19 or 20. See pages 123 and 124 for illustration of cable spacing in enclosed trenches.

Schedule 3.12 – Correction factors cables in enclosed trenches.

Cond-uctor cross-section-al area. mm²	Installation Method									
	18				19			20		
	2x1c 1x3c 1x4c	3x1c 2x2c – –	4x1c 2x3c 2x4c –	6x1c 4x2c 3x3c 3x4c	6x1c 4x2c 3x3c 3x4c	8x1c 4x3c 4x4c –	12x1c 8x2c 6x3c 6x4c	12x1c 8x2c 6x3c 6x4c	18x1c 12x2c 9x3c 9x4c	24x1c 16x2c 12x3c 12x4c
4	0·93	0·90	0·87	0·82	0·86	0·83	0·76	0·81	0·74	0·69
6	0·92	0·89	0·86	0·81	0·86	0·82	0·75	0·80	0·73	0·68
10	0·91	0·88	0·85	0·80	0·85	0·80	0·74	0·78	0·72	0·66
16	0·91	0·87	0·84	0·78	0·83	0·78	0·71	0·76	0·70	0·64
25	0·90	0·86	0·82	0·76	0·81	0·76	0·69	0·74	0·67	0·62
35	0·89	0·85	0·81	0·75	0·80	0·74	0·68	0·72	0·66	0·60
50	0·88	0·84	0·79	0·74	0·78	0·73	0·66	0·71	0·64	0·59
70	0·87	0·82	0·78	0·72	0·77	0·72	0·64	0·70	0·62	0·57

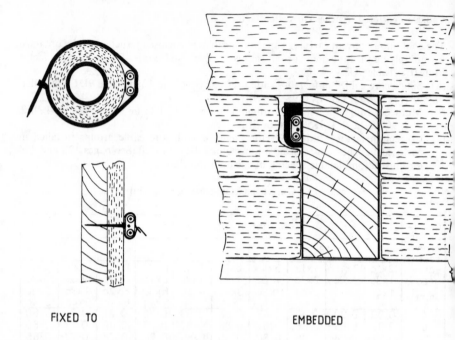

FIXED TO   EMBEDDED

Figure 3.21   Cables fixed to or embedded in thermal insulation.

Basic cable installation design data

The tabulated current carrying capacity and voltage drop data in the IEE current rating
Tables may be applied as the relevant data under the following basic conditions:–

(1)	Frequency 50 to 60 Hz $\pm 2\%$.
(2)	Ambient temperature 30°C.
(3)	Conductors identical equally and fully loaded.
(4)	One multicore cable run separately, alternatively one circuit of single core cables bunched or grouped, alternatively clearance between adjacent cables is two cable diameters or more.
(5)	The cable type is appropriate for the methods of installation and environment.
(6)	Maximum conductor operating temperature is not exceeded (see Schedule 3.11).
(7)	Power factor is not worse than 0.6 for conductors up to 120mm^2 or 0.8 lagging for larger conductors.
(8)	The overcurrent protective devices are HBC fuses to BS88 or BS1361 alternatively a circuit breaker to BS4752 Part 1 or an MCB to BS3871.

Where any of the above conditions differ or when the cable is totally embedded in
thermal insulation see Figure 3.21 or where the overcurrent protection device is a
semi-enclosed fuse then an appropriate correction factor must be applied for each
condition to correct the tabulated current carrying capacity data to the relevant data.

Cable grouping correction factors

Examples of cable grouping correction factors (C_g) related to cable type and method of installation.

Single core cables

Where more than one circuit is bunched or grouped the tabulated current carrying capacity data must be adjusted by a factor related to the number of circuits loaded more than 30% and correction factors applied as Figure 3.22.
Example of loaded circuits in trunking to determine correction factor.

Circuit	L1	L2	L3	N	CPC	Loaded
1	1	1	1	1	1	> 30%
2	1	1	1		1	< 30%
3	1			1	1	> 30%
Total	3		12			2

Correction factor for 2 No. loaded circuits (Figure 3.22) enclosed in trunking = 0.80

Multicore cables

Where two or more multicore cables are bunched or grouped the tabulated current carrying capacity data must be adjusted by a factor related to the number of cables loaded more than 30% and correction factors applied as Figure 3.22.

Where the spacing between adjacent cables is equal to or greater than two cable diameters correction factors may be omitted.

In the above example three single core cable circuits are bunched and enclosed in cable trunking, circuits No. 1 and No. 3 are loaded more than 30% of their grouped current rating and circuit No. 2 is assumed loaded less than 30% of its grouped current rating, if this is the case instead of using a correction factor for three circuits = 0.7, circuits No. 1 and No. 3 could be sized more economically using the correction factor for two circuits loaded more than 30% = 0.8 to confirm circuit No. 2 design current is less than 30% of its grouped current rating:-
(a) 3 circuits enclosed Table 9B Column 3 correction factor = 0.7.
(b) 1.0mm² SCPVC three phase current rating Table 9D, installation method 8, reference method 3, Column 5 current rating = 12.0A.
(c) Circuit No. 2 design current equals = 2.0A.
(d) Circuit No. 2 30% of its grouped current rating $(0.3 \times 0.7 \times 12.0A) = 2.5A$.
As the design current of circuit No. 2 is less than 30% of its grouped current rating the correction factor (C_g) applied to circuits No. 1 and No. 3 is 0.8 and 0.7 for circuit No. 2.

Cable grouping factors (C_g) used to determine the maximum continuous current rating of single and multicore cables installed in a group and loaded more than 30% of their grouped current rating.

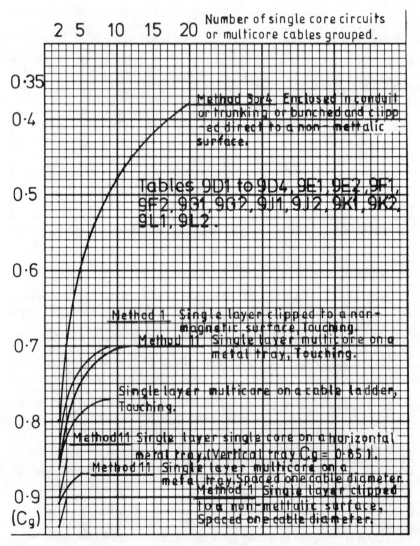

Figure 3.22   *Correction factors for groups of cables enclosed, clipped direct, on cable tray and cable ladder, cables touching or spaced (projected from IEE Table 9B).*

Annex 2 to Practice 3 – Notes on the selection of types of cable and flexible cord for particular uses and external influences *(IEE Appendix 10: reproduced by kind permission of the Institution of Electrical Engineers).*

For compliance with the requirements of Chapter 52 for the selection and erection of wiring systems in relation to risks of mechanical damage and corrosion, this appendix lists in two tables types of cable and flexible cord suitable for uses intended. These tables are not intended to be exhaustive and other limitations may be imposed by the relevant regulations, in particular those concerning maximum permissible operating temperatures.

Information is also included in this appendix on protection against corrosion of exposed metalwork of wiring systems.

Protection against corrosion of exposed metalwork of wiring systems

In damp situations, where metal cable sheaths and armour of cables, metal conduit and conduit fittings, metal ducting and trunking systems, and associated metal fixings, are liable to chemical or electrolytic attack by materials of a structure with which they may come in contact, it is necessary to take suitable precautions against corrosion.

Materials likely to cause such attack include:–

– materials containing magnesium chloride which are used in the construction of floors and dadoes,

– plaster undercoats contaminated with corrosive salts,

– lime, cement and plaster, for example on unpainted walls,

– oak and other acidic woods,

– dissimilar metals liable to set up electrolytic action.

Application of suitable coatings before erection, or prevention of contact by separation which plastics, are recognised as effectual precautions against corrosion.

Special care is required in the choice of materials for clips and other fittings for bare aluminium-sheathed cables and for aluminium conduit, to avoid risk of local corrosion in damp situations. Examples of suitable materials for this purpose are the following:–

– Porcelain,

– Plastics,

– Aluminium,

– Corrosion-resistant aluminium alloys,

– Zinc alloys complying with BS1004,

– Iron or steel protected against corrosion by galvanizing, sheradizing, etc.

(continued on page 153)

IEE Table 10A
Applications of cables for fixed wiring

Type of cable	Uses	Additional precautions (if any)
PVC- or rubber-insulated non-sheathed	In conduits, cable ducting or trunking, but not in such conduits etc. buried underground	–
Light circular pvc-insulated and sheathed	(i) General indoor use other than embedding (ii) Underground in conduit or pipes	Additional protection where exposed to severe mechanical stresses
Flat pvc-insulated and sheathed	(i) General indoor use (ii) On exterior surface walls, boundary walls and the like (iii) Overhead wiring between buildings (iv) Underground in conduits or pipes	Additional protection where exposed to severe mechanical stresses
Split-concentric pvc-insulated	General	–
Consac	General	–
Mineral-insulated	General	With overall pvc covering where exposed to the weather or risk of corrosion, or where installed underground, or in concrete ducts
PVC-insulated and armoured	General	With overall pvc covering where exposed to the weather or risk of corrosion, or where installed underground, or in concrete ducts
Paper-insulated lead-sheathed	General	(i) With armouring where exposed to severe mechanical stresses or where installed underground (ii) With serving where installed in concrete ducts

NOTES: 1 – The use of cable covers (preferably conforming to BS2484) or equivalent mechanical protection is desirable for all underground cables which might otherwise subsequently be disturbed.

2 – Cables having pvc insulation or sheath should preferably not be used where the ambient temperature is consistently below 0°C. Where they are to be installed during a period of low temperature, precautions should be taken to avoid risk of mechanical damage during handling.

Applications of flexible cords

Type of flexible cord	Uses
60°C rubber-insulated braided twin and three-core	Indoors in household or commercial premises where subject only to low mechanical stresses
60°C rubber-insulated and sheathed	(i) Indoors in household or commercial premises where subject only to low mechanical stresses (ii) Occasional use outdoors
60°C rubber-insulated sheathed and screened	Portable hand-lamps on construction sites or similar applications
60°C rubber-insulated oil-resisting and flame-retardant sheath	(i) General, unless subject to severe mechanical stresses (ii) Fixed installations protected in conduit or other enclosure
85°C rubber-insulated HOFR sheathed	General, including hot situations e.g. night storage heaters and immersion heaters
85°C heat resisting pvc-insulated and sheathed (to BS6500 (1969))	General, including hot situations e.g. for pendant luminaires
150°C rubber-insulated and braided	(i) At high ambient temperatures (ii) In or on luminaires
185°C glass-fibre-insulated single-core twisted twin and three-core	For internal wiring of luminaires only and then only where permitted by BS4533
185°C glass-fibre-insulated braided circular	(i) Dry situations at high ambient and not subject to abrasion or undue flexing (ii) Wiring of luminaires
Light pvc-insulated and sheathed	Indoors in household or commercial premises in dry situations, for light duty
Ordinary pvc-insulated and sheathed	(i) Indoors in household or commercial premises, including damp situations, for medium duty (ii) For cooking·and heating appliances where not in contact with hot parts (iii) For outdoor use other than in agricultural or industrial applications

Protection against corrosion (continued)

Contact between bare aluminium sheaths or aluminium conduits and any parts made of brass or other metal having a high copper content, should be especially avoided in damp situations, unless the parts are suitably plated. If such contact is unavoidable, the joint should be completely protected against ingress of moisture. Wiped joints in aluminium-sheathed cables should always be protected against moisture by a suitable paint, by an impervious tape, or by embedding in bitumen.

Annex 3 to Practice 3 – Notes on methods of support for cables and conductors
(IEE Appendix 11)

Some of the means to satisfy the Regulations covering supports, bends and space factors are given in this Annex. However, it is open to a qualified Electrical Engineer to seek other ways of compliance.

General statements for cables

(1) Cables installed in conduit or trunking do not require further support UNLESS the vertical run exceeds 5m. Cables in a vertical run exceeding 5m will require intermediate support to prevent undue stress at the top of the run.
(2) Horizontal runs of sheathed and/or armoured cables on reasonable smooth surface in relatively inaccessible locations need no fixing.
(3) Horizontal cables installed in caravans passing through joists set at intervals not exceeding 400mm and being firmly embedded in thermal insulating material do not need any supports or fixings. Where inaccessible in ceiling, floor or wall spaces, cable supports should be provided at 250mm intervals (horizontal runs) or 400mm (vertical runs).
(4) All other cables need some form of supports (clips, cleats, etc.) and the recommended maximum spacing is given in this Annex.

Temporary cable runs

For construction sites and other temporary installations cables should be so supported that undue strain at any termination or joint is prevented.

Spacing of supports for cables run in accessible positions

Schedule 3.13 and Figure 3.23 give the requirements of the Regulations in respect of the bending radii of cables and the fixing centres of their supports.

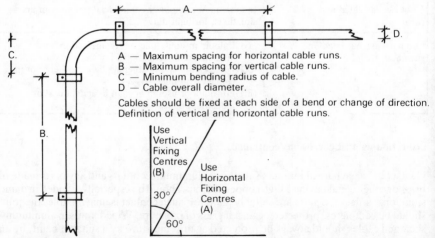

A — Maximum spacing for horizontal cable runs.
B — Maximum spacing for vertical cable runs.
C — Minimum bending radius of cable.
D — Cable overall diameter.

Cables should be fixed at each side of a bend or change of direction.
Definition of vertical and horizontal cable runs.

Use Vertical Fixing Centres (B)

Use Horizontal Fixing Centres (A)

30°

60°

Figure 3.23   Cable bending radii and fixing centres.

Schedule 3.13 – Cable bending radii (mm) and fixing centres (mm) (see Figure 3.23)

Overall Cable diameter (D) mm	Non-armoured cables — Stranded copper or aluminium rubber or pvc insulated with or without sheath including lead						Armoured — Any type			Armoured or non-armoured — Solid aluminium or copper shaped conductors, pvc			Paper insulated lead sheath			Mineral insulated copper or aluminium sheath with or without pvc		
	General			Caravans			General			General			General			General		
Figure 3.23	A	B	C	A	B	C	A	B	C	A	B	C	A	B	C	A	B	C
3-9	250	400	D x 3	150	250	D x 3	–	–	D x 6	–	–	D x 8	–	–	D x 12	600	800	D x 6
9-10	250	400	D x 3	150	250	D x 3	350	450	D x 6	350	450	D x 8	350	450	D x 12	900	1200	D x 6
10-15	300	400	D x 4	150	250	D x 4	350	450	D x 6	350	450	D x 8	350	450	D x 12	900	1200	D x 6
15-20	350	450	D x 4	150	250	D x 4	400	550	D x 6	400	550	D x 8	400	550	D x 12	1500	2000	D x 6
20-25	400	550	D x 4	150	250	D x 4	450	600	D x 6	450	600	D x 8	450	600	D x 12	*	*	*
25-40	400	550	D x 6	150	250	D x 6	450	600	D x 6	450	600	D x 8	450	600	D x 12	*	*	*
Over 40	*	*	D x 6	150	250	D x 6	*	*	D x 6	*	*	D x 8	*	*	D x 12	*	*	*

Note.
*Use manufacturer's recommendation. A = Horizontal run; B = Vertical run; C = Minimum bending radius.

Practice 4

Conduit, trunking, ducting and ducts

Selection and erection *(Regulations 521-10 to 521-12, 523-5 and 523-6, 523-14 to 523-18 and 527-10 to 527-12)*

Conduit and conduit fittings must be selected from Schedules 4.1 and 4.2. A complete conduit system (other than a factory assembled conduit system) must be installed before cables are drawn in. Running couplings and pipe unions must not be temporarily uncoupled in order to draw in cables.

A prewired, factory assembled conduit system should incorporate suitable tolerances to cater for variations in building site dimensions so that no part of the system will be under stress during the erection on site. During and after installation, precautions must be taken to prevent distortion of conduit and injury to cable ends by other construction activities.

Trunking, ducting and fittings must comply with one of the following British Standards:

BS4678 – "Steel trunking and ducting", or

BS476 Part 5 – "Insulating material having ignitability characteristic 'P'"

Figure 4.1 shows a selection of fittings which can be applied to a metal trunking system. Figure 4.2 illustrates various forms of cable enclosure and supports. Conduits, trunking and all cable enclosures must be suitable for the extremes of ambient temperature that will be met in normal use and account taken of the normal operating temperature of the cables installed in them. Where a pvc or similar thermoplastic box is used to support a luminaire or is in contact with it, the box temperature must not exceed 60°C and the load on the box not be greater than 3kg.

The normal maximum temperature of cable enclosures must not be overlooked when determining the box temperature.

As warm air rises, the air temperature at the top of a cable enclosure such as rising main busbars, duct, ducting or trunking system may increase to a high level due to heat generated by conductors. Heat barriers shall be fitted at intervals not exceeding five metres or at each floor level, whichever distance is less. Fire barriers may also serve as heat barriers.

In non-sealed conduit systems drainage holes should be provided where water might collect, for example a drainage hole should be provided at the end of a switch drop.

Entries to finished ducts, ducting or trunking are to be placed so as to prevent ingress of water or be protected against ingress. See Figure 4.3

Schedule 4.1 – Conduit and Conduit Fittings

British Standard	Protection			Finish			Standard diameter, thread — Imperial (inches)							Metric (mm)						Conduit — Type					Conduit fittings — Type					
	2	3	4	G	EP	E	½	¾	1	1¼	1½	2	2½	16	20	25	32	38	50	MS	PVC	SD	SW	EX	MI	MS	PVC	C	P	M
BS31			●	●			○	●	●	○	●	●	○							●		●			●	○		●	○	
"		●			●		○	○	○	○	●	●	○							●					●	○		●	○	
"	●					●	○	○	○	○										●					●	○		●	○	
BS4568			●	●										○	●	●	●	○	○	●			●		●	○		●	○	
"		●			●									○	●	●	●	○	○	●			●		●	○		●	○	
"	●					●								○	●	●	●	○	○	●			●		●	○		●	○	
BS4607	●					●								○				●	●		●			●			●			●

MS – Mild Steel.
MI – Malleable iron.
PVC – Polyvinylchloride.
E – Enamelled.
EP – Electro-zinc plated outside.
G – Hot dipped galvanised.
C – Cast.
P – Pressed welded.
M – Moulded.
SD – Solid drawn.
SW – Seam welded.
EX – Extruded.

Class 2 – Medium protection both inside and outside
Class 3 – Medium heavy protection (inside as Class 2, outside as Class 4).
Class 4 – Heavy protection both inside and outside.
Class 1 is referred to in BS31 and BS4568 but is not included in the above Table.
● – Preferred size or types
○ – Other sizes or types

Schedule 4.2 – Flexible Conduit and Adaptors

British Standard	Flexible conduit size and type											Construction					Gland thread size and type													
	Imp Inches				Metric mm				Duty								Imp Inches				Metric mm				Duty			Metal		
	½	¾	1½	2	16	20	25	32	GP	WP	L	GS	AP	SO	C	PVC	½	¾	1½	2	16	20	25	32	GP	WP	L	B	A	S
BS731	○	○	●	●	○	●	●	●	●			●					○	○	●	●	○	●	●	●	●			●		
"	○	○	●	●	○	●	●	●		●			●				○	○	●	●	○	●	●	●		●		●		
"	○	○	●	●	○	●	●	●			●			●			○	○	●	●	○	●	●	●			●		●	
"	○	○	●	●	○	●	●	●							●		○	○	●	●	○	●	●	●						●
BS4607 medium									●																●					
BS4607 heavy	○	○	●	●	○	●	●	●	●							●	○	○	●	●	○	●	●	●	●					

GP – General purpose
WP – Water proof
L – Liquid tight
B – Brass
A – Aluminium
S – Steel

GS – Galvanised steel spiral with deep interlocked joint.
AP – Galvanised steel, asbestos packed joint
SO – Galvanised steel, asbestos packed joint, PVC sheathed overall
C – Composite interleaved aluminium and paper tapes
PVC – Corrogated Polyvinylchloride tube and gland
● Preferred sizes etc. ○ – Other sizes etc.

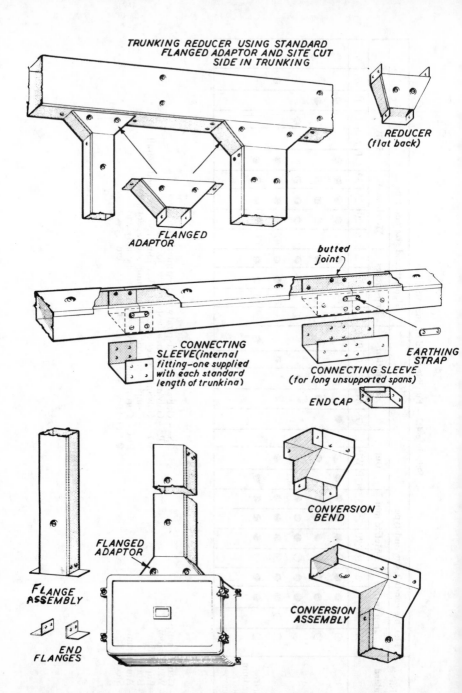

Figure 4.1 Shows a selection of fittings which can be applied to a metal trunking system and which conforms to the requirements of Regulation 521-12.

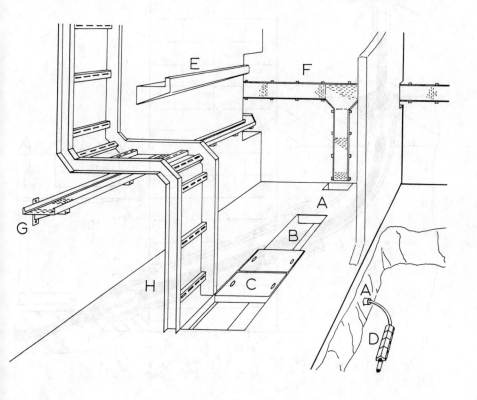

*Figure 4.2   Various forms of cable enclosure and supports: A – Duct (Enclosed cable way or pipe);
B – Open cable trench; C – Enclosed cable trench; D – Cable tiles (Protection external to
building); E – Cable Shelf (part of the building); F – Vertical cable tray; G – Horizontal
cable tray; H – Ladder rack.*

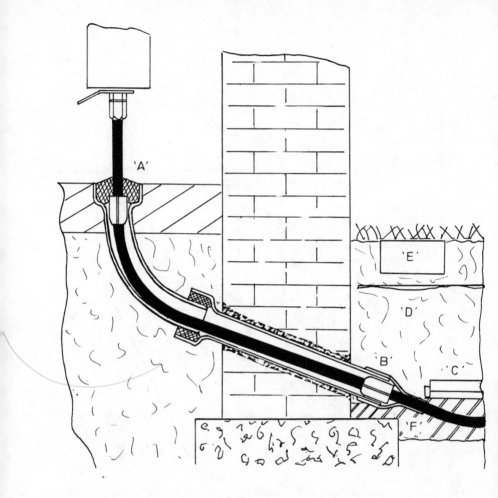

Figure 4.3   Protection of entries to finished ducts, ducting or trunking.

Protection against ingress of water (and vermin) (Regulation 523-15)

   A – Cable located by a split wooden pipe bung and filled with a weak mix of sand and cement to facilitate easy removal when required.

   B – Cable located by a split wooden pipe bung filled with plastic compound and covered with bitumastic tape or a heat shrink sleeve.

Protection of direct buried cables by location marking and cable tiles (Regulation 523-33)

   C – Hard burned clay or concrete interlocking tiles.

   D – Plastic marker tape.

   E – Block type concrete marker with lead insert for cable route reference code.

   F – Sand or riddled soil cable cover and bedding.

In onerous dusty conditions, conductor enclosures and joints must meet the requirements of IP5X (BS5490). This means that the enclosure must provide complete protection of persons against contact with live or moving parts within the enclosure and the enclosure must offer protection against the entry of harmful deposits of dust.

Metalwork should not be exposed to corrosive materials unless it is of a protected type.

Wiring systems which have associated non-metallic parts should not be placed in contact with other materials which would lead to the wiring system being chemically affected e.g. oil, creosote, unless the non-metallic parts are suitably protected. Further examples of substances which affect non-metallic materials are those used against woodworm and similar pests.

Further details of methods of protection against corrosion of wiring system metalwork are given in the Annex 2 to Practice 3.

Non-acidic or corrosive fluxes should not be used.

Joints in aluminium cables and other soldered joints should be protected against corrosion and attack by acidic fluxes by thorough cleaning followed by painting with suitable paint or binding with impervious tape or bitumen embedding.

Great care should be taken to remove any burrs from ends of conduit. Care must also be taken when installing and connecting cable trunking, or conduits into a trunking system that no sharp edges are left which may damage cables. (See Figure 3.9). The use of bushes is recommended at all boxes not incorporating spout entries.

Where cable drawn into conduit is subject to a connection, suitable boxes shall be provided at the cable junction. See Figure 4.4

Joints made in duct and ducting systems, or between those systems and another type of duct (ducting or conduit) shall be mechanically sound and made so that drawn in cables cannot be damaged. This also applies to cable outlets from a duct or ducting system.

Identification, Accessibility and Fire Barriers *(Regulations 524-2, 526-2 and 528-1)*.

Where conduits are installed in situations which normally require piped services to be separately identified by colour (boiler houses, plant rooms, service ducts or voids in buildings) then the requirements of BS1710 "Identification of pipelines" shall apply. The specified colour for electrical conduits is orange.

Note this is the standard colour on mineral insulated metal sheathed cables which are sheathed overall with pvc.

Inspection type conduit fittings and accessories (circular boxes with two or more entries, inspection couplers, tees or elbows with covers fixed by screws) should be installed in such a way that access to inspection covers is maintained to allow for future wiring and rewiring. Other building trades should be discouraged from covering or entrapping conduit fitting inspection covers.

No electrical installation within a building shall reduce the integrity of any wall ceiling or floor in respect of its ability to withstand the spread of fire. Where the electrical installation must pass through a building element (wall, floor, etc.), great care should be taken. Openings made in such elements to allow the installation of cables or conduits, or cable trunking, ducts or ducting must be made good in such a way as to restore the fire integrity of the building element. Figure 4.5 illustrates a typical cable transit utilised as a fire seal in wall. Figure 4.6 also illustrates how the fire integrity of walls and floor is maintained. Additionally internal fire barriers must be fitted within trunking, ducting or ducts in which cables, conduits or conductors are installed, where these pass through fire compartment walls or floors. See Figure 4.7

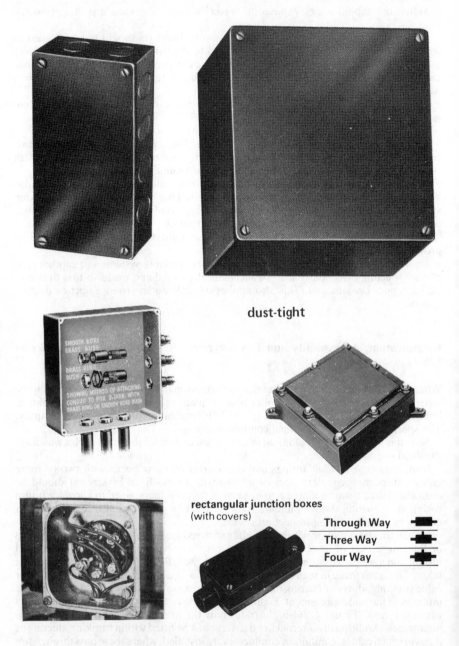

dust-tight

rectangular junction boxes
(with covers)

Through Way	
Three Way	
Four Way	

Figure 4.4   A selection of junction boxes. Junction boxes are available in sheet steel metal either with knockouts or left blank, also constructed in cast iron, both types can be obtained in black enamelled or galvanised finish.

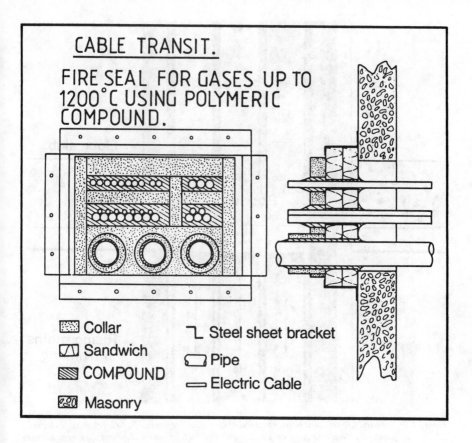

Figure 4.5   A cable transit used to maintain the fire integrity of a building element.

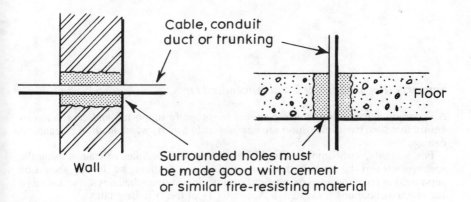

Figure 4.6   Cable passing through walls and floors.

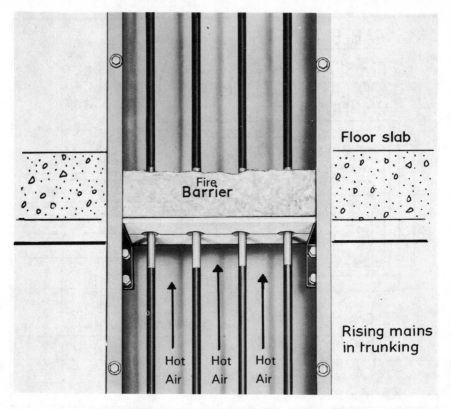

Figure 4.7 *Internal fire resistant barrier to prevent spread of fire at each floor level in cable channel, duct, ducting, trunking or shaft. Such fire barriers may also serve as heat barriers required by Regulation 523-6 provided they are fixed at intervals not exceeding five metres.*

Supports *(Regulation 529-2 and Appendix 11)*

All conduit, ducting and trunking should be properly supported and care taken to ensure that such cable enclosures are not subject to activity which leads to mechanical damage.

For conduits, such supports should be purpose made saddles or clamps using the spacing between the supports recommended below. Trunking or ducting should be supported as recommended or in manufacturers' literature. Schedules 4.3 and 4.4 give the recommendations contained in Appendix 11 of the IEE Regulations.

Schedule 4.3 – Conduit maximum fixing centres (Metres)

Size		Metal		Plastic		Pliable		From
mm	Inch	Horizontal	Vertical	Horizontal	Vertical	Horizontal	Vertical	Bend
16	–	0.75	1.00	0.75	1.00	0.30	0.50	0.30
20.25	–	1.75	2.00	1.50	1.75	0.40	0.60	0.30
32	1½	2.00	2.50	1.75	2.00	0.60	0.80	0.30
–	2	2.25	2.50	2.00	2.00	0.80	1.00	0.30

Schedule 4.4 – Trunking maximum fixing centres (Metres)

Size (mm)	Metal		Plastic		From
	Horizontal	Vertical	Horizontal	Vertical	Bend
25 x 16. 32 x 12.5. 40 x 16. 40 x 25.	–	–	0.50	0.50	0.30
40 x 40. 50 x 50.	1.75	2.00	1.25	1.25	0.30
85 x 20.	–	–	1.25	1.25	0.30
75 x 50. 100 x 50.	3.00	3.00	1.50	2.00	0.30
75 x 75. 100 x 75 100 x 100. 150 x 75. 150 x 100. 150 x 150.	3.00	3.00	1.75	2.00	0.30

Particular care should be taken with rigid pvc conduits, and the method of support adopted should allow for thermal movement along the length of the conduit which will occur with changes of temperature. Supports must be capable of coping with such movement within the normal temperature range. All supports used must be strong enough to cope with normal mechanical stresses and strains during the life of the installation (i.e. resting of ladders against conduits). Figure 4.8 illustrates several types of conduit fixings.

For the method to be employed when conduit is used to span distribution between buildings, see item A in Figure 3.11.

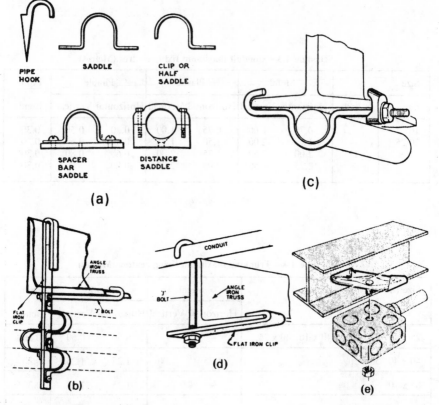

Figure 4.8   Types of conduit fixings:
   (a)   various supports
   (b)   bracket
   (c)   girder clamp
   (d)   Angle iron truss clamp
   (e)   Fastener clip

Conduit fittings *(Regulations 529-4 to 529-6)*

Solid elbows or tees are allowed only in the following positions:
(i)   Immediately adjacent to: a conduit terminal box; a luminaire; a conduit inspection fitting; or
(ii)   Not more than 500 mm from a fitting which will afford permanent access, provided that total run of conduit between two points of permanent access is 10 m (or less) and there is not more than one right angle (or two 45°) bends in the run in addition to the solid elbow. See Figure 4.9)

Pre-manufactured conduit bends shall comply with BS4568 or BS4607.

Bends made on site shall have an inner radius which is at least 2.5 times the outside diameter of the conduit (see Figure 4.10) or such larger radius as would be needed to comply with Regulation 529-3 (see Practice 3 – Schedule 3.12). Also every bend in a duct or ducting shall be of an inner radius which complies with Regulation 529-3.

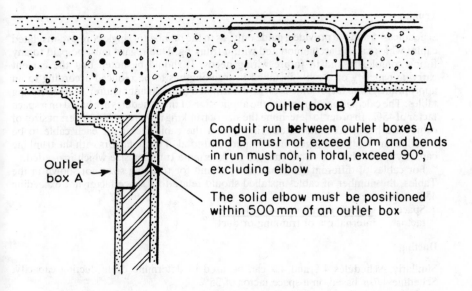

Outlet box B

Conduit run between outlet boxes A and B must not exceed 10m and bends in run must not, in total, exceed 90°, excluding elbow

The solid elbow must be positioned within 500 mm of an outlet box

Outlet box A

Figure 4.9   Illustration of the limitation in the use of solid elbows.

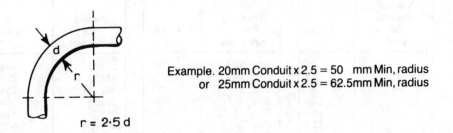

r = 2·5 d

Example. 20mm Conduit x 2.5 = 50   mm Min, radius
or 25mm Conduit x 2.5 = 62.5mm Min, radius

Figure 4.10   Bending radius of conduit bend other than bends to BS4568 or BS4607.

Cable capacity of wiring systems *(Appendix 12)*

Appendix 12 of the IEE Regulations describes a method of determining the number of cables of the same size, or of differing sizes, that can be drawn into a particular size of trunking and conduit. This method satisfies the requirement of the Regulations that the number of cables installed in trunking shall be such that no damage is caused to the cables or to the enclosure during installation.

Trunking

Schedules 4.5 and 4.6 provide a guide only, as to the number of single core pvc-insulated cables which can be accommodated within trunking. Due regard must be paid to any fitting complexity and to future wiring needs. It should be noted that the current carrying capacity of a cable installed in trunking has to be reduced according to an appropriate group factor which can be determined from a manufacturer's current rating tables. The calculations derived by the application of the Schedules are based on a space factor of 45%. In order to determine the size of trunking required when different sizes of cables are being accommodated, first obtain the cable factor for each cable to be installed and add these together. Compare that total of those factors with the trunking capacity factor shown in Schedule 4.6 to determine trunking size which is needed.

For cables of different types and/or sizes and for trunking sizes not shown in the Tables, the number of cables installed should relate to a space factor not exceeding 45%, where:

$$\frac{\text{Space}}{\text{factor}} = \frac{\text{sum of overall csa of cables}}{\text{internal csa of trunking or duct}} \%$$

Ducting

Similarly, Schedules 4.5 and 4.7 can be used to determine cable ducting capacity. Schedule 4.7 is based on a space factor of 35%.

Schedule 4.5 – Factors for single core pvc-insulated cables to be installed in trunking or ducting.

Nominal conductor size mm²	Factor
1.5+	7.1
1.5*	8.1
2.5+	10.2
2.5*	11.4
4	15.2
6	22.9
10	36.3
16	50.3
25	75.4
35	95.0
50	133
70	177
95	227

+ Solid
* Stranded

Schedule 4.6 – Factors for trunking

Trunking size mm x mm	Factor
50 x 37.5	767
50 x 50	1037
75 x 25	738
75 x 37.5	1146
75 x 50	1555
75 x 75	2371
100 x 25	993
100 x 37.5	1542
100 x 50	2091
100 x 75	3189
100 x 100	4252
150 x 75	4743
150 x 100	6394
150 x 150	9697
200 x 100	8572
225 x 150	14652
300 x 150	19447

Schedule 4.7 – Factors for ducting

Ducting size mm x mm	Factor
25 x 25	166
33 x 25	226
38 x 25	253
50 x 25	343
75 x 25	513
100 x 25	693
112 x 25	784
25 x 38	257
33 x 38	349
38 x 38	391
50 x 38	530
75 x 38	794
100 x 38	1072
112 x 38	1214

Conduit

Schedules 4.8 to 4.10 can be used to determine the number of single core pvc-insulated cables which can be drawn into steel and pvc, light and heavy gauge conduits.

Schedule 4.8 – Capacity of conduits for single core pvc-insulated cables

Cable size: Nominal conductor size mm²	Length of run metres	20mm straight	one bend	two bends	three bends	four bends	25mm straight	one bend	two bends	three bends	four bends	32mm straight	one bend	two bends	three bends	four bends
1.0 solid	1.0	20	18	17	16	13	36	33	32	28	24	63	59	56	51	43
	1.5	20	18	16	14	11	36	33	30	26	20	63	57	53	46	37
	2.0	20	17	16	13	9	36	32	28	24	18	63	56	51	43	33
	2.5	20	17	15	12	8	36	31	27	22	16	63	54	48	40	29
	3.0	20	16	14	11	–	36	30	26	20	–	63	53	46	37	–
	3.5	18	16	13	10		32	29	25	19		56	52	45	35	
	4.0	17	16	13	9		32	28	24	18		56	51	43	33	
	4.5	17	15	12	9		31	28	23	17		55	50	41	31	
	5.0	17	15	12	8		31	27	22	16		54	48	40	29	
	6.0	16	14	11	–		30	26	20	–		53	46	37	–	
	7.0	16	13	10	–		29	25	19	–		52	45	35	–	
	8.0	16	13	9	–		28	24	18	–		51	43	33	–	
	9.0	15	12	9	–		28	23	17	–		50	41	31	–	
	10.0	15	12	8	–		27	22	16	–		48	40	29	–	
1.5 solid	1.0	17	13	13	11	9	29	24	23	21	17	51	43	40	37	31
	1.5	17	13	12	10	8	29	24	22	19	15	51	41	38	34	27
	2.0	17	13	11	9	7	29	23	21	17	13	51	40	37	31	24
	2.5	17	12	11	8	6	29	22	20	16	11	51	39	35	29	21
	3.0	17	12	10	8	–	29	22	19	15	–	51	38	34	27	–
	3.5	13	11	10	7		23	21	18	14		41	38	32	25	
	4.0	13	11	9	7		23	21	17	13		40	37	31	24	
	4.5	12	11	9	6		23	20	16	12		40	36	30	22	
	5.0	12	11	8	6		22	20	16	11		39	35	29	21	
	6.0	12	10	8	–		22	19	15	–		38	34	27	–	
	7.0	11	10	7	–		21	18	14	–		38	32	25	–	
	8.0	11	9	7	–		21	17	13	–		37	31	24	–	
	9.0	11	9	6	–		20	16	12	–		36	30	22	–	
	10.0	11	8	6	–		20	16	11	–		35	29	21	–	
1.5 stranded	1.0	14	13	13	11	9	25	24	23	21	17	45	43	40	37	31
	1.5	14	13	12	10	8	25	24	22	19	15	45	41	38	34	27
	2.0	14	13	11	9	7	25	23	21	17	13	45	40	37	31	24
	2.5	14	12	11	8	6	25	22	20	16	11	45	39	35	29	21
	3.0	14	12	10	8	–	25	22	19	15	–	45	38	34	27	–
	3.5	13	11	10	7		23	21	18	14		41	38	32	25	
	4.0	13	11	9	7		23	21	17	13		40	37	31	24	
	4.5	12	11	9	6		23	20	16	12		40	36	30	22	
	5.0	12	11	8	6		22	20	16	11		39	35	29	21	
	6.0	12	10	8	–		22	19	15	–		38	34	27	–	
	7.0	11	10	7	–		21	18	14	–		38	32	25	–	
	8.0	11	9	7	–		21	17	13	–		37	31	24	–	
	9.0	11	9	6	–		20	16	12	–		36	30	22	–	
	10.0	11	8	6	–		20	16	11	–		35	29	21	–	
2.5 solid	1.0	11	10	9	8	7	20	18	17	15	12	35	31	30	27	23
	1.5	11	9	9	7	6	20	17	16	14	11	35	30	28	25	20
	2.0	11	9	8	7	5	20	17	15	12	9	35	30	27	23	17
	2.5	11	9	8	6	4	20	16	14	11	8	35	29	26	21	15
	3.0	11	9	7	6	–	20	16	14	11	–	35	28	25	20	–
	3.5	9	8	7	5		17	15	13	10		30	27	24	18	
	4.0	9	8	7	5		17	15	12	9		30	27	23	17	
	4.5	9	8	6	4		16	15	12	9		29	26	22	16	
	5.0	9	8	6	4		16	14	11	8		29	26	21	15	
	6.0	9	7	6	–		16	14	11	–		28	25	20	–	
	7.0	8	7	5	–		15	13	10	–		27	24	18	–	
	8.0	8	7	5	–		15	12	9	–		27	23	17	–	
	9.0	8	6	4	–		15	12	9	–		26	22	16	–	
	10.0	8	6	4	–		14	11	8	–		26	21	15	–	

Schedule 4.9 – Capacity of conduits for single core pvc-insulated cables

Cable size		Size of conduit														
Nominal conductor size mm²	Length of run metres	20mm					25mm					32mm				
		straight	one bend	two bends	three bends	four bends	straight	one bend	two bends	three bends	four bends	straight	one bend	two bends	three bends	four bends
2.5 stranded	1.0	10	10	9	8	7	18	18	17	15	12	32	31	30	27	23
	1.5	10	9	9	7	6	18	17	16	14	11	32	30	28	25	20
	2.0	10	9	8	7	5	18	17	15	12	9	32	30	27	23	17
	2.5	10	9	8	6	4	18	16	14	11	8	32	29	26	21	15
	3.0	10	9	7	6	–	18	16	14	11	–	32	28	25	20	–
	3.5	9	8	7	5		17	15	13	10		30	27	24	18	
	4.0	9	8	7	5		17	15	12	9		30	27	23	17	
	4.5	9	8	6	4		16	15	12	9		29	26	22	16	
	5.0	9	8	6	4		16	14	11	8		29	26	21	15	
	6.0	9	7	6	–		16	14	11	–		28	25	20	–	
	7.0	8	7	5	–		15	13	10	–		27	24	18	–	
	8.0	8	7	5	–		15	12	9	–		27	23	17	–	
	9.0	8	6	4	–		15	12	9	–		26	22	16	–	
	10.0	8	6	4	–		14	11	8	–		26	21	15	–	
4.0 stranded	1.0	7	7	6	5	4	13	12	11	10	9	24	22	20	19	16
	1.5	7	7	6	5	4	13	12	11	9	7	24	21	19	17	13
	2.0	7	6	5	4	3	13	11	10	9	6	24	20	19	16	12
	2.5	7	6	5	4	3	13	11	10	8	6	24	20	18	14	11
	3.0	7	6	5	4	–	13	11	9	7	–	24	19	17	13	–
	3.5	6	6	5	3		12	11	9	7		21	19	16	13	
	4.0	6	5	4	3		11	10	9	6		20	19	16	12	
	4.5	6	5	4	3		11	10	8	6		20	18	15	11	
	5.0	6	5	4	3		11	10	8	6		20	18	14	11	
	6.0	6	5	4	–		11	9	7	–		19	17	13	–	
	7.0	6	5	3	–		11	9	7	–		19	16	13	–	
	8.0	5	4	3	–		10	9	6	–		19	16	12	–	
	9.0	5	4	3	–		10	8	6	–		18	15	11	–	
	10.0	5	4	3	–		10	8	6	–		18	14	11	–	
6.0 stranded	1.0	5	5	4	4	3	9	9	8	7	6	15	15	15	14	11
	1.5	5	5	4	4	3	9	9	8	7	5	15	15	14	12	10
	2.0	5	4	4	3	2	9	8	7	6	5	15	15	14	11	9
	2.5	5	4	4	3	2	9	8	7	6	4	15	15	13	11	8
	3.0	5	4	4	3	–	9	8	7	5	–	15	14	12	10	–
	3.5	5	4	3	2		8	8	6	5		15	14	11	9	
	4.0	4	4	3	2		8	7	6	5		15	14	11	9	
	4.5	4	4	3	2		8	7	6	4		15	13	11	8	
	5.0	4	4	3	2		8	7	6	4		15	13	11	8	
	6.0	4	4	3	–		8	7	5	–		14	12	10	–	
	7.0	4	3	2	–		8	6	5	–		14	12	9	–	
	8.0	4	3	2	–		7	6	5	–		14	11	9	–	
	9.0	4	3	2	–		7	6	4	–		13	11	8	–	
	10.0	4	3	2	–		7	6	4	–		13	11	8	–	
10.0 stranded	1.0	3	2	2	2	2	5	5	4	4	3	9	9	8	7	6
	1.5	3	2	2	2	1	5	5	4	4	3	9	8	8	7	5
	2.0	3	2	2	2	1	5	4	4	3	2	9	8	7	6	5
	2.5	3	2	2	1	1	5	4	4	3	2	9	8	7	6	4
	3.0	3	2	2	1	–	5	4	4	3	–	9	8	7	5	–
	3.5	2	2	2	1		4	4	3	2		8	7	6	5	
	4.0	2	2	2	1		4	4	3	2		8	7	6	5	
	4.5	2	2	1	1		4	4	3	2		8	7	6	4	
	5.0	2	2	1	1		4	4	3	2		8	7	6	4	
	6.0	2	2	1	–		4	4	3	–		8	7	5	–	
	7.0	2	2	1	–		4	3	2	–		7	6	5	–	
	8.0	2	2	1	–		4	3	2	–		7	6	5	–	
	9.0	2	1	1	–		4	3	2	–		7	6	4	–	
	10.0	2	1	1	–		4	3	2	–		7	6	4	–	

Schedule 4.10 – Capacity of conduits for single-core pre-insulated cables

Cable factors for short straight runs

Type of conductor	Conductor cross-sectional area mm²	Factor
Solid	1	22
	1.5	27
	2.5	39
Stranded	1.5	31
	2.5	43
	4	58
	6	88
	10	146

Cable factors for long straight runs, or runs incorporating bends

Type of conductor	Conductor cross-sectional area mm²	Factor
Solid or stranded	1	16
	1.5	22
	2.5	30
	4	43
	6	58
	10	105

Conduit factors for short straight runs

Conduit dia mm	Factor
16	290
20	460
25	800
32	1400

Conduit factors for runs incorporating bends

Length of run m	Conduit diameter mm																			
	Straight				One bend				Two bends				Three bends				Four bends			
	16	20	25	32	16	20	25	32	16	20	25	32	16	20	25	32	16	20	25	32
1	Covered by above Tables				188	303	543	947	177	286	514	900	158	256	463	818	130	213	388	692
1.5					182	294	528	923	167	270	487	857	143	233	422	750	111	182	333	600
2					177	286	514	900	158	256	463	818	130	213	388	692	97	159	292	529
2.5					171	278	500	878	150	244	442	783	120	196	358	643	86	141	260	474
3					167	270	487	857	143	233	422	750	111	182	333	600				
3.5	179	290	521	911	162	263	475	837	136	222	404	720	103	169	311	563				
4	177	286	514	900	158	256	463	818	130	213	388	692	97	159	292	529				
4.5	174	282	507	889	154	250	452	800	125	204	373	667	91	149	275	500				
5	171	278	500	878	150	244	442	783	120	196	358	643	86	141	260	474				
6	167	270	487	857	143	233	422	750	111	182	333	600								
7	162	263	475	837	136	222	404	720	103	169	311	563								
8	158	256	463	818	130	213	388	692	97	159	292	529								
9	154	250	452	800	125	204	373	667	91	149	275	500								

Practice 5

Circuits and systems

This Section covers the requirements (or the recommendations) of the Regulations in respect of:
(a) Segregation of circuits (Regulations 525-1 to 525-9)
(b) Maximum demand and diversity (IEE Appendix 4)
(c) Standard circuit arrangements which meet the requirements of the Regulations.
Additional information on the design of circuits can be found elsewhere in this publication and Schedule 5.1 indicates those sources.

Schedule 5.1 – Principal Regulations concerning circuits

Refer to	for further information on
Principles 3	Final circuits
Practice 2 & 2A	Safety extra low voltage circuits Class II circuit protective conductors Disconnecting times Reduced low voltage circuits
Practice 7	Combined protective and neutral conductors Ring circuit protective conductors Earth fault loop impedance
Practice 8	Isolation Switching of circuits

Segregation of circuits *(Regulations 525-1 to 525-9)*

In Practice 2 – Safety Protection it was emphasised that segregation between low voltage circuits and extra-low voltage circuits is required by the Regulations. Therefore where a low-voltage installation includes telecommunications, fire alarm or emergency lighting circuits all of which are connected to the main supply system, the special precautions outlined below must be followed. Essentially these precautions prevent electrical and physical contact between cables of the different circuits. For further guidance on the categories of circuit involved see Figure 5.1. If cables of a low voltage circuit (other than those for fire alarms or emergency lighting) are to be installed in the same enclosure as cables of a telecommunication system connected to a public utility system, such as that of British Telecom then it is necessary to obtain the approval of that organisation. Cables between battery chargers and mains circuit self-contained luminaires are not acknowledged as being emergency lighting circuits.

Schedule 5.2 gives further details of the requirements of the Regulations in respect of the segregation of cables of different categories of circuit.

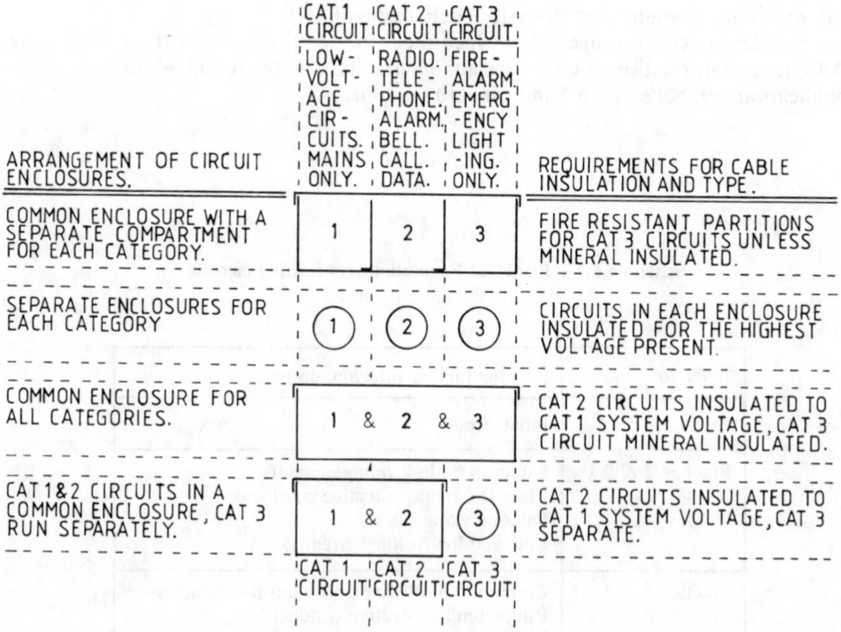

ARRANGEMENT OF CIRCUIT ENCLOSURES.	CAT 1 CIRCUIT — LOW-VOLTAGE CIR-CUITS. MAINS ONLY.	CAT 2 CIRCUIT — RADIO. TELE-PHONE. ALARM. BELL. CALL. DATA.	CAT 3 CIRCUIT — FIRE-ALARM. EMERGENCY LIGHT-ING. ONLY.	REQUIREMENTS FOR CABLE INSULATION AND TYPE.
COMMON ENCLOSURE WITH A SEPARATE COMPARTMENT FOR EACH CATEGORY.	1	2	3	FIRE RESISTANT PARTITIONS FOR CAT 3 CIRCUITS UNLESS MINERAL INSULATED.
SEPARATE ENCLOSURES FOR EACH CATEGORY	(1)	(2)	(3)	CIRCUITS IN EACH ENCLOSURE INSULATED FOR THE HIGHEST VOLTAGE PRESENT.
COMMON ENCLOSURE FOR ALL CATEGORIES.	1 & 2 & 3			CAT 2 CIRCUITS INSULATED TO CAT 1 SYSTEM VOLTAGE, CAT 3 CIRCUIT MINERAL INSULATED.
CAT 1&2 CIRCUITS IN A COMMON ENCLOSURE, CAT 3 RUN SEPARATELY.	1 & 2		(3)	CAT 2 CIRCUITS INSULATED TO CAT 1 SYSTEM VOLTAGE, CAT 3 SEPARATE.

Figure 5.1   Illustration of the segregation of:
Category 1 (low voltage mains circuits other than for fire alarm or emergency lighting);
Category 2 (extra-low voltage and telecommunication circuits supplied from safety source;
Category 3 (fire alarm and emergency lighting circuits).

Schedule 5.2 – Segregation of cables in different categories of circuit

Circuit cables	Requirements of Regulations	Alternative
Category 1 (low voltage from mains supply other than fire alarm or emergency lighting)	Not in same enclosure as cables of Category 2 (radio, telephone, sound distribution, intruder alarms, bell/call and data transmission) circuits supplied from a safety source	If Category 2 cables insulated to highest voltage of Category 1 circuit, the same enclosure acceptable
Category 2	Not in same enclosure as Category 3 (fire alarm, or emergency lighting) circuit. BS5266 *"Emergency Lighting"* recommends the segregation of Category 3 circuit cables from other cables.	None
Category 1 and Category 2 in common enclosure	Category 1 cables to be partitioned from Category 2 cables. At outlet boxes or controls, switchplates or blocks the two categories of circuit cables must be separated as shown in Figure 5.2	If Category 2 cables insulated to highest voltage of Category 1 circuit, the same enclosure is acceptable
Category 3 in channel or trunking with Category 1 and/or Category 2	Category 3 cables to be segregated from other cables by continuous partitions. At common outlets in a trunking system the partition must be continued.	If mineral insulated cables with sheath not exceeding 70°C are used for fire alarm or emergency lighting circuits, the partitions are not required unless they are specified in BS5266 or BS5839 *"Fire detection and alarm systems in buildings"*
Category 1 and Category 2 in common cable or cord	Category 2 cables to be insulated individually or as a group to highest voltage of Category 1 circuit. At outlet boxes or controls, switchplates or blocks the two categories or circuit cables must be separated by rigid screen or barrier. See Figure 5.2	Separate Category 2 cables from those of Category 1 by earthed metal braid having current carrying capacity of Category 1 cable cores.
Category 1 and Category 3	These circuits shall not be contained in a common cable or cord. See also BS5266 *"Emergency Lighting"*, BS6259 *"Sound Distribution Systems"* and BS6330 *"The reception of sound and television broadcasting"*.	None

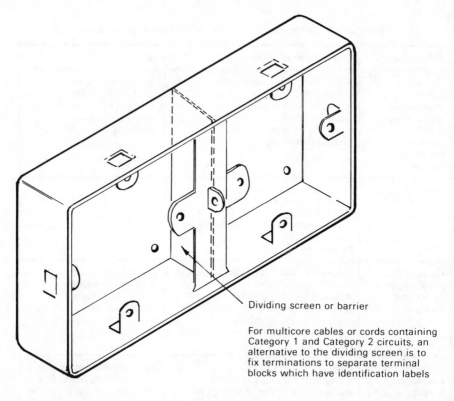

Dividing screen or barrier

For multicore cables or cords containing Category 1 and Category 2 circuits, an alternative to the dividing screen is to fix terminations to separate terminal blocks which have identification labels

Figure 5.2   Segregation of Category 1 and Category 2 circuits contained in a common enclosure, at outlet box to meet requirements of the Regulations.

Maximum demand and diversity *(IEE Appendix 4)*

The maximum demand of a simple final circuit with commonly used equipment is calculated from values given in Table 4A of the IEE Regulations, but the values given in that Table may need to be varied by the installation designer with a suitable degree of knowledge and experience of the diversity applicable to a particular installation. The contents of Table 4A are shown in Schedule 5.3 together with a simple example of its use.

Schedules 5.4 to 5.6, which are based on Table 4B of the IEE Regulations, should be used for circuits feeding a number of final circuits, or the total current of the separate final circuits may be added together and a diversity allowance applied to this total by a responsible designer. Other methods, used by a qualified electrical engineer, are permitted. Before choosing the cable size the voltage drop must be checked. It should be noted that no diversity is permissible for thermostatically controlled water heaters, floor warming installations or thermal storage space heating installations.

Schedule 5.3 – Current demand of points other than standard circuit arrangements and an example of use

Outlet point or equipment	Assumed load	Simple Example				
		No. of outlets say:	Total load (kW)	Assumed Current (A)	Diversity factor say:	Design current (A)
Socket outlet 2A:	0.5A	12	–	6.0	25%	1.5
† Other socket outlets:	Rated current	4 x 15A	–	60.0	50%	30.0
* Light outlet (per lamp holder):	100W	10	1.0	4.2	50%	2.1
Domestic cooker:	10A + 30% remainder + 5A if auxilliary socket fitted	1	10.7	44.6	(see Fig. 5.9)	25.4
Other stationary equipment	BS current rating or normal current	–	–	–	–	–
		Total load current and rating of overcurrent protective device				**59A**

Footnotes:

† For standard circuits using BS1362 socket outlets, see text "Standard circuit arrangement" herein.

* Fluorescent lamps are assessed on the lamp current and the control gear current, or 1.8 x lamp watts in the absence of detailed information.

Note. Points for electric clocks, shower units (BS3052) and sockets (BS4573), bell transformers and other equipment rated up to 5VA maximum can be neglected.

It is also important to understand that distribution boards must be rated for total connected loads before a diversity factor is applied. The allowances for diversity given in Schedule 5.4 to Schedule 5.6, should not be applied to larger premises. For those locations the diversity must be assessed on the basis of previous experience.

To illustrate the meaning of diversity and maximum demand in a simple way, the various items of load in a small installation are shown in Figure 5.3 with their periods of use, as an example of the principle involved.

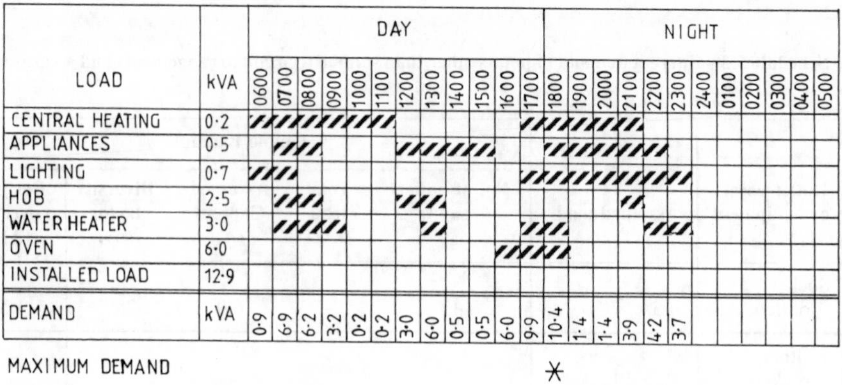

LOAD	kVA	0600	0700	0800	0900	1000	1100	1200	1300	1400	1500	1600	1700	1800	1900	2000	2100	2200	2300	2400	0100	0200	0300	0400	0500
					DAY											NIGHT									
CENTRAL HEATING	0·2	/////	////	////	////	////	////							/////	////	////									
APPLIANCES	0·5		////					////	////					////	////	////									
LIGHTING	0·7	////												////	////	////	////	////							
HOB	2·5		////				////							////											
WATER HEATER	3·0		/////	////			////				////				////	////									
OVEN	6·0							////	////																
INSTALLED LOAD	12·9																								
DEMAND	kVA	0·9	6·9	6·2	3·2	0·2	0·2	3·0	6·0	0·5	0·5	6·0	9·9	10·4	1·4	1·4	3·9	4·2	3·7						

MAXIMUM DEMAND   ✳

Figure 5.3   *Illustrating the meaning of diveristy and maximum demand for various items of installed load in a small installation.*

Schedule 5.4 – Allowances for Diversity (IEE Table 4B) for single house or flat

Purpose	Initial allowance	Remainder
Lighting	none	66% of total
Heating and power: (other than items below)	Total up to 10A	+ 50%
Cookers	10A	+ 30% + 5A if auxilliary socket
Motors	–	–
Water heaters (instant type)	Full load of largest and second largest heaters	+ 25%
Standard socket outlet and cooker circuits (Appendix 5)	Full load of largest circuit	+ 40%
Other socket outlets and fixed equipment	Full load of largest point	+ 40%

Schedule 5.5 – Allowances for Diversity (IEE Table 4B) for Small Shops, Offices and other business premises

Purpose	Initial allowance	Remainder
Lighting	none	90%
Heating and power: (other than items below)	Full load of largest appliance	+ 75%
Cookers	Full load of largest appliance + 80% of second largest	+ 60%
Motors (not lifts)	Full load of largest motor + 80% of second largest	+ 60%
Water heaters (instant type)	Full load of largest and second largest heaters	+ 25%
Standard socket outlet and cooker circuits	Full load of largest circuit	+ 50%
Other socket outlets and fixed equipment	Full load of largest point	+ 75%

Schedule 5.6 – Allowances for Diversity (IEE Table 4B) for Small Hotels, Boarding and Guest Houses

Purpose	Initial allowance	Remainder
Lighting	none	75% of total
Heating and power including cookers but other than items below	Full load of largest appliance + 80% of second largest	+ 60%
Motors (not lifts)	Full load of largest motor	+ 50%
Water heaters (instant type)	Full load of largest and second largest heaters	+ 25%
Standard socket outlet and cooker circuits	Full load of largest circuit	+ 50%
Other socket outlets and fixed equipment	Full load of largest point + 75% of every point in dining rooms and other main rooms	+ 40%

Standard Circuit Arrangements to comply with the Regulations (See also Practice 1, 3, 4, 5, 6, 7 and 8 for other references. *(IEE Appendix 5).*

Designs for standard or more commonly used circuits which comply with the Regulations are detailed below. It is important when standard circuits are to be installed that the designer checks that the requirements of the Regulations in respect of protection against electric shock and earthing, are also met. Standard circuits are given in IEE Appendix 5 as follows:–
    Final circuits using BS1363 socket outlets;
    Final circuits using BS196 socket outlets;
    Final radial circuits using BS4343 socket outlets;
    Cooker final circuits in domestic premises.
Table 5A of the Regulations details three types of final circuit utilising BS1363 socket outlets. Remember that kitchen areas may need separate circuits. Separate radial circuits need to be provided to immersion heaters in tanks having a capacity in excess of 15 litres.

It is permitted to use other circuit arrangements provided they meet the requirements of the Regulation (Principles 3) and are specified by a qualified electrical engineer.

Examples of some standard circuits are shown in Figures 5.4 to 5.11.

Figure 5.8 illustrates the types of BS196 socket outlets which are suitable for use in non-domestic premises. It shows front views of socket-outlets complying with BS196 and indicates some alternative keyway positions. Socket-outlets for use on ring circuits have, in addition, external keys (which have no code letters) to lock out unfused plugs. The socket-outlets and plugs have recesses and projections respectively at positions B for single pole fusing and at P for double pole fusing.

Industrial installations – BS4343 socket-outlets

The requirements of a final radial circuit for BS4343, 16A socket outlets (not including those with pilot contacts) are shown in Figure 5.9.

Cooker circuits

The requirements for domestic cooker circuits are shown in Figures 5.10 and 5.11. It should be noted, however, that a circuit rated between 15A and 50A may supply two or more cooking appliances within one room.

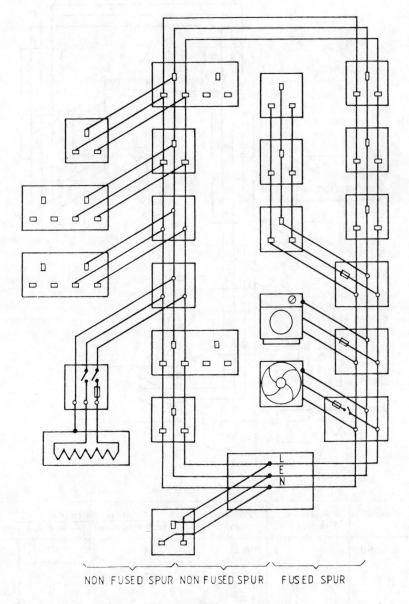

NON FUSED SPUR   NON FUSED SPUR   FUSED SPUR

Figure 5.4   Ring circuit with BS1363 socket outlets: maximum floor area served; 100m²
            Cable size: Copper conductor, rubber or pvc-insulated – 2.5mm²
                        Copperclad aluminium, pvc-insulated – 4.0mm²
                        Mineral insulated copperclad – 1.5mm²
            Overcurrent protective device – 30A or 32A
            Socket outlets served – unlimited

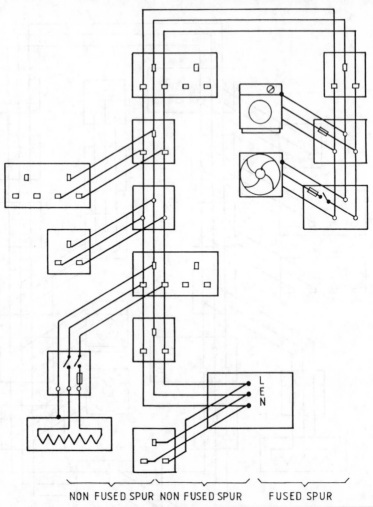

NON FUSED SPUR NON FUSED SPUR   FUSED SPUR

Circuit	Maximum floor area (m²)	Protective device	Cables permitted (mm²)		
			pvc- or rubber-insulated	pvc-insulated	micc
A2 Radial	50	30A or 32A cartridge fuse or circuit breaker	4 copper	6 aluminium/ copperclad	2.5
A3 Radial	20	20A any type	2.5 copper	4 aluminium/ copperclad	1.5

Figure 5.5 Radial Circuits A2 and A3 with BS1363 socket outlets.

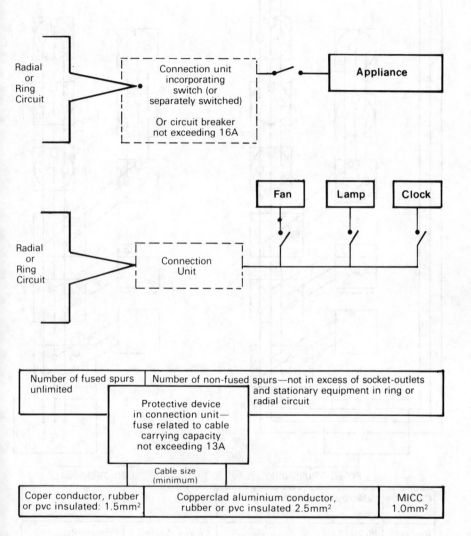

Figure 5.6   Spurs connected to radial or ring circuits using BS1363 socket outlets.

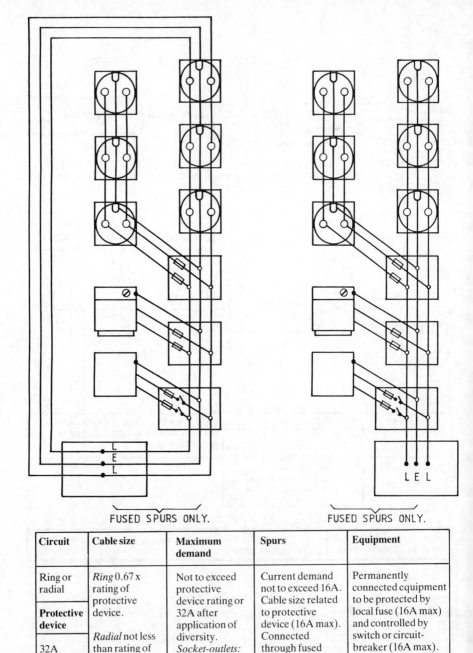

FUSED SPURS ONLY.   FUSED SPURS ONLY.

Circuit	Cable size	Maximum demand	Spurs	Equipment
Ring or radial	*Ring* 0.67 x rating of protective device.	Not to exceed protective device rating or 32A after application of diversity. *Socket-outlets:* unlimited.	Current demand not to exceed 16A. Cable size related to protective device (16A max). Connected through fused connection unit.	Permanently connected equipment to be protected by local fuse (16A max) and controlled by switch or circuit-breaker (16A max). No allowance for diversity.
Protective device				
32A Max	*Radial* not less than rating of protective device.			

Figure 5.7   Requirements for non-domestic ring and radial circuits with BS196 socket outlets.

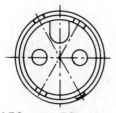
250 volts 50~ for
single or double pole
fused plugs (Code CQ)

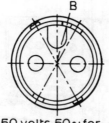
250 volts 50~ for
single pole fused plugs
(Code B/CQ)

250 volts 50~ for
double pole fused plugs
(Code P/CQ)

Figure 5.8   Types of BS196 socket-outlets suitable for use in non-domestic premises.

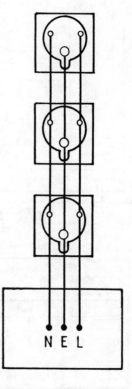

Circuit	Cable size	Maximum demand	Socket outlets
Radial	Rating of protective device (minimum)	Rating of protective device or 20A (max)	Unlimited subject to load and diversity
Protective device			
20A (max)			

Figure 5.9   Radial circuit for BS4343 socket-outlets (16A) suitable for number of phases and used mainly for industrial purposes.

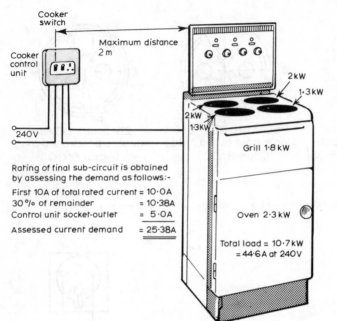

Cooker switch

Cooker control unit

Maximum distance 2 m

240V

2 kW
1·3 kW
2 kW
1·3 kW

Grill 1·8 kW

Oven 2·3 kW

Total load = 10·7 kW
= 44·6 A at 240V

Rating of final sub-circuit is obtained by assessing the demand as follows:-

First 10A of total rated current = 10·0A
30% of remainder = 10·38A
Control unit socket-outlet = 5·0A

Assessed current demand = 25·38A

Figure 5.10   Method of applying diversity to determine the circuit rating for a typical cooker in domestic premises.

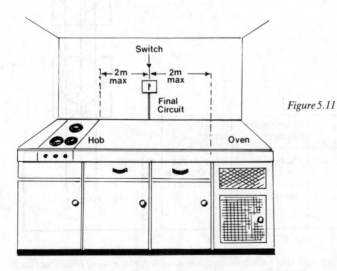

Switch

2m max   2m max

Final Circuit

Hob   Oven

Figure 5.11   Illustrating maximum permissible distance between a stationary cooking appliance, or two such appliances (in one room), and the controlling switch. Attention is drawn to the need to afford discriminative operation of excess-current protective device.

Practice 6

Overcurrent Protection

The fundamental safety requirements in respect of overcurrent protection will be met if a positive answer can be given to all the questions posed in Schedule 6.1. Detailed requirements for overcurrent protection are set out in the text which follows Schedule 6.1.

Overcurrent protection – general *(Regulations 431-1, 431-2 and 436-1)*

Devices for the automatic disconnection of a circuit must be provided to protect live conductors when an overload (sound circuit) or short circuit (faulty circuit) occurs and where these devices are separate, both forms of protection should be coordinated (see later text – "overcurrent protective devices – coordination").

An exception to this rule (Regulation 436-1) is where the characteristics of the supply source limit the possibility of overcurrents larger than the current carrying capacity of the cable. Compliance with Regulations 433-1 to 433-3 concerning *overload protection* (see later text) is deemed to satisfy the requirements for *protection against overcurrents* (overload current and short circuit current) of a similar level. It has to be borne in mind that protection of current using equipment, or any associated flexible cord, however connected, is not necessarily given by the protective devices provided for the circuit conductors. In particular, this fact needs to be taken into account in the design of non-fused socket-outlet circuits and where a flexible cord of an incorrect rating could be inadvertently connected.

Overcurrent protective devices *(Regulations 432-1 to 432-4)*

Overcurrent protective devices may be of the following types:
1. Circuit breaker incorporating overload release
2. Fuses
3. Circuit breaker in conjunction with fuses in the tripping circuit
4. Circuit breaker with overload and short circuit release

In each case the device chosen shall have a functional capacity to make and/or break the overcurrent specified in the text which follows.

Schedule 6.1 – Fundamental safety requirements for overcurrent protection

(Regulations 13-7 and 13-12)

Positive answer required to all the following questions	Notes and ASEE Comment
Is the installation and every circuit therein protected against overcurrent by fuses or circuit breakers?	The definition of "Installation" is an assembly of electrical equipment to fulfil a specific purpose and having certain co-ordinated characteristics. This means that unless the word "installation" is further qualified it can be applied to a complete installation or to any section of it
Is every circuit protected against overcurrent by a device which will operate automatically and safely for the protected circuit?	The term overcurrent includes overload current and short-circuit current
Are the devices employed of adequate breaking (and making) capacity?	Breaking capacity is the maximum prospective breaking current that a device is stated to be capable of breaking.
When operated, is the device suitably located and constructed to: (a) prevent danger from overheating, arching or the scattering of hot metal particles? (b) permit re-connection of supply without danger?	If the supply authority has switch- or fuse-gear at the installation's origin, it may not be necessary to duplicate that overcurrent protection equipment between the origin and the installation's main distribution point. See definition "origin of an installation" (see Principles 2)
Has an inspection been made to ensure there are no fuses or non-linked circuit breakers in the neutral conductor?	"Neutral conductor" – a defined term – is that conductor which is connected to the neutral point on the supply system. See also definition of "Live part" (Principles 2) which includes a neutral conductor. In Great Britain, it can be assumed that in any public electricity supply the neutral point of the supply is permanently earthed. Overseas supply authorities may have different requirements.

Overcurrent protection related to type of circuit and distribution system
(Regulations 473-9 to 473-14)

A device to detect an overcurrent must be provided in each phase conductor and must operate to protect that conductor without interrupting the supply to the other live conductors, except where danger could occur with such an arrangement. For example, in the case of 3-phase motors, where 'single phasing' caused by such an interruption of one phase could damage the motor, it is necessary to provide alternative forms of protection. This protection can best be provided by motor starter with single-phase protection characteristics that provides for all the phase conductors to be disconnected simultaneously. An alternative method is by utilising a circuit breaker with linked poles, so that a fault on one phase will automatically disconnect all phases. It is not necessary to provide overcurrent detection or disconnection for the neutral conductor of a TN or TT system, providing always that its cross-section is equal to the phase conductors. Should a reduced neutral conductor be used, the short circuit protection of the neutral must be assured by the device protecting the phase conductor and the circuit load should be equally shared between the phase conductors. If not, then an overcurrent detection device must be provided for the neutral conductor. When the neutral is overloaded, this should lead to the phase conductors being disconnected, but not necessarily the neutral. It should be noted however that the neutral cross-section must satisfy the requirement of the Regulations (see Practice 3).

In IT systems the neutral conductor should not be divided into a distribution system. If this is not practicable, overcurrent detection must be provided for the neutral conductor of each circuit arranged to disconnect the neutral and its complementary live conductor simultaneously.

For IT systems it should be noted that each distributed neutral conductor need not have means of overcurrent detection if it is protected against short circuit at the origin of the circuit or the circuit is protected by a residual current operated device having a rated residual current not greater than 0.15 times the neutral conductor current carrying capacity, so that all live conductors (including neutral) are disconnected simultaneously.

Overcurrent protective devices – selection and erection *(Regulations 514-2, 531-1, 531-2 and 533-1 to 533-5)*

Protective devices are required to be labelled, marked and arranged so that related circuits can be readily identified. A convenient way is to group circuits at a distribution board and to provide a circuit chart. See also Practice 10 – Warning Notices (etc).

For earthed neutral (TN) systems (see Practice 7) an overcurrent protective device used for protection against electric shock by indirect contact should be selected so that it operates before the associated protective conductor reaches a final temperature exceeding that permitted by Schedule 7.7. This final temperature is 160°C for pvc insulated protective conductors, 220°C for rubber insulated and 250°C for conductors insulated with thermosetting plastic. The overcurrent device protecting socket-outlet circuits must operate on an earth fault within 0.4 seconds and devices protecting fixed equipment circuits within 5 seconds, except for bathrooms where this value for fixed equipment circuits is also 0.4 seconds (see Practice 2 – Regulation 413-4). The foregoing requirements in respect of protective devices also apply to systems which have independently earthed exposed conductive part as in TT systems (see Practice 7), but in a TT system the use of residual current devices is preferred to overcurrent protective devices because the value of earth fault loop impedance of such systems is variable depending upon moisture levels at each earth electrode.

If an earth fault occurs on an IT system (one which is not earthed or one which is earthed through a high impedance), only a limited fault current may flow. However, the system becomes an earthed system through the first earth fault, and the IT system becomes either a TT system or a TN system. If a second fault occurs whilst the first fault persists, the risks of shock are the same as for a TT or TN system. Therefore the requirements for protective devices are the same as those for the TN system referred to above.

Every fuse or circuit-breaker should be marked with the nominal current rating appropriate to the protected circuit or that rating should be indicated adjacent to the device (see Practice 10). Preferably, where un-instructed or non-skilled persons are likely to replace fuse links without supervision it should not be possible inadvertently to insert a fuse having a higher nominal current rating. The type of fuse link to be used and its fusing factor, should also be indicated.

If fuses are likely to be removed or replaced while a circuit is live, it should be possible to do so without danger. Thus they must be of the fully shrouded type. (See Figure 6.1)

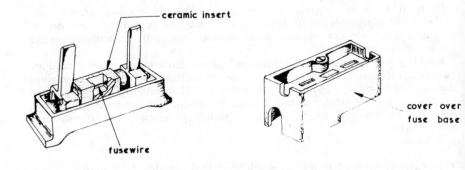

Figure 6.1   Domestic semi-enclosed (rewireable) fuse of the fully shrouded type can be removed or replaced whilst the protected circuit is energised.

Cartridge fuse links are preferred. Elements for semi-enclosed fuses should be fitted to the directions of the manufacturer of the fuse carrier or should be in a single copper wire or tinned copper wire (see Schedule 6.2).

Where likely to be operated by unskilled personnel, the circuit breaker setting for overcurrent release should be non-adjustable. If adjustable, a key or tool should be needed to adjust the calibration and to give a visible indication of the actual overcurrent setting achieved.

Schedule 6.2 – Sizes of fuse elements of plain or tinned copper wire, for use in semi-enclosed fuses

Nominal current of fuse (A)	Nominal diameter of wire (mm)	Approx. Imperial equivalent (in)	(swg)
3	0.15	0.006	38
5	0.2	0.0084	35
10	0.35	0.0136	29
15	0.5	0.020	25
20	0.6	0.024	23
25	0.75	0.028	22
30	0.85	0.032	21
45	1.25	0.048	18
60	1.53	0.056	17
80	1.8	0.072	15
100	2.0	0.080	14

Overcurrent protective device – discrimination *(Regulation 533-6)* and coordination *Regulation 435-1)*

Proper discrimination in the operation of overcurrent protective devices is essential to avoid interruption of other circuits. Thus their characteristics and settings must be such that a fault on one circuit will not disconnect another circuit. The fuse or circuit-breaker nearest the fault should be the only one which operates, although other devices may be receiving some aspect of the fault contribution.

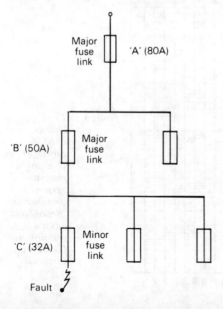

Figure 6.2   Illustrating the principle of discrimination between overcurrent protective devices.

If discrimination is to be assured in the event of fault or overload between two protective devices in a circuit, the minor protective device should be selected to operate first and leave the major protective device unimpaired.

An accurate selection of protective devices can only be made by reference to the individual I^2t (ampere^2/second) characteristics described in a manufacturer's literature.

An example will demonstrate the principle. In Figure 6.2, 'A' is a BS88 fuselink rated at 80A, 660V (breaking capacity 80kA), which will discriminate with 'B' a 50A 660V fuselink (breaking capacity 80kA) at a fault level of 300A. Reference to time/current characteristics of each device 'A', 'B' and 'C' will show that the operating time for the 32A fuse is 0.15 second and the 50A fuselink operating time is one second. Reference to Figure 6.3 will show that let-through current (total I^2t) of the minor protective device (3.1kA) does not exceed the pre-arcing current of the 50A major device (6.5kA) and the pre-arcing current of the 80A major device (20.7kA). Thus discrimination is achieved.

Discrimination between and coordination of protective devices is an involved subject, however, and one which needs more detailed treatment than is possible here. Further reading on this subject is available in the under-mentioned publications:

(a)   "Electric Fuses" by A. Wright and P.G. Newbery published 1982, by Peter Peregrinus Ltd.

(b)   BS88 : Part 1 : 1975 Appendix B Selection of Fuselinks published by British Standards Institution.

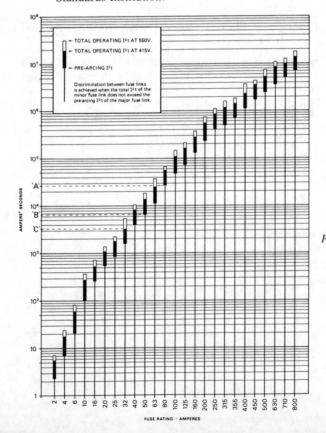

Figure 6.3 I^2t characteristics of BS88 cartridge fuses. Overcurrent protective devices-coordination (Reproduced by kind permission of GEC Fusegear Limited).

The technical literature issued by manufacturers of fuselinks often contains guidance on fuse discrimination.

The energy let through of a protective device for short circuit protection should not exceed the fault rating of the overload protective device. This means that the characteristics of the devices should be co-ordinated to prevent damage to the overload protective device.

BS4941 describes coordination which is acceptable where motor starters are involved and points out that the coordination of overload and short circuit protective devices is necessary to avoid damage to the overload device by a short circuit current. It is advisable to seek guidance from the manufacturer of the motor starter. In other words when the overload protective device is of such small magnitude and will not withstand the short circuit current it must be backed up by an HBC fuse capable of protecting the overload protective device and the circuit wiring.

Overload current protection *(Regulations 433-1 to 433-3)*

Circuit breakers or fuses must be capable of disconnecting the circuit before an overload leads to a temperature rise in the conductors which may cause damage to cables, joints, and their surroundings etc. Co-ordination between conductors and protective devices is of paramount importance; to satisfy this requirement the following conditions apply:

(a)   the design current (I_B) of the circuit must not be greater than the nominal rating or setting (I_n) of the related overload protective device.

(b)   the current carrying capacity of circuit conductors (I_z) (see Practice 3) must not be less than the nominal rating or setting (I_n) of the related overload protective device.

(c)   the current which operates the protective device (I_Z) must not exceed the current carrying capacity (I_Z) of the smallest conductor x 1.45.

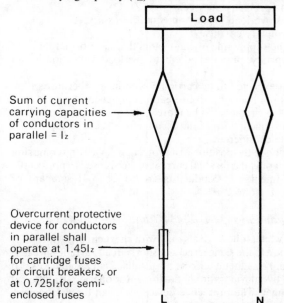

Load

Sum of current carrying capacities of conductors in parallel = I_z

Parallel conductors to be equal in all respects (type, csa, length, disposition) with no branch circuits and carrying equal currents

Overcurrent protective device for conductors in parallel shall operate at 1.45I_z for cartridge fuses or circuit breakers, or at 0.725I_z for semi-enclosed fuses

L   N

Not applicable to ring circuits

Figure 6.4   Overload protection of conductors in parallel.

Conditions (a) and (b) above can be summarised as follows:

The design current of circuit must be equal to or less than the nominal current rating or setting of the overload protective device and the latter must be equal to or less than the current carrying capacity of the smallest circuit conductor.

Fuses to BS88 or BS1361 or circuit breakers to BS3871 Part 1 or BS4572 Part 1, which satisfy (b) above are also deemed to satisfy (c) above. If the rating of a semi-enclosed fuse to BS3036 is not more than that of the smallest circuit conductor x 0.725 it also satisfies (c). This is because re-wirable fuses have a fusing factor of 2. Put another way, where BS3036 fuses are used, the current rating of the cable should not be less than 1.38 times the fuse rating.

Circuits designed having due regard to the provisions of the Regulations in respect of maximum demand and diversity (see Principles 3) should not be subjected to frequent or small overloads of long duration.

For circuits using parallel conductors, the term "rating of the smallest conductor" used previously is the total current carrying capacity of all the conductors connected in parallel, provided they are all equal in type, cross sectional area, length and without branch connections. The concept of this requirement is shown in Figure 6.4. (But see also later reference to the protection of conductors in parallel against short-circuit).

Overload protective devices – position *(Regulations 473-1 and 473-4)*

At the point where the current carrying capacity of conductors is decreased due to a change in cross-section, environmental conditions, type of cable or conductor or installation method, overload protection must be provided. Where this is not practicable the overload protection device may be located at any point in the conductor run, but it is not permissible to connect branch circuits between the point of reduction in current-carrying capacity and the protective device.

In the following circumstances overload protection is not necessary:

1. For current transformer secondary circuits.
2. If the protective device on the supply side of conductors that have been rated at a reduced current carrying capacity, provides adequate overload protection for all the conductors.
3. If an overload current is not expected to be carried by conductors because of the load characteristics, such as the load of a fixed heating appliance.
4. If the accidental opening of the circuit could be more dangerous than the overload current e.g. supplies to electromagnets, machine exciter circuits, etc. In these cases an overload alarm should be considered.

The foregoing provisions relating to the position of a protective device or its omission are applicable to an IT system but only if a residual current device is used to protect the conductors or the circuit equipment and conductors are to Class II standard or equivalent insulation (see Practice Notes 2).

Short circuit protection *(Regulations 434-1 to 434-7 and 473-5 to 473-8)*

It should be noted that the text which follows deals only with short circuits which may occur between conductors common to the same circuit. A short circuit current can cause danger due to the thermal and magnetic effects it produces in conductors, at terminations, and joints. Protective devices for conductors must operate in sufficient time to prevent this kind of danger. The protective device used can be of a nominal current rating higher than that of the protected conductor. If the device which provides protection against short-circuit also provides overload protection and has a nominal rating not higher than the cable rating, the short circuit rating of the cable is deemed to be adequate.

The prospective short circuit current shall be verified at every relevant point of the installation by calculation or measurement. This assessment may be limited to that of the incoming supply protective device if the value calculated or measured by instruments is smaller than the breaking capacity of the smallest protective device in the installation. Figure 6.5 demonstrates this requirement.

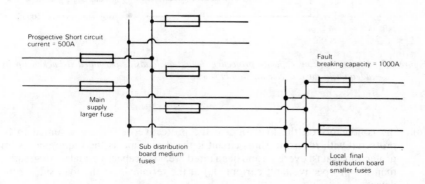

Figure 6.5   *Assessment of prospective short circuit current may be limited to protective device at source of supply if value calculated is less than fault breaking capacity of smallest protective device within the installation.*

Short circuit protection devices must comply with the following:
(a)   The rated short circuit breaking capacity of a protective device shall be of a value equal to or greater than the prospective fault current (I_p) on the load side of the device. See Figure 6.6.

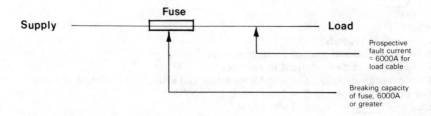

Figure 6.6   *Rated short circuit capacity of protective device, equal or greater than prospective fault current on load.*

(b)   a protective device with a lower breaking capacity than the prospective fault current on the load side of the device is permissible if another device having the required breaking capacity is installed on the supply side. This refers to the use of HBC fuse links to back-up circuit breakers, see Figure 6.7.

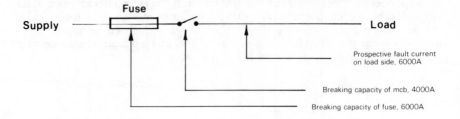

Figure 6.7 Lower breaking capacity protective device on loadside permitted if backed up by adequately rated device on supply side.

(c)   the conductors on the load side of the protective device are assumed to be protected with regard to short circuit if the device meets the requirements for protection against overload and has a rated breaking capacity equal to, or greater, than the prospective fault current (I_p) at the terminals on the load side of the device.

Normally, cable makers quote short-circuit ratings for cables which have regard to the formula which is referred to in the text which follows.

Schedule 6.3 provides data on the breaking capacities of the various protective devices. These capacities should be confirmed by reference to the literature of the manufacturer of the protective device actually employed.

Where for any reason the overload protective device is not also used for short-circuit protection the Regulations state that a short circuit current must be interrupted before the circuit conductors reach their maximum permissable temperature rise. Therefore the maximum operating time of the protective device must be confirmed to prevent the permitted conductor temperature rise being exceeded. This time can be established from the following equation:

$$t = \frac{k^2 S^2}{I^2}$$

where

t   = time in seconds
S   = cross-sectional area of conductor in mm^2
I   = short circuit rms current in amperes
k   = constant dependent on conductor metal and insulant (See Schedule 6.4)
For example if k = 115 S = 10mm^2 and I = 5000A
then $t = \frac{115^2 \times 10^2}{5000^2} = 0.053$ seconds

Note: This is the maximum time that a fault current of 5000 amperes can be applied to the cable. Therefore the protective device must disconnect the supply to the cable in less than 0.053 seconds. The operating times of protective devices at various short circuit currents are to be found in the appropriate manufacturers' literature.

Parallel conductors may be protected as described in the text on "Overload Protection" and are co-ordinated for the selection of the protective device. Attention must be given to the case of a short circuit condition not affecting all of the conductors. In other words the protection device must operate in such a time as to protect one conductor as if it were carrying the whole of the fault current.

Schedule 6.3 Rated Breaking Capacity of Devices
(These capacities must be confirmed by reference to manufacturers' literature)

Type of Protective Device	British Standard	Voltage Range	Current Range	Cat of Duty	Rated Breaking Capacity kA	Test PF	Primarily Designed for use in
Semi enclosed fuse " "	3036 " "	240V to earth " "	Up to 100 " "	S1 S2 S4	1·0 2·0 4·0	0.9 0.8 0.8	Domestic & General " "
Cartridge fuse	1362	Up to 250V	Up to 13A	–	6·0	0.3 – 0.4	Plugs, Domestic & similar
MCB " " " " " "	3871 Pt 1 " " " " " "	Up to 415V " " " " " "	Up to 100 " " " " " "	M1 M1-5 M2 M3 M4 M6 M9	1·0 1·5 2·0 3·0 4·0 6·0 9·0	0.85 – 0.9 0.8 – 0.85 0.75 – 0.8 0.75 – 0.8 0.75 – 0.8 0.75 – 0.8 0.55 – 0.6	Final circuits " " " " " "
Cartridge fuse	88	Up to 1000Vac Up to 1500Vdc	Up to 1250	–	40kA at 250Vdc 80kA at 415Vac ≤ 20kA > 20kA	0.2 – 0.3 0.1 – 0.2	Industrial & General
Cartridge fuse Cartridge fuse	1361 Type I 1361 Type II	240Vac 415Vac	5 – 45 60, 80, 100	– –	16.5 33.0	0.3 0.3	Domestic & similar "

(continued)

Circuit breakers (including MCCB)	4752 Part 1	Up to 1000Vac Up to 1200Vdc	not limited	P1 or P2	Short circuit current	Feeders or main cables
					< 1500	0.95
					> 1500-3000	0.9
					> 3000-4500	0.8
					> 4500-6000	0.7
					> 6000-10000	0.5
					> 10000-20000	0.3
					> 20000-50000	0.25
					> 50000	0.2

Note: P1 = B – MB duty. P2 = B – MB – MB duty. P2 to be suitable for full service after test.

Schedule 6.4 – k factors for particular conductor metal and insulant

Cable Insulation	Conductor metal	'k' factor
PVC	Copper Aluminium	115 76
60°C rubber 85°C rubber	Copper/Aluminium Copper/Aluminium	141/93 134/89
90°C thermosetting	Copper Aluminium	143 94
Paper	Copper Aluminium	108 71
Mineral	Copper cond/sleeve Aluminium	115/135 87

Short circuit protective devices – position

In a similar way to that described earlier for overload protection, wherever the current-carrying capacity of conductors decreases due to change in cross-section, surrounding conditions, type of conductor or form of installation, then short-circuit protection must be provided at the point of change.

A relaxation of this requirement is allowed if the protective device is located on the load side, away from the point of change in current carrying capacity by not more than 3 metres, and if the risks of short circuit, fire and personal danger are suitably minimised and the admissable limits of conductor temperature are not exceeded. Likewise the location of the short circuit protective device need not apply providing there is adequate short circuit protection on the supply side to give protection to the conductors on the load side.

Provided that unprotected conductors are installed in a way which minimises danger from fire or to persons, short circuit protective devices can be omitted in the following circumstances:
(a) where they are contained on control panels related to generators, transformers, rectifiers or batteries.
(b) in certain measuring circuits.
(c) where they could cause danger (see "Position of overload protective devices").

In general the relaxation of the requirement that the short circuit protective device should be located at the origin of the circuit applies to situations like a switchboard where reduced cross section conductors are connected direct to a busbar system.

Practice 7

Earthing, Earth leakage and Earth Fault Currents

The precautions to be taken against earth leakage and earth fault currents will be met if a positive answer can be given to all the questions posed in Schedule 7.1. The requirements of the IEE Regulations concerning earthing arrangements are described later in this Section.

Types of system earthing *(IEE Appendix 3)*

Essential particulars of the supply, which must be obtained for any new installation or extension thereto must particularly include the earthing arrangement and the earth fault current path, upon which the protective measures depend. The installation and the supply source comprise a 'system', the former belonging to the consumer and the latter belonging to the supply undertaking in the case of public supply. Where the user incorporates his own source of supply, this is included in the terms 'electrical installation of the premises' and 'electrical system', but it should be separately considered in determining the type of system, whether TN, TT, or IT.

Principles 2 – Definitions, provides descriptions of various supply systems e.g. TN, TT, IT under 'Systems'. Figures 7.1 to 7.6 are diagrams of these systems.

It can be taken that a supply given under the Electricity Supply Regulations 1937 has a direct and permanent connection to earth at one or more points. The supply undertaking may provide the consumer's main earthing terminal. Any special requirements for PME system installations should be obtained from the supply undertaking as PME approval granted by the Secretary of State for Energy or the Secretary of State for Scotland may be subject to different conditions in each case. The same permission is necessary for supplies under the Electricity Supply Regulations 1937 in which the neutral needs to be earthed or combined with a protective conductor.

But this is not required in the case of a private supply.

The consumer or his agent must be responsible for the suitability of the earth fault protective equipment for the whole of the earth fault current path and its impedance.

Schedule 7.1 – Precautions against earth leakage and earth fault currents

(Regulations 13-8 and 13-11)

Positive answer required to all the following questions	Notes and ASEE Comment
Are all the equipment enclosures, etc properly earthed so that leakage currents from defective insulation of conductors, or from a short-circuit between conductors, are discharged without danger?	Bonding to protective conductors should maintain conducting metalwork at near earth potential under fault conditions
Alternatively, have other effective means been employed?	Residual current devices or fault voltage operated devices should be used to disconnect the supply before metalwork becomes charged to a dangerous level.
Is every circuit arranged to prevent persistant dangerous earth leakage currents?	Regulation 26 of the 'Electricity Supply Regulations 1937' limits a leakage from a consumer's installation to one-tenth thousandth part of the maximum current.
Are circuits protected by overcurrent devices?	See Practice 6.
Has a residual current or voltage operated device been installed where the prospective earth fault current is insufficient to operate an overcurrent protective device?	See text "Limitation of earth fault loop impedance" for method of calculating earth fault current
Has extraneous metalwork been connected to the installation's main earthing terminal if simultaneous contact between earthed metalwork of electrical services and building, or other services metalwork is possible?	See Practice 2 – "Automatic disconnection of supply"

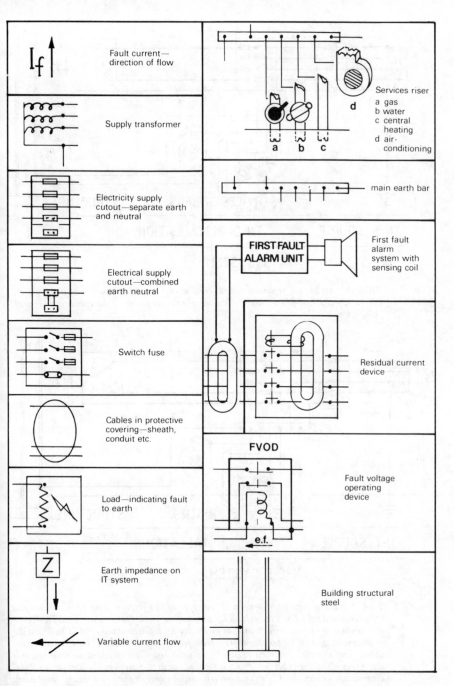

Figure 7.1   Key to symbols used in Figures 7.2 to 7.6.

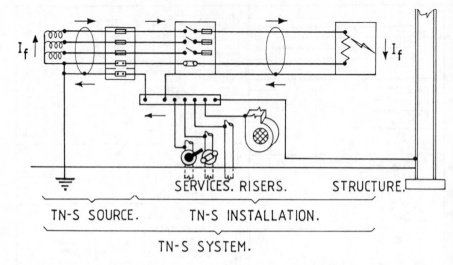

Figure 7.2 *TN-S systems have a separate neutral conductor (N) and a separate protective earth conductor (PE), the latter may be the metallic outer cover of the cable or a separate conductor.*

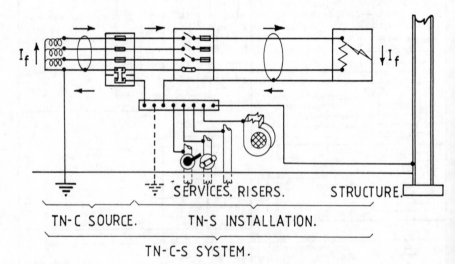

Figure 7.3 *TN-C-S systems are a combination of two types of distribution, type TN-C throughout the source and type TN-S thoughout the installation. In this arrangement the TN-C type of distribution may also be known as protective multiple earthing (PME) in which the protective earth neutral conductor (PEN) is formed by the metallic outer cover of the cable. The metallic outer cover of the cable is usually connected to several earth electrodes along the cable route and some times at the consumers installation. In PME distribution cables the PEN conductor is also known as the combined neutral earth conductor (CNE).*

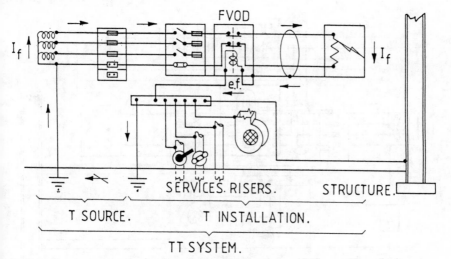

FVOD

I_f I_f

e.f.

SERVICES. RISERS.   STRUCTURE.

T SOURCE.   T INSTALLATION.

TT SYSTEM.

Figure 7.4   *In TT systems the neutral point is connected to an earth electrode at the source and an*
independant earth electrode is provided for the installation. All exposed conductive
parts and any extraneous conductive parts of the installation are connected to the
installation earth electrode which should be located outside the resistance area of any
metallic service pipes entering the building.
The installation should be protected against overcurrent by fuses or circuit breakers or
residual current devices. Where a fault voltage operated device (FVOD) is used all
exposed and extraneous conductive parts shall be connected to the installation earth via
the coil of the FVOD although residual current devices are preferred because that part of
the earth fault loop between the source and installation earth electrodes may vary due to
seasonal change.

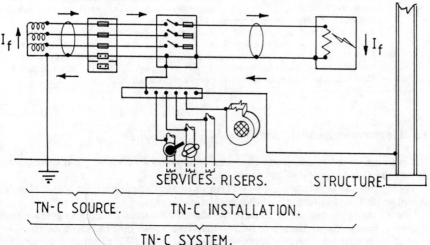

I_f I_f

SERVICES. RISERS.   STRUCTURE.

TN-C SOURCE.   TN-C INSTALLATION.

TN-C SYSTEM.

Figure 7.5   *TN-C systems have a combined protective earth neutral conductor (PEN) throughout*
both source and installation. When this type of distribution is used throughout an
installation such as in earthed concentric wiring systems permission must always be
obtained from the appropriate authority.

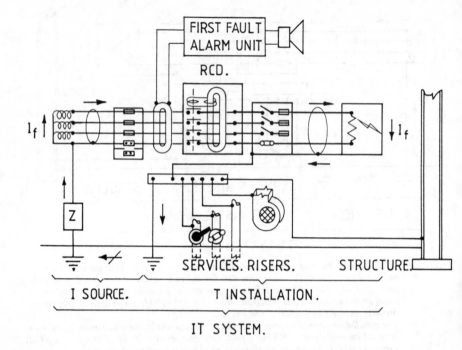

Figure 7.6   *In IT systems all live conductors are isolated from earth, alternatively the neutral or other live conductor at source can be connected to earth via a high impedance or artificial neutral point for stability. As the system is not earthed in the conventional sense use protective devices (RCD) or fault voltage operated devices (FVOD) for earth leakage and fuses or circuit breakers for over current protection.*
Earth electrodes are provided at appropriate points of installation to connect simultaneously accessible exposed and extraneous conductive parts together and to earth. Residual current devices are preferred. Insulation monitors must be provided to give an alarm or disconnection when a first fault occurs. IT systems cannot be used for Public supplies under the Electricity supply regulations 1937.

Earthing arrangements *(Regulations 541-1 to 542-9)*

All earthing methods and protective conductors should be chosen and installed to ensure the safe operation of the associated equipment.

The earthing system may be divided into sections as required. Each section has to comply with the requirements of the Regulations.

Usually the resistance of earth electrodes should not exceed 1 ohm. For guidance on lightning protection systems see British Standard Code of Practice BS6651 *"The protection of structures against lightning"*. Figures 7.7 and 7.8 illustrate the earthing arrangements of a typical lightning protection system.

The resistance of earth electrodes for lightning conductor systems need not exceed 10 ohms.

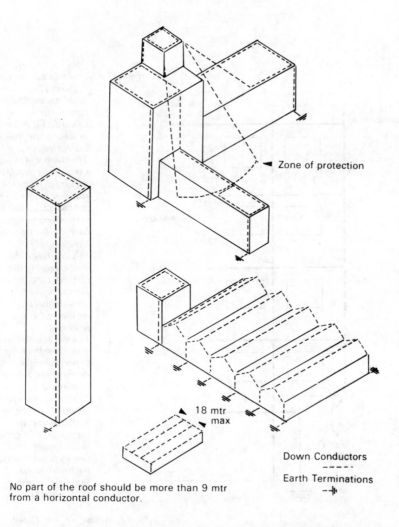

◄ Zone of protection

▲ 18 mtr
max

Down Conductors
- - - - -
Earth Terminations
⊣⊢

No part of the roof should be more than 9 mtr
from a horizontal conductor.

*Figure 7.7   Air Termination Network for Lightning Protection is that part of a lightning conductor
system which is intended to intercept lightning discharges. These can vary from a vertical
conductor for a tower to a system of horizontal conductors for flat roofs. Horizontal
Conductors are required for roofs of large horizontal dimensions. No part of the roof
should be more than 30ft (9m) from a Horizontal Conductor. All metallic projections
should be bonded and form part of Air Termination Network. If there is considerable
variation in height of structure lower portions should in addition to their own Down
Conductors be bonded to the Down Conductors of the taller portions.*

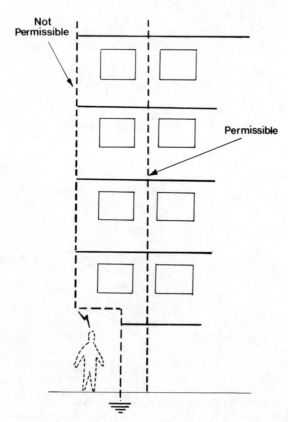

Not Permissible

Permissible

Figure 7.8   Down Conductors for Lightning Protection: Building cantilevered from the first storey upwards. Care should be taken not to form re-entrant loops.

The number of Down Conductors should be decided as follows:– A structure having a base not exceeding 1000 ft² (100 m²) may only have one Down Conductor.

In a structure with a base exceeding 1000 ft² (100 m²) the number of Down Conductors should equal the smaller of the following:

1. One, plus one for every 3000 ft² (300 m²) or part thereof in excess of first 1000 ft² (100 m²) or

2. One for every 100 ft (30 m) of perimeter.

3. For a structure exceeding 100 ft (30 m) in height additional considerations apply, see British Standard Code of Practice CP326: 1965.

Areas Between	Down Conductors	
100m² – 400m²	TWO	2
400m² – 700m²	THREE	3
700m² – 1000m²	FOUR	4
1000m² – 1300m²	FIVE	5
1300m² – 1600m²	SIX	6
1600m² – 1900m²	SEVEN	7

Every installation shall have a consumer's earth terminal which shall be connected to Earth by at least one of the methods detailed below:–

(i) The consumer's main earthing terminal on a TN-S system should be connected to the earthed point of the source of supply. This connection may be via the sheath and/or armour of the supply authority's cables or equipment. (See Figure 7.2)

(ii) The consumer's main earthing terminal on a TN-C-S (PME) system will be connected by the supply authority to the neutral of the source. (See Figure 7.3).

(iii) The consumer's main earthing terminal on a TT or IT system should be connected to an installation earth electrode by an earthing conductor. (See Figures 7.4 and 7.6).

On TN-C installations comprising earthed concentric wiring or any system where the neutral and earth conductor is combined to form a protective earth neutral conductor (PEN), the external conductor within the consumer's installations should be connected to the consumer's earth terminal. In TN-C supply systems the consumer's earth terminal is connected to the neutral of the supply. Further information on Combined Protective and Neutral Conductors, see later text.

Earthing arrangements must meet the following requirements:
(a) Resistance between consumer's main earth terminal and earth point of supply (TN system) or to Earth (TT or IT system) must be related to the installation which they serve.
(b) Carry earth faults and earth leakage currents with no detrimental effects to the installation.
(c) Be of sufficient mechanical strength to withstand any external conditons or be provided with additional mechanical protection.
(d) Be inspected and tested regularly to determine effectiveness.

In earthing systems electrolytic action can occur between dissimilar metals. In the presence of leakage currents and dampness electroytic action is accelerated. For example, certain combinations of dissimiliar metals may form an electroytic cell as indicated by Schedule 7.2, for instance the copper sheath of a cable fixed to galvanised cable tray would create a situation where action between dissimilar metals could take place therefore either the cable or the tray must be protected to ensure separation e.g. apply a pvc sheath to the cable or to the tray.
When two or more installations have separate earthing systems, any protective conductor installed between the installations shall be capable of carrying the maximum fault current likely to flow. Alternatively the protective conductor should be insulated and earthed in one installation only. Where the protective conductor is within a cable it should be earthed within the installation that contains the protective device associated with that cable.
When emergency lighting and fire alarm systems are wired in mineral insulated metal sheathed cable, attention must be given to the bonding of their sheaths, because under fault conditions heavy earth currents from associated installations could be present.

Schedule 7.2 – Electrolytic Potential Differences of the Elements in Volts

Element	A		B
	Fc	Fh	Fc
Magnesium	+ 2.8	+ 2.54	+ 2.06
Aluminium	+ 1.559	+ 1.276	+ 1.56
Zinc	+ 1.053	+ 0.770	+ 1.06
Cadmium	+ 0.703	+ 0.420	+ 0.71
Iron	+ 0.940	+ 0.660	+ 0.90
Nickel	+ 0.480	+ 0.197	+ 0.61
Tin	+ 0.475	+ 0.192	+ 0.66
Lead	+ 0.4121	+ 0.1293	+ 0.68
Copper	− 0.046	− 0.329	− 0.04
Arsenic	− 0.010	− 0.293	− 0.04
Antimony	− 0.183	− 0.466	− 0.24
Mercury	− 0.467	− 0.750	− 0.46
Silver	− 0.515	− 0.798	− 0.48

Note: Column 'A', refers to metals in contact with solutions of the corresponding metal ions containing one ionmol per litre. Column 'B' refers to metals in contact with solutions of the corresponding metal ions. Fc gives the potential difference against the calomer electrode. Fh gives the potential difference against the hydrogen electrode. The relations between these two is Fh − Fc − 0.283 volts.

Two elements may form an electrolytic cell, the voltage being approximately the difference between the values given in the Schedule. If two metals which are in contact have a difference of electrolytic potential greater than about 0.6 volt there is a risk of serious electrolytic corrosion, the metal higher up the list being the one to corrode. Thus, zinc protects iron by sacrifical corrosion, but tin may increase the rate of corrosion of iron if the protective layer is pierced.

Earth electrodes *(Regulations 542-10 to 542-15)*

The types of earth electrodes recognised by the Regulations are:
(a) Earth rods or pipes.
(b) Earth tapes or wires.
(c) Earth plates.
(d) Earth electrodes embedded in foundations.
(e) Metallic reinforcement in concrete structures.
(f) Underground metallic pipe systems excluding public gas and water systems.
(g) Lead sheaths and metallic covering of underground cables.

Figure 7.9 shows a typical earth electrode installation and Figure 7.10 shows the layout of a concrete inspection pit.

More than one earth rod may have to be installed to achieve a satisfactory earth reading. Alternatively copper tapes, copper plates, copper grids or cast iron pipes surrounded by a conducting material may have to be installed in certain areas. Sites on granite or sandstone may require other earthing methods.

Local soil conditions are a major factor in the efficiency of earth electrodes and the requisite number of electrodes should be installed to ensure the value of resistance to earth is met. Schedule 7.4 illustrates that the chemical composition of soil affects its resistivity. See Schedule 7.3 for resistivity of various soils. See Practice 11 for measurement of earth electrode resistance.

Extremes of weather can also influence the resistance of earth electrodes and in the selection of electrode type and in calculating the depth at which they should be embedded, account should be taken of that possibility. Figure 7.11 shows how the increased moisture content of soil can rapidly decrease its resistance. It demonstrates that below 20% moisture content the resistance of red clay soars. Wherever possible the earth electrode should be installed deep enough to reach the "water table" or "permanent moisture level". Where severe low temperature conditions exist, upper soil levels can become frozen. Earth electrodes should be buried below the frost layer. Schedule 7.5 illustrates the effect of temperature on resistivity. Figure 7.12 illustrates what happens to a satisfactory earth electrode resistance reading taken during a wet season, compared to the readings obtained during a dry or frosty season.

Often permanent moisture and frost free soil levels are deep below the surface and the only way to reach them is by driving extensible rod earth electrodes. Figure 7.13 shows the relationship between depth of earth rod and the resistance for soil of uniform moisture content. Where rocks lie just below the surface parallel driven shorter rods, plates, mats or buried conductors, or a combination of them, can be used if they are buried as deep as possible to avoid freezing or drying out. Often parallel rods are driven too closely together and this decreases their effectiveness.

Figure 7.14 illustrates that the distance between rods should be greater than the rod length.

The choice of earth electrode type and material will be influenced by the need for it to withstand corrosion and the possibility of an increase in the earth resistance of the electrodes due to corrosion, should be allowed for when designing the earthing arrangements.

Public gas and water systems must not be utilised as earth electrodes but on the consumer's side such metalwork should be bonded and connected to the main equipotential bonding conductor at the main earth terminal position. (See Practice 2).

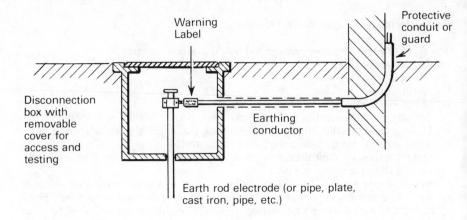

Figure 7.9 Typical earth electrode installation.

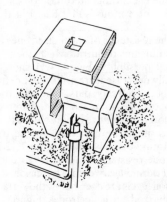

Figure 7.10 Layout of a concrete inspection pit for the earth electrode.

Schedule 7.3 – Resistivity of various soils

Soil	Resistivity, ohm-cm
Marshy Ground	200-270
Loam and Clay	400-15,000
Chalk	6,000-40,000
Sand	9,000-800,000
Peat	20,000 upwards
Sandy Gravel	30,000-50,000
Rock	100,000 upwards

Wherever possible, dry, sandy, rocky ground should be avoided; however, in many installations no choice is available.

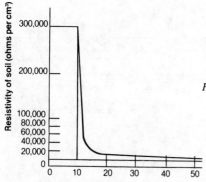

Figure 7.11   Variation of soil resistivity with moisture content (red clay soil).

Schedule 7.4 – Effect of salt on soil resistivity
(sandy loam, moisture content 15%)

Added salted (per cent by weight of moisture)	Resistivity (ohm-centimetres)
0	10,700
0.1	1,800
1.0	460
5	190
10	130
20	100

Care should be taken where streams, rivers or high seasonal rain fall are liable, over a period of time, to wash away soil salts.

Schedule 7.5 – Effect of temperature on resistivity
(For sandy loam, 15.2% moisture)

Temperature C	F	Resistivity ohm-cm
20	68	7,200
10	50	9,900
0	32 (water)	13,800
0	32 (ice)	30,000
− 5	23	79,000
−15	14	330,000

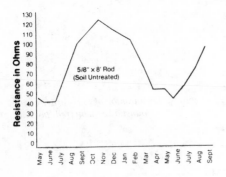

Figure 7.12 A typical earth electrode resistance cycle due to seasonal variations in weather conditions.

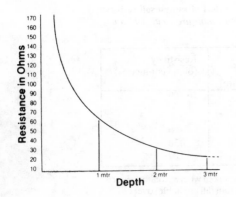

Figure 7.13 The relationship between depth of driven earth rod and resistance of soil of uniform moisture content.

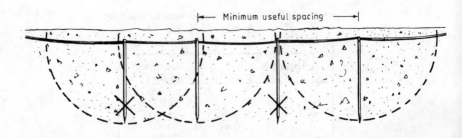

Figure 7.14 Illustrates that distance between earth electrode rods should be greater than depth of the rods.

Metallic coverings and lead sheaths of cables may be used as earth electrodes if they are not liable to deterioration through corrosion and the consent of the cable owner has been obtained and arrangements are made to monitor that no future changes of use of the cable will affect its adequacy as an earth electrode.

Figures 7.7 to 7.13 and Schedules 7.3 to 7.5 are reproduced by kind permission of W.J. Furse & Co Ltd.

Earthing conductors *(Regulations 542-16 to 542-18)*

Earthing conductors are required to meet the conditions given in Schedule 7.6. If the earthing conductor is in tape or strip form its dimensions must be chosen with regard to the possibility of mechanical damage and corrosion. Conductors of aluminium and copper clad aluminium should not be employed as final connections to earth electrodes.

A substantial clamp together with a permanent label with indelible wording should be used to connect the earthing conductor to the earth electrode (see Practice 10).

Main earthing terminals or bars *(Regulations 542-19 to 542-20)*

To connect the circuit protective conductors, main bonding conductors, and any functional earthing conductors (if required), to the earth conductor, every installation should have an accessible main earthing terminal or earth bar. Provision must be made for the disconnection of the main earthing terminal from the means of earthing to permit the resistance measurement of earthing arrangements. Disconnection of the means of earthing from the earth terminal, should be possible only by the use of tools.

Protective conductors *(Regulations 543-1 to 543-19)*

The cross-sectional area of every protective conductor (not for equipotential bonding) must be either calculated or selected as indicated in the text which follows. Schedule 7.6 shows the minimum cross sectional areas of separate protective conductors. Separate means that the protective conductor is not an integral part of a cable, nor formed by conduit, ducting or trunking, nor contained within such an enclosure.

Calculated csa

For disconnection times up to 5 seconds, the cross-sectional area of protective conductors must be calculated from the formula $S = \dfrac{\sqrt{I^2 t}}{k}$, which can be further expressed in the following terms:

$$\text{Cross sectional area (mm}^2) = \sqrt{\frac{\left(\text{Fault current at protective device}\right)^2 \times \left(\text{time of operation, in seconds, of protective device}\right)}{\text{protective conductor factor, k}}}$$

For example, if the maximum short circuit current through the protective device is 4000A, when its operating time is 5 seconds and the 'k' factor is 115, then the cross sectional area of a pvc-insulated protective conductor in the cable will not be less than:

$$= \frac{\sqrt{4000^2 \times 5}}{115} = 77.77\text{mm}^2$$

Schedule 7.6 – Minimum cross sectional areas of separate earthing and protective conductors and buried earthing conductors

Cross Sectional Area of Conductor (minimum) mm²	Earthing and protective conductors. Surface		Earthing conductors only Buried in ground			
	Mechanically Protected	Not Mechanically Protected	Mechanically Protected		Not Mechanically Protected	
			Protected Against Corrosion	Not Protected Against Corrosion	Protected Against Corrosion	Not Protected Against Corrosion
2.5	●		●			
4.0		●				
16 (copper)					●	
16 (Coated Steel)					●	
25 (Copper)				●		●
50 (Steel)				●		●

but this result gives a non-standard size of protective conductor and the nearest larger standard size 95mm² should be used.

The fault current is that for a fault of negligible impedance and the time taken for the protective device to operate also relates to that fault current. The limiting capability of the circuit impedances and the breaking capacity of the protective device should be allowed for in assessing the fault current and the time of operation used in the above equation.

Schedule 7.7, based on Tables 54B, 54C and 54D in the 15th edition of the Regulations, provides details of 'k' factors of protective conductors.

More detailed information on the cross sectional areas of protective conductors is given in Appendix 8 of the Regulations. This is summarised with examples in the text which follows.

Where a protective conductor is common to several circuits, its cross-sectional area should be calculated having regard to the worst condition for fault current and operating time within those circuits or be selected to match the largest circuit phase conductor.

Schedule 7.7 – Value of k for protective conductors

Insulation material: Final temperature: Conductor material:	PVC 160° Cu Al St Pb	85° Rubber 220°C Cu Al St Pb	90°C thermo-plastic 250°C Cu Al St Pb
Separate insulated Protective conductors, (eg not part of a cable) or bare conductors touching the cable covering: (Insulating material may also be the cable covering). Initial temperature assumed – 30°C for each type of insulation	143 95 52 –	166 110 60 –	176 116 64 –
Protective conductors as a core in a cable or bunched with cables. Initial temperature assumed – 70°C (PVC); 85°C (Rubber); 90°C (thermoplastic)	115 76 – –	134 89 – –	143 94 – –
Protective conductors being the sheath or armour of a cable. Initial temperature assumed – 60°C (PVC); 75°C (Rubber); 80°C (thermoplastic)	– 81 44 22	– 93 51 26	– 98 54 27

Cu = Copper; Al = aluminium; St = Steel; Pb = Lead

Schedule 7.8 provides k values for bare conductors with no risk of heat damage to adjacent materials, and with an initial temperature of 30°C assumed. It is based on Table 54E of the 15th edition.

Schedule 7.8 – Values of k for bare conductors *(Initial temperature 30°C)*

Conditions	Copper (Cu)	Aluminium (Al)	Steel (St)
* Visible conductors in limited areas Final temperature 500°C (Cu and St) 300°C (Al)	228	125	82
In normal situations Final temperature 200°C	159	105	58
With fire risk Final temperature 150°C	138	91	50

* The figures refer only to situations where the connections are not affected by temperature.

Limitation of earth fault loop impedance for compliance with Regulation 543-1
(IEE Appendix 8)

As previously mentioned, the cross sectional area of a protective conductor, except an equipotential bonding conductor, should be calculated or selected. The cable to be utilised will often settle whether calculation or selection is appropriate.

The use of flat twin, three core and twin cables pvc-insulated pvc-sheathed with protective conductors (to BS6004 Table 5) requires the application of the formula given earlier for the calculation of cross sectional area of the protective conductor. See the following examples.

Example 1. – BS1361 Type 1 Fuse

Assume 2.5mm² cable with incorporated protective conductor feeding an immersion heater fused at 15 amperes with a k factor of 115.
For fixed appliance, fuse operating time (maximum) required is 5 seconds. For time 5 seconds – current flowing is 47A. (See Figure 7.15).
Using the formula previously referred to:

$$S = \sqrt{\frac{I^2 \times t}{K}} \ \ mm^2$$

In this case
$$I = 47A$$
$$t = 5 \text{ second}$$
$$K = 115$$
$$\therefore S = \sqrt{\frac{47^2 \times 5}{115}} \ \ 0.91mm^2$$

In this example the 2.5mm² pvc-insulated pvc-sheathed cable normally incorporates a protective conductor of 1.5mm² which is more than adequate.

Miniature circuit breaker Type 3 to BS3871

Type 3 breakers must trip at between 7 and 10 times rated current.
If the worst case is taken: a 6A breaker will trip at 60A. See Figure 7.16 (c).

$$\therefore Zs = \frac{240}{60} = 4 \text{ ohms}$$

$$S = \sqrt{\frac{(60)^2 \times 0.4}{143^*}}$$

$$= 0.26mm^2$$

Nearest standard size 1.0mm²
* Assuming protective conductor not included in the cable sheath, Schedule 7.7.

When dissimilar metals are used for phase and protective conductors, the protective conductor has to have the same conductance as that of a cable chosen by the above method.

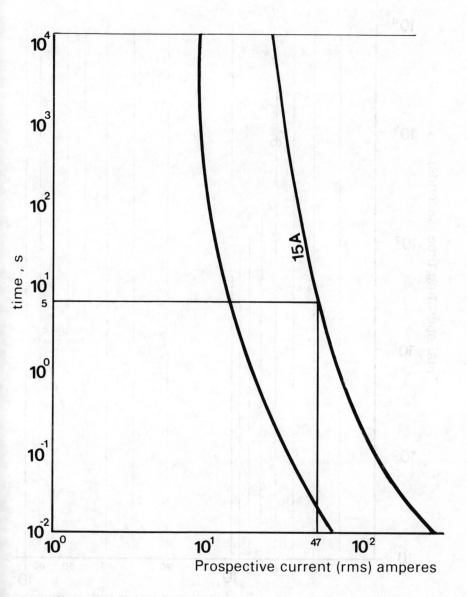

Figure 7.15 Time/current characteristics of BS1361 fuses.

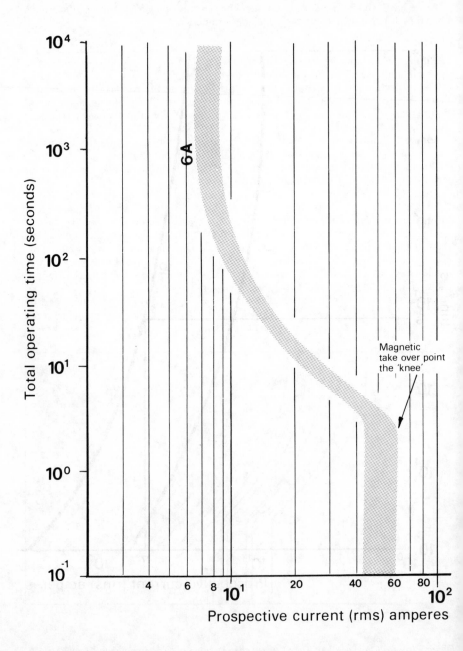

Figure 7.16   (c)Time/current characteristics for Type 3 miniature circuit breakers to BS3871.

As we have seen it is possible to estimate the time for which a conductor will accept a known fault current by using the adiabatic formula.

$$t = \frac{K^2 S^2}{I^2} \text{ seconds}$$

Strictly this formula is for cables of $10mm^2$ or greater for times up to 5 seconds. The approximation is still useful for smaller cables.

The protection given by some Type 3 miniature circuit breakers (mcb) is shown in Figure 7.16 (a) which compares the mcb characteristics with that of the adiabatic curves for the smaller cable sizes. General protection is indicated if the adiabatic line is beyond the 'knee' of the mcb curve.

For small cables being protected by very rapid circuit breaker action (for example 5 milliseconds) the above explanation can be an over simplification.

Due to the varying degrees of assymmetry possible, it is more realistic to compare I^2t let through of the mcb to the maximum I^2t for the cable.

From the abiabatic formula it can be seen that for a given time $I^2t = K^2 S^2$.

So $K^2 S^2$ values for various cables can be calculated and plotted on the maximum I^2t let through energy curves for an mcb. Figure 7.16 (b) shows some such curves.

The prospective fault current at the point of installation must be calculated and the point at which this occurs on the mcb curve noted. If it occurs at the line representing the $K^2 S^2$ operating limit of the chosen cable, then full protection will be achieved. For example a 2.5mm cable will be protected by a 32A mcb up to 9kA, whereas a $1.5mm^2$ cable would not. See Figure 7.16(b).

Value of fault loop impedance external to the circuit (Ze) can be determined by deducting from the value of Zs, the value $R_1 + R_2$ (calculated from cable manufacturer's data) or $0.25 (R_1 + R_2)$ in case of ring circuits.

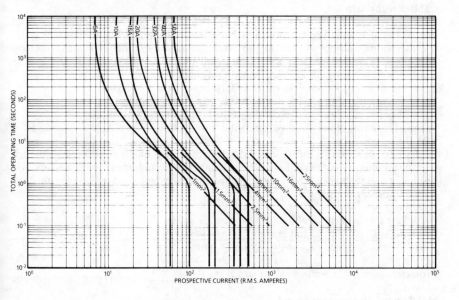

Figure 7.16   (a) Comparison of Time/Current characteristics of Type 3 miniature circuit breakers and common copper/pvc conductor sizes. (Illustrations by courtesy of Bill Switchgear Ltd).

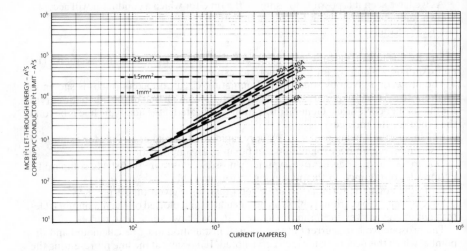

Figure 7.16 (b) Comparison of I^2t maximum let-through energy of Type 3 miniature circuit breakers with cable safety curve of common copper/pvc conductor sizes. (Illustrations by courtesy of Bill Switchgear Ltd).

Cable already selected

Where the size and type of cable has been selected already on the basis of other considerations, in order to evaluate protective conductor size the total earth fault loop impedance (Z_s) must be calculated. The inductance of a cable under 35mm^2 can be ignored, and the formula $Z_s = Z_E + R_1 + R_2$ used where:

Z_E = Earth fault loop impedance external to the circuit concerned.

R_1 = Resistance of phase conductor to farthest point of utilisation.

R_2 = Resistance of protective conductor to farthest point of utilisation.

When used in ring circuits without spurs the formula to be used is $Z_s = Z_E + 0.25 R_1 + 0.25 R_2$.

The value of R_1 and R_2 are calculated before the ring is finally completed. Although the calculations are vectorial, for this purpose arithmetic additions can be used and will result in a slightly higher value. See calculation for earth fault loop impedance for BS88 Part 2 fuses, set out below.

Example:

BS88 Part 2 fuse with time limit of 0.4 seconds

From Figure 7.17 Earth fault current (I_f) = 110A

Earth loop impedance (Z_s) = $\dfrac{240V}{110A}$ = 2.18 ohms

Protective conductor (not in cable) size $S = \sqrt{\dfrac{(110)^2 \times 0.4}{143}}$

= 0.49mm.^{2} Nearest size 1mm.^{2}

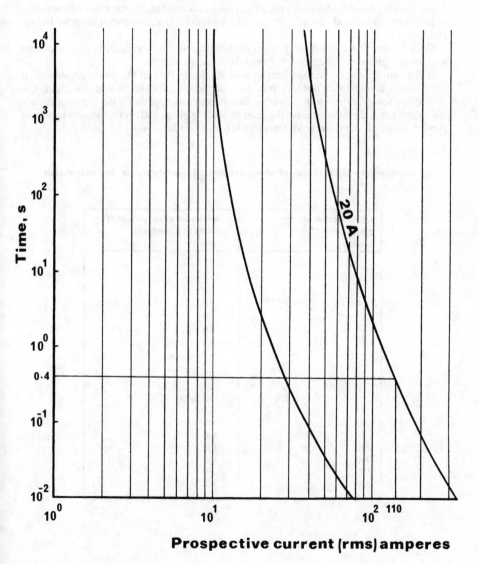

Figure 7.17   Time/current characteristics – BS88 Part 2 fuses.

Selected csa of protective conductors

The Regulations provide an alternative method of selecting the size of protective conductors through a relationship between the sizes of phase and protective conductors of the same material, as follows:

Up to 16mm^2 phase conductors; protective conductor must be the same size (minimum).

Between 16mm^2 and 35mm^2 phase conductors; protective conductor must be 16mm^2 (minimum).

Over 35mm^2 phase conductors; protective conductor must be half the cross sectional area of the phase conductor or the nearest standard size.

If the protective conductor material is dissimilar to that of the phase conductor, it must have a conductance not less than that of conductors of similar material. Schedule 7.10 gives some information on protective conductors together with the appropriate fixing centres. Schedule 7.9 gives the relative sizes of phase and protective conductors of similar materials for a range of standard sizes of conductors.

Schedule 7.9 – Relative sizes of phase and protective conductors of similar materials

Cross-section of phase conductors (mm^2)	Minimum cross-section of protective conductor (mm^2)
1	1
1.5	1.5
2.5	2.5
4.0	4.0
6.0	6
10	10
16	16
25	16
35	16
50	25
70	35
95	50
120	50 or 70
150	70
185	95
240	120
300	150
400	185
500	240
630	300

Schedule 7.10 – Protective conductors. Maximum fixing centres of copper and aluminium tapes, standard tape sizes, CSA and DC reistance.

Approx CSA (mm²)	Approx dc resistance 20°C Ohm/km		Tape width (mm)	Tape thickness (mm)									Fixing centre (metres)
	Copper	Aluminium		1.5		2	3		4	5	6		
				CU	AL	AL	CU	AL	CU	CU	CU	AL	
18.75	0.969	1.599	12.5	X	X								0.25
37.50	0.516	0.855	12.5				O						0.25
30.00	0.611	1.013	20	O									0.40
40.00	0.484	0.801	20			O							0.40
60.00	0.313	0.517	20				O	X					0.40
37.50	0.516	0.855	25	O									0.50
75.00	0.244	0.405	25				X	X					0.50
100.00	0.184	0.304	25						O				0.50
150.00	0.124	0.206	25								X	O	0.50
93.00	0.197	0.327	31				O						0.62
186.00	0.097	0.161	31							O			0.62
114.00	0.161	0.266	38				O						0.76
190.00	0.095	0.158	38						O				0.76
228.00	0.079	0.132	38							O			0.76
150.00	0.124	0.206	50				O						1.00
200.00	0.090	0.150	50						O				1.00
300.00	0.060	0.100	50							X			1.00
300.00	0.060	0.100	50									O	1.00

Notes: X – Standard tape with or without pvc sheath.
O – Standard tape no sheath.

Tapes should be fixed by saddles to manufacturers' recommendations, alternatively (tape width X 20) subject to a maximum of 1 metre and should be supported at bends or joints. Tapes should not be drilled for fixing unless adequate cross section is used to compensate for loss of section due to drilling.

Schedule 7.10 has been based on good practice and best available data – it is not specified in the IEE Regulations.

Protective conductors formed by metal conduits, trunking etc may need to be supplemented to achieve the maximum prescribed impedance to clear a fuse or trip a circuit breaker in 0.4 seconds or 5 seconds, as appropriate.

Types of protective conductor

Protective conductors must comply with the Regulations as regards identification by colour (see Practice 3) and also must comply with the following requirements:

1. A cable containing a protective conductor must comply with the British Standard for that cable (see Practice 3). A protective conductor of 10mm² or less, should be of copper or copper-clad aluminium.

2. In a final ring circuit the protective conductor must be arranged as a ring in the same way as the phase conductors with each end of the protective conductor connected to the earth terminal of the circuit. This does not refer to the metal cable covering or enclosure.

3. Protective conductors formed by the metal enclosures of factory made switchboards, distribution boards and busbar trunking, etc must be designed to satisfy to the need for (i) protection against detrimental mechanical, chemical or electrochemical effects (ii) have a conducting sectional area not less than that which is calculated by the previously mentioned formula, and (iii) have provisions for connecting other protective conductors at all branch points on the assemblies.

4. The sheath and/or armour or metallic covering of a cable used as a protective conductor must meet the requirements stipulated at items (i) and (ii) of item 3.

5. Cable trunking or conduit systems used as protective conductors must have a conductivity not less than that calculated by the use of the previously mentioned formula; joints must comply with the Regulations and preserve electrical continuity as described later herein and they must have means of connecting other protective conductors where required.

6. Socket outlets or accessories that are earthed via the protective metal enclosure(s), such as conduit or trunking, of the wiring system, must also have a short protective conductor between the terminal attached to the accessory enclosure or between the trunking and the accessory earth terminal. This connection is essential to guarantee continuity between the socket outlet or other accessory and the accessory box or trunking. (An insulated coverplate is shown in Figure 7.18).

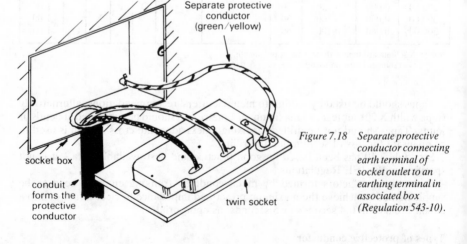

Figure 7.18   Separate protective conductor connecting earth terminal of socket outlet to an earthing terminal in associated box (Regulation 543-10).

7. It is prohibited to use flexible metal conduit as a protective conductor. A separate protective conductor must be fixed to the outside of the flexible conduit and terminated on the equipment at each end. The protective conductor should be calculated in accordance with the formula previously described, or selected from Schedule 7.6.

8. Exposed metal enclosures of equipment must not be used as a protective conductor for other equipment. The method adopted should be as shown in Figure 7.19.

9. Metalwork, such as conduit or trunking, enclosing cables is not permitted for use as a combined protective earth and neutral (PEN) conductor, or as a neutral conductor in TN-C or TN-C-S systems.

10. Conductive parts not forming part of the electrical installation must not be used as protective conductors. Permanently fixed and reliable extraneous metal parts may, however, be utilised for supplementary bonding.

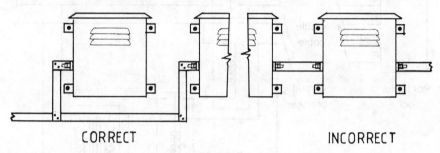

CORRECT   INCORRECT

Figure 7.19   Exposed metal enclosures of equipment must not be used as a protective conductor of other equipment.

Preservation of electrical continuity

Protective conductors must be installed so that they are safeguarded against detrimental mechanical, chemical and electrodynamic effects. A separate protective conductor of a cross-sectional area up to 6mm^2 (other than copper strip) must be insulated as for a single core non-sheathed cable to BS6004. Where a non-insulated protective conductor up to 6mm^2 section within a cable is exposed at terminations or joints it must be insulated with sleeving to BS2848. The insulating sleeving should be coloured green/yellow.

Protective conductor connections must be accessible (excepting joints in metal conduits, ducting and trunking).

Switches must not be fitted in protective conductors, but test links or joints may be provided if the use of a tool is necessary for disconnection (see Figure 7.20).

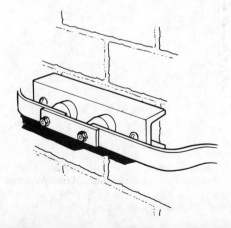

Figure 7.20   Test link in protective conductor. (Illustration by courtesy of W.J. Furse & Co Ltd).

The operating coil of an earth monitoring device must not be connected in the protective earth conductor but should be in the pilot conductor (see Figure 7.21).

Metal conduit joints must be screwed or securely clamped for good electrical continuity. Simple slip and pin-grip sockets are not permitted.

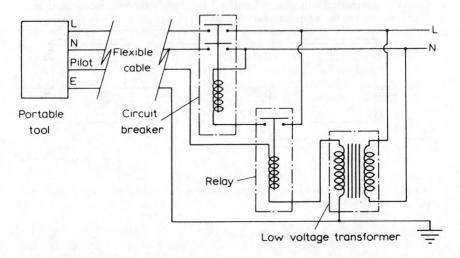

Figure 7.21 Coil of earth monitoring device in pilot conductor (Regulation 543-18).

Residual current devices *(Regulations 531-3 to 531-8(a) and 412-14)*

Where residual current devices are utilised, all the phase conductors of the circuit must be disconnected by the device. See Figure 7.22.

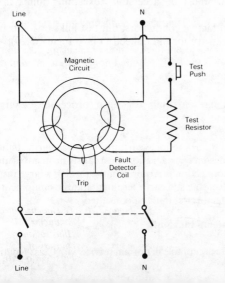

Figure 7.22 A residual current device.

The value of the tripping current (amperes) times the earth loop impedance (ohms) must not be greater than 50 for residual current devices. If a fault voltage operated device is used the total earth fault loop impedance should not exceed 500 ohms (see Schedule 2.15 and Figure 7.4).*

Where the current using equipment characteristics are known, verification is required that the vectorial sum of the leakage currents on that part of the installation on the load side of the device are compatible with the device. This vectorial sum must be less than one half of the nominal residual operating current of the device.

For TT and IT systems recognition needs to be taken of the variation of earthing resistance due to climatic variations, etc.

On large installations the earthing arrangements may need to be subdivided due to the magnitude of total inherent leakage currents. Where residual operating currents of 30mA or less are used this sub-division may also be necessary on smaller installations.

When a separate auxiliary supply is required to operate a residual current device:–
1. The device shall have a 'fail-safe' mechanism that will operate automatically if the auxiliary supply fails.
Or
2. A supply will automatically be available upon failure of the auxiliary supply.

Residual current devices must be located outside the influence of other equipment's magnetic fields unless it has been verified that their operation will not be affected by those other magnetic fields.

When used in conjunction with an overcurrent device a residual current device must be able to withstand any thermal or mechanical stress under fault conditions on the load side of the point where it is installed. This will depend on the characteristics of the short circuit current at this point and the characteristics of the device providing short circuit protection.

A residual current device (RCD) alone must not be relied on to protect against direct contact. An RCD giving indirect contact protection will reduce the risk during direct contact if the RCD has a rated operating current not exceeding 30mA and is designed to operate within 40ms when the residual current rises to 150mA during direct contact, providing one of four protective measure required by Regulation 412-1 is also effective, these measures are (i) insulation of live parts. (ii) barriers or enclosures. (iii) obstacles. (iv) out of reach. Where residual current devices are connected in series and danger could arise from multiple tripping under fault conditions, the minor RCD must be selected to operate before the major devices. The acceptable method of ensuring discrimination is to select RCD tripping times such that the RCD required not to trip to prevent danger has a longer response time during fault.

Combined protective and functional earthing for data processing equipment
(Regulations 545-1 to 545-8)

Protective earthing is more important than functional earthing, where an earth connection covers both functions the overriding design consideration must satisfy protective earthing. Where a low noise or "clean" earth connection is required in the form of a large insulated earth conductor run separately between the site earth terminal and the equipment clean earth terminal the equipment manufacturer should be consulted.

Equipment with earth leakage currents up to 3.5mA

Earth leakage currents up to 3.5mA are acceptable in normal service with Class 1 stationary
*See note to Schedule 2.15.

or movable equipment to BS6204. For a single item no precautions are necessary: a plug and socket can be used.

Equipment leakage currents exceeding 3.5mA

Connect equipment to fixed wiring or use a plug and socket to BS4343.

RCD protection

If the supply passes through an RCD the equipment earth leakage current shall not exceed one quarter of the RCD nominal tripping current.

'TT' system supply

In 'TT' systems the equipment earth leakage current (I) multiplied by twice the installation earth electrode resistance (2R) must not exceed 50. Where these limitations cannot be met the equipment should be supplied through a double wound transformer. The centre point of the transformer secondary winding shall be connected to (1) exposed conductive parts, (2) circuit protective conductors, (3) high integrity duplicated protective conductors (each not less than 4mm^2 CSA) between the transformer and the item of equipment.

Equipment with earth leakage currents exceeding 10mA

A duplicated high integrity protective earth connection is necessary between the source of the final circuit and the equipment. Duplicated conductor arrangements are (i) two separate insulated conductors (4mm^2 CSA or more) each having separate earthing terminals, (ii) two conductors of a multicore cable or one conductor of a multicore and the metal armour, sheath or braiding of the cable (note:- the CSA of all conductors of a multicore when added together shall equal or exceed 10mm^2), (iii) one separate insulated conductor not less than 2.5mm^2 CSA connected in parallel with an enclosure such as a metal conduit, trunking or ducting, (iv) a protective conductor in an earth monitored circuit arranged to disconnect the supply on failure of the protective conductor. Where the total earth leakage current does not exceed 10mA in a final circuit supplying a number of data processing units via socket outlets the final circuit shall have a duplicated protective circuit as items (i) to (iii) or an earth monitored protective conductor as (iv).

Combined Protective and Neutral Conductors (PEN) *(Regulations 546-1 to 546-8)*

A system having a combined protective and neutral (PEN) conductor may only be used when it is authorised by the appropriate Secretary of State for Energy. A PEN system can be installed in situations where electrical energy is obtained from (a) privately owned transformers, or converters connected so that there is no metallic connection with the supply authority service, or (b) from a privately owned generating plant.

The types of conductors acceptable as PEN conductors providing that the protected circuit is not supplied through a residual current device are:–

(a) conductors of cables with a minimum cross sectional area of 10mm^2 copper or 16mm^2 aluminium.

(b) the outer conductor of a concentric cable manufactured in accordance with British Standards having a minimum cross sectional area of 4mm^2 and installed in accordance with the directions below:

(i)   The outer conductor of a concentric cable can serve only one circuit, although a twin or multicore cable may serve a number of points which are contained in one final circuit.

(ii) The conductance of the outer conductor of a concentric cable should be not less than the conductance of the internal conductor of the singlecore cable; one internal conductor of a multicore cable; the internal conductors connected in parallel when a twin or multicore cable serving several points in a final circuit is connected in the form of a ring circuit.

(iii) The conductance of the outer conductor of a concentric cable should be maintained at all joints and terminations by means of additional conductors installed in accordance with the foregoing requirements (see Figure 7.24)

(iv) The outer conductor of a concentric cable shall not incorporate means of switching or isolation.

(v) The PEN conductor in every cable shall be insulated or have sufficient insulation for the highest voltage applied to the cable.

When neutral and earth conductors are installed separately at any point in the installation they must then not be connected together beyond that point. The PEN conductor must be connected to a terminal bar designated for the protective earthing conductor at the point of separation and the neutral conductor to a separate terminal bar.

Figure 7.24   An earth tail sealing pot used in concentric wiring systems where protective conductor has to be maintained (Regulation 546-5).

Main equipotential bonding conductors *(Regulations 547-2 to 547-3)*

The cross sectional area of the main equipotential bonding copper conductor should be not less than half the cross sectional area of the earthing conductor, subject to a minimum size of 6mm² and a maximum of 25mm². When PME conditions apply the supply undertaking must be consulted regarding sizes of protective conductors.

Main equipotential bonding connections to the main gas and water services should be as near as possible to the main point of entry into the building ensuring that the bonding is made to the metal pipework on the consumer's side of any insulating section of that surface. The bonding shall be made on the consumer's side of a gas meter between the meter outlet union and branch pipework connections preferably within 600mm of the gas meter. (See Practice 2).

Supplementary bonding conductors *(Regulations 547-4 to 547-7)*

Supplementary bonding can be provided by:

(a) Permanent and reliable extraneous conductive parts e.g. has satisfactory metal to metal joints.

(b) Supplementary bonding conductors.

(c) A combination of items (a) and (b).

Pipework brackets and equipment of other services such as water, gas etc are prohibited from use as protective conductors, but may be used for supplementary bonding.

The cross sectional areas of supplementary bonding conductors connected between two exposed conductive parts, or between two extraneous conductive parts should not be smaller than any associated protective conductor connected to the exposed conductive part and should not be smaller than 2.5mm^2 (mechanically protected) and 4mm^2 (not mechanically protected). Subject to the previously mentioned minima, a protective conductor between exposed and extraneous conductive parts may be half the size of that connected between exposed conductive parts.

A label (see Practice 10) must be attached firmly in a visible position at every point of connection of every conductor which bonds extraneous conductive parts.

Copperclad aluminium or aluminium conductors must not be used for bonding connections to water pipes liable to condensation during normal conditions.

Prevention of mutal detrimental influences between electrical services and exposed metalwork of other services *(Regulations 525-10 to 525-12)*.

Where contact may occur between fixed metal work (eg of the various services) and metal sheaths or armour of low voltage cables (or metal conduit, trunking, bare protective conductors, etc associated with such cables), they must be either effectively segregated or bonded together. The bonding of gas and water services as described earlier does not provide a substitute for this requirement. The bonding of metalwork to other services should be confirmed with the respective reponsible undertaking. British Telecom cables should not be bonded or earthed without authority to do so having been obtained.

Cables operating at low voltage and without metal sheaths must also be segregated from fixed metal work.

Excepting where common supervision of multiple services is provided, non-electrical services shall not be installed with electrical services in a common enclosure (see Code of Practice 413 for information on this requirement).

In a lift or hoist shaft, no other services shall be installed other than the cables and conduits serving the lift and its associated equipment, e.g. telephone alarm, emergency lighting or shaft lighting etc. See Figure 7.25.

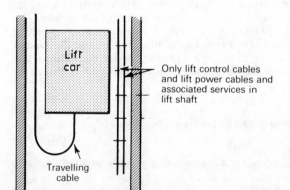

Only lift control cables and lift power cables and associated services in lift shaft

Lift car

Travelling cable

Lift shaft

Figure 7.25 Illustrating the requirements of Regulation 525-12.

Practice 8

Isolation and switching

The fundamental requirements for isolation and switching are given in Regulations 13-14 and 13-15.

Schedule 8.1 poses questions which if answered positively will ensure that the fundamental safety requirements as to isolation and switching are met. The full requirements of the Regulations as to isolation and switching are summarised in this Section.

Schedule 8.1 – Fundamental requirements for Isolation and Switching

(Regulations 13-14 and 13-15)

Positive answer required to all the following questions	Notes and ASEE Comment
Has effective and readily operable means been provided to cut off the voltage supply to every installation, circuit and item of equipment, to prevent or remove danger?	If the supply authority has a switch- or fuse-gear at the installation's origin, it may not be necessary to duplicate that means of isolation between the origin and the installation's main distribution point.
Has effective, readily accessible, easily operable and suitably located means been provided to disconnect each electric motor from the supply, to prevent danger?	The means of disconnection may be an isolating switch, Key switch, pull wire trip switch, or plug and socket-outlet, etc.

Basic requirements for switchgear *(Regulations 530-1 to 530-3)*

Where it is required to disconnect all live conductors including the neutral conductor, the phase switches must open simultaneously with or before (a) the neutral switch opens (b) or before the neutral link can be removed. On closing, the neutral switch shall close first or close simultaneously with all phase switches. Figure 8.1 illustrates several types of disconnecting devices.

Single pole switchgear shall not be connected in the neutral conductor or any system designated TN or TT.

The maximum voltage that can develop across a fuse or circuit breaker under fault conditions shall not exceed a voltage that would impair the fuse or circuit breaker.

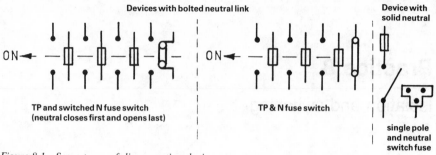

Figure 8.1   Some types of disconnecting device.

Position of switches

The questions contained in Schedule 8.2 indicate where switches are to be located in order to meet the requirements of the Regulations. The full effect of the Regulations as to switching and isolation devices is summarised in the text.

Schedule 8.2 – Position of switches

Positive answer required to all the following questions	Notes and ASEE Comment
Has an inspection been made to confirm that no switch or circuit breaker has been inserted in an earthed neutral conductor? If a linked switch or circuit-breaker has been installed to break an earthed neutral conductor, will it also break all the associated phase conductors in the sequence required by the Regulations?	"Neutral conductor" – a defined term – is that conductor which is connected to the neutral point on the transmission system. See definition of "Live part" includes a neutral conductor. In Great Britain, it can be assumed that in any public electricity supply the neutral of the supply is permanently earthed. Overseas supply authorities may have different requirements.
Have all single pole switches been installed in the phase conductor only?	"Phase conductor" – a defined term – is a conductor, other than the neutral conductor.
Has any switch installed in an earthed neutral conductor been linked so as to break all the associated phase conductors?	

New terminology

The Regulations introduce new terminology for isolation and switching. There are four concepts embodied in the theme of the Regulations which deal with isolation and switching. The first, "isolation", is a defined term (see Principles 2). Isolation is essentially an "off-load" disconnection which occurs when there is no load current flowing through the opening contacts of an isolating device. Isolation alone, should be undertaken only by electrically skilled persons.

The second concept is "mechanical maintenance" also a defined term (see Principles 2). This measure relates to the protection of persons undertaking non-electrical tasks such as cleaning. It is an "on-load" function.

A third concept is "emergency switching" (defined term – see Principles 2) also an "on load" function. The Regulations in this field co-relate with those of the Electricity (Special) Regulations of the Factories Act.

Lastly, the concept of "functional switching" (not a defined term) which covers the switching necessary for the proper normal control and functioning of electrical equipment.

Devices suitable as isolators include: isolators (disconnectors); switch-disconnectors (isolating switches); plugs and socket outlets; fuse-links; links; circuit breakers having the required contact separation.

Devices suitable for switching off for mechanical maintenance include: switches; circuit breakers; control switches operating contactors; plugs and socket outlets.

Devices suitable for emergency switching must be a single switching device which directly cuts off the incoming supply or a combination of several items of equipment which by single initiation results in the cutting off of the appropriate supply. Plugs and sockets must not be used for emergency switching.

To sum up the requirements for isolation and switching fundamental for safety are to provide on-load switches or contactors, off-load isolators or other means of isolation to cut off all voltage from every main cable, sub-mains cable, final circuit, item of switchgear and every item of equipment where danger could arise. This does not exclude the use of the supply authority switchgear for isolation of the main cable feeding an installation, if the supply authority agrees. In addition to normal isolation and switching, a means of disconnection sited to prevent danger has to be provided for every electric motor.

General *(Regulations 460-1 and 460-2, 476-1, 537-1, 514-1)*

The fundamental safety rules for isolation (off-load disconnection) and switching (making and breaking current in normal or overload conditions) given in Regulations 13-14 and 13-15 are effectively repeated in Regulation 460-1 which requires that a means of isolation or switching that is manually operated, not automatic, shall be provided to remove or prevent danger arising from the use of electrical machines, equipment or installations, the exceptions being no switch or isolator should be connected in the PEN conductor of a TN-C system or in the protective conductor of a TN-S system. In a TN-S system the neutral conductor can be permanently connected without the means of isolation or disconnection being provided except in the case of a high voltage discharge lighting installation auto transformer where a means of isolating both poles of the supply shall be provided.

Where any of the functions for isolation, isolation for mechanical maintenance, functional switching and emergency switching are combined in one device, that device shall satisfy the requirements for each function used and shall be selected and erected as described later in this Section.

Conversely, not all devices are suitable for all functions. For example it is doubtful if a moulded case circuit breaker or a miniature circuit breaker would meet the requirements of switching off for mechanical maintenance.

In order to avoid confusion or possible danger great stress is made in the Regulations of the need to label equipment. The purpose of such items of equipment, where this is not obvious, needs to be clearly indicated to comply with the Regulations and appropriate warning notices located on, adjacent to, the equipment switch or controls (see Practice 10).

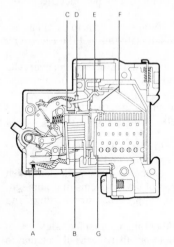

Figure 8.2   A diagram of a miniature circuit breaker. When a short-circuit occurs the fault current energises the solenoid (B) and attracts the plunger (C). The knob (D) then strikes the moving contact (E) with considerable kinetic energy and forces the contacts apart in less than 1 millisecond at rated breaking capacity. Devices for switching off for mechanical maintenance are required to be manually initiated and have OFF and OPEN positions which are indicated only when those positions on each pole have been achieved. (Illustration by courtesy of MEM Ltd).

Isolation *(Regulations 461-1 to 461-5 and 476-2 to 476-6)*

The requirements for isolation are that all live conductors of every circuit shall be isolated by means of a switch, circuit breaker, contactor, fuse link and carrier or other suitable means. It is permitted to isolate a group of circuits by the same means of isolation where appropriate but under no circumstances shall the PEN conductor of a TN-C system or the protective conductor of a TN-S system be isolated or disconnected in service. Where equipment is isolated for maintenance or is at rest in service and a danger could result from unintentional re-connection, suitable interlocking, locking or permit to work systems shall be implemented to prevent danger. Figure 8.3 illustrates the application of group isolation to a number of circuits supplying electric motors.

Where access can be gained to live parts that cannot be switched off by a common isolating device warning notices shall be used to warn of the danger and/or positive interlocking provided to ensure access is gained only when it is safe to work, similarly access to live parts connected to Power Factor correction capacitors etc., shall have warning notices and instructions on the safe method of discharging any energy remaining after switch off.

Switches, circuit breakers, contactors, fuse link and carrier or other isolating device shall be identified with the circuit they control.

Isolation should be possible at the origin of an installation leaving all equipment safe for maintenance, where an isolator provides maintenance facilities for a circuit breaker it shall be interlocked to ensure the isolator cannot be switched with the circuit breaker closed unless it is under the control of skilled persons only.

Where the main isolator is at some distance from the equipment to be isolated it shall be designed to be secured to prevent re-enclosure by others, if locks or removable handles are used to prevent unauthorised re-closure any other key or handle in the same installation shall be of a different type.

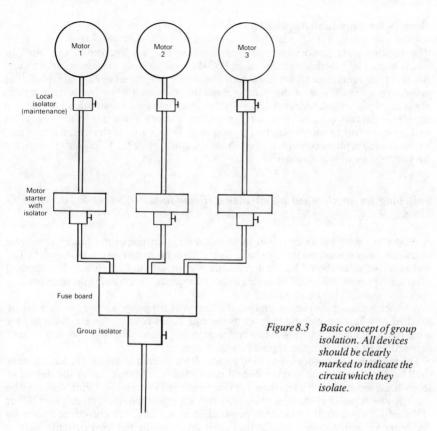

Figure 8.3 Basic concept of group isolation. All devices should be clearly marked to indicate the circuit which they isolate.

Isolators for motor circuits shall isolate the motor, the control equipment and automatic circuit breakers etc., associated with the motor. Isolators for high voltage discharge lighting luminaires shall be an integral part of the luminaire so as to isolate the supply when the cover is opened, alternatively an isolator shall be mounted adjacent to the luminaire or be secured by a switch with a locked or removable handle or by a lock on the door of a distribution board.

Figure 8.4 shows a self contained discharge luminaire with interlocking device.

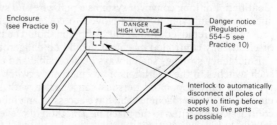

Figure 8.4 A means of complying with the isolation requirements for self-contained high-voltage discharge lighting fittings.

Devices for isolation *(Regulations 537-1 to 537-7)*

The requirements for devices used for isolation are: all live conductors shall be disconnected by a distance not less than BS5419 for disconnectors (semiconductors do not meet the requirements for isolators); the distance between open contacts shall be visible from the outside of the switch or reliably indicated when the correct contact separation is reached for all poles; isolators must meet all requirements to prevent unintentional reclosure by vibration or any other unlikely cause and have a means for locking in the off position; isolators should be linked multipole devices; if single pole units are used in phase conductors they should be close together; TN-S neutrals must not be switched by non-linked devices.

Switching for mechanical maintenance *(Regulations 462-1 to 462-3, 476-7 to 476-8 and 537-8 to 537-11)*

A means to switch off to carry out mechanical maintenance of machinery should be provided where it is necessary to prevent danger to persons carrying out such work. The means of isolation should be sited conveniently for use and identified. The method adopted to prevent the switch or device re-activating machinery during the maintenance operation should also be identified.

A switch for mechanical maintenance shall be provided where a heated surface can be touched or where an electric magnet or the like could cause a danger. Switches for mechanical maintenance mounted on an appliance, luminaire etc., shall not have exposed live parts when the appliance etc. is opened.

The requirements for devices used to switch off for mechanical maintenance are, they shall be connected in the main circuit, if connected in a control circuit the degree of safety achieved shall not be less than a device connected in the main circuit, they shall be manually switched or initiated with a visible contact gap or reliable indicator for OFF or ON functions and shall be selected or installed in a manner to prevent reclosure by accidental or unintentional means, they shall interrupt the full load current safely.

Emergency switching *(Regulations 463-1 to 463-5, 476-9 to 476-13)*

The requirement for emergency switching applies to every part of an installation where rapid disconnection will prevent or remove danger, a direct acting switch or remote emergency device shall disconnect by a single action to cut off the supply, in the case of machinery that will run on after disconnection it may be necessary to momentarily reverse the drive (plugging a motor) and/or apply brakes to prevent or remove danger.

All devices used for emergency switching shall be immediately accessible and identified. For long conveyor systems a pull wire and switch or pressure sensitive cable and control unit should be employed to cover the total area where danger is to be prevented or removed. Emergency stopping should be provided where electrical driven or electrically controlled machinery could be dangerous.

Emergency switches shall always be accessible and care should be used when siting such switches, if the operation of an emergency switch could cause danger it may be a type that only appointed persons can operate with a key. A person operating an electrically driven machine shall have access to an emergency switch, if more than one control switch is fitted to the machine a method of preventing unexpected re-starting by others shall be applied.

Figure 8.5 is a wiring diagram and a schematic of one manufacturer's direct-on-line motor starter with overload protection and no-volt protection. It incorporates two types of emergency switching (1) emergency stop push buttons (automatic locking variety which require a resetting opertion before the starter can be operated) and (2) a motor circuit isolating switch (capable of breaking stalled current and making fault current) which can be operated to isolate the motor in emergencies.

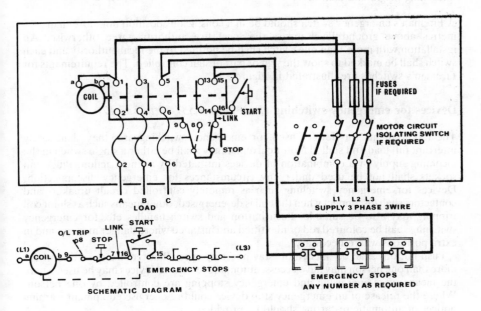

Figure 8.5 Diagram of Motor Starter circuit with means of emergency switching. (Illustration by courtesy of Crabtree Electrical Industries Ltd).

Fireman's emergency switch

An emergency switch for use by Firemen shall be provided for exterior high voltage signs such as neon signs and for high voltage interior discharge lighting installations. Signs in a closed market or shopping arcade are considered to be an exterior installation, a temporary sign installation used indoors for exhibitions is not an exterior installation a Fireman switch is not required for a portable sign or luminaire up to 100W if fed from an accessible socket outlet.

Exterior installations

A Firemans's emergency switch must be sited outside the building adjacent to the sign discharge lamps; alternatively a notice adjacent to the sign discharge lamps should clearly identify the position of the switch, the switch should have a name-plate fixed adjacent to it.

Interior installations (operating unattended)

A Fireman's emergency switch must be sited in the main entrance unless the local fire authority agree to another position.

Mounting height and control

A Fireman's emergency switch should be in a conspicious position not more than 2.75 metres above ground level unless the local fire authority agree otherwise. An installation with more than one switch shall be notified to the local authority and each switch shall be marked to show the sign or part of sign controlled. The requirements for Fireman's switches are illustrated in Figure 8.6.

Devices for emergency switching *(Regulations 537-12 to 537-17)*

The requirements for devices used for emergency switching are: they shall safely interrupt full load and stalled motor currents, they shall be either a single switch in the incoming supply or a combination of devices intitiated by a single action. Plugs and sockets shall not be used under any circumstances for emergency disconnection. Devices for emergency switching such as remotely controlled circuit breakers and contactors shall disconnect when the coil is de-energised, other means such as shunt coil tripping may also be suitable. Push button and switch handles etc. for emergency switching shall be coloured red or identified and installed where danger may rise and in extra positions where necessary.

Push buttons shall be latched or 'stay put' stop types that require re-setting where more than one person may have access, automatic re-setting devices may be used where the means of re-energising and emergency stopping are controlled by one person. Where the release of an emergency stop device could re-energise equipment warning notices of automatic restarting should be provided.

Emergency Fireman's switches shall be coloured RED with a plate not less than 150 x 150mm marked FIREMAN'S SWITCH in letters not less than 13mm fixed in a near position legible from ground level, the switch shall be clearly marked ON, OFF the OFF position at the top so that the switch can be pushed to the OFF position from ground level with a pole, the switch to latch in the OFF position, the name plate shall bear the name of the installing company or, if different, the name of the maintenance contractor.

A Fireman's switch which compiles with the Regulations is illustrated in Figure 8.6.

Other requirements for switching *(Regulations 476-14 to 476-20)*

Where emergency switching is not necessary and the requirements of the Regulations summarised earlier herein do not apply then the provisions set out below must be applied. This is done *either* by using isolating switches or switching off for maintenance as described earlier *or* by functional switching (for normal operation) *or* by suitable extra switching.

Every installation shall have a main switch or circuit breaker to break all live conductors, in three phase four wire AC installations the neutral may be a link and only the phase conductors switched, in which case the neutral link shall be bolted or in contact before the three linked phase switches can close: it follows the neutral link shall remain closed until the phase switches open. In some four pole fuse switches and

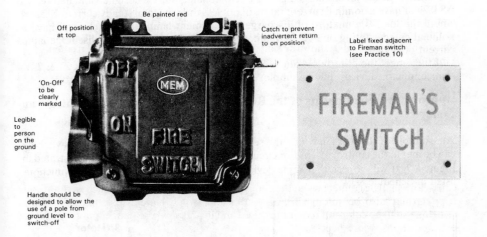

Off position at top

Be painted red

'On-Off' to be clearly marked

Catch to prevent inadvertent return to on position

Label fixed adjacent to Fireman switch (see Practice 10)

Legible to person on the ground

Handle should be designed to allow the use of a pole from ground level to switch-off

FIREMAN'S SWITCH

Figure 8.6   A Fireman's switch which complies with the requirements of Regulations (illustration by courtesy of MEM Ltd).

switches, all poles open and close simultaneously. Every circuit and final circuit shall have a switch or other means of interrupting the supply on load under any fault condition, a number of circuits may be switched as a group.

Appliances or luminaires shall be controlled by a load breaking and supply disconnection device that are separated from the luminaire or appliance and fixed in accessible location, this does not include luminaires or appliances intended to be connected to the supply by a plug and socket. Where silica glass sheathed or bare heating elements of an appliance can be touched the switch shall be a linked switch breaking all phases and neutral conductors. If the controlling device is mounted on the appliance or luminaire it shall meet all the requirements of a switching device fitted for mechanical maintenance of the appliance or luminaire. This requirement also applies to any separately located means of interrupting the supply.

A complete lighting or heating installation may be controlled by one or more load disconnecting devices in another room.

Every cooking appliance other than a portable appliance shall be controlled by a switch positioned not more than 2 metnres from the appliance, two appliances such as an electric hob and separate oven can be controlled by the same switch if each appliance is sited within 2 metres of the switch (See Figure 5.11).

Devices for functional switching *(Regulation 537–18 and 537–20)*

Functional switching may be carried out by a plug and socket up to 16A ac or dc rating, where the rating is higher than 16A ac a plug and socket may be used if it has a high enough breaking or disconnecting capacity for the load. Plugs and sockets with a rating higher than 16A shall not be used on dc and shall not be used for emergency switching under any circumstances.

Switches for use on discharge lighting circuits shall either be designed and marked to BS3676 or have a nominal current rating of not less than the total steady current X 2 and where the load is a mixture of discharge and filament lamps the switch shall have a nominal current rating of 1 X the filament lamp current plus 2 X the discharge lamp current or higher.

If they meet the criteria set out in Schedule 1.3 and Schedule 1.4 (pages 23 & 24), semiconductor devices may be employed for functional switching and control.

Applying the requirements of the Regulations for Isolation and switching – an example

An example of the ways in which the several requirements for isolating and switching can be met in the control of a motor circuit is described in Schedule 8.3 and illustrated in Figure 8.7. It will be seen that some devices can perform several of the twelve functions listed in Schedule 8.3.

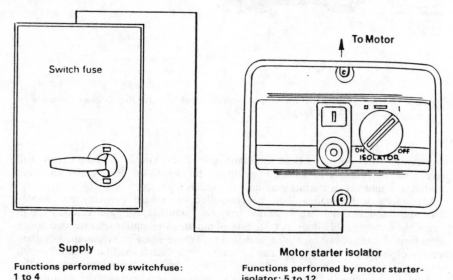

Supply

Functions performed by switchfuse:
1 to 4

Motor starter isolator

Functions performed by motor starter-
isolator: 5 to 12

Figure 8.7 Demonstrating how the several requirements for the isolating and switching of a motor circuit can be performed by one device (illustration by courtesy of MEM Ltd).

Schedule 8.3 – The twelve functions needed to control a motor circuit

(see Figure 8.7)

Item No.	Function	Comment
1	Isolation of electrical service (supply end)	There may be need to isolate the supply to work on the starter or control devices at the motor end of the circuit.
2	Back up protection for local switch and starter (supply end)	Provision needs to be made to provide back up for any let through fault on the starter or devices at the motor end, such as a circuit breaker or a fuse.
3	Short circuit protection of cables (supply end)	Those feeding the local device or devices need short circuit protection.
4	Overload protection on cables (supply end)	Between this device or devices and the device or devices at the motor end.
5	Isolate the electric service	There may be need to switch off the supply locally – to change motor for instance.
6	Switch for mechanical maintenance	To service the machine the motor is driving – an on load isolator with 'lock off' facilities.
7	Emergency switch	To isolate in an emergency preferably red in colour with no prospect of automatic reset, or latch off facility.
8	Functional switch	Switching off machine when not in use.
9	No-volt release	Should voltage drop below required level, power failure and requirements of Regulations 552-4 (see Practice 9): also actuated by emergency stop button.
10	Overload protection of motor	To prevent damage to motor due to overload and "single-phasing" fault.
11	Short circuit protection for cables	Conductors connecting the starter to the motor need protection from damage by a short circuit. Starter should carry the let through current of the overload protective device under fault conditions.
12	Overload protection cables	Conductors between the starter and motor also need protection from damage by overload; this is usually a function of the starter.

Figure 8.7 shows how a switchfuse, fuse switch or circuit breaker could perform functions 1-4 if correctly selected. It also shows how a starter isolator could perform functions 5-12 if the starter is correctly chosen for the motor concerned. Thus it can be seen that two devices are capable of performing twelve functions. It would be possible to use other types of device but the method described appears to be the most appropriate way to meet these requirements.

Protection against undervoltage *(Regulations 451-1 to 451-6 and 535-1)*

Persons and animals can be endangered by simple unexpected situations such as a reduction in or loss of artificial lighting or a sudden stopping, starting or erratic operation of electrically driven machines commonly used for agricultural, industrial, commercial and domestic purposes.

Incidents may act directly as with a total loss of artificial lighting or indirectly with machinery by a mechanical malfunction due to an obscure electrical cause such as a design failure to protect against dangerous situations arising from severe variations in the supply voltage. Common effect of voltage variation on lighting are:- (1) reduction of light level (tungsten). (2) Loss of light for several minutes (discharge). (3) Momentary loss of light (tungsten & fluorescent). (4) Total loss of light (except emergency). (5) Sudden restoration of light (tungsten & fluorescent). (6) Delayed restoration of light (discharge). (7) Panic, accidental injury or loss of life.

Common effects of voltage variation on some mechanical functions are:- (1) fluctuations of power. (2) Reduction of power. (3) Momentary loss of power. (4) Partial loss of power. (5) Total loss of power. (6) Sudden restoration of power. (7) Partial restoration of power. (8) Process timers out of sequence. (9) Loss of continuous processes. (10) Loss of process materials. (11) Loss of production. (12) Damage to some plant. (13) Irrational action, panic, accidental injury or loss of life.

The regulations require the electrical design engineer and the installation engineer to verify through discussion with those responsible for installing, operating or maintaining the machine or process that:- (1) Variations in the supply voltage are unlikely to cause danger. (2) Precautions against foreseen damage has been provided. (3) Future risk of such damage is acceptable. (4) Collectively all equipment will function so as to ensure safety when the supply voltage fluctuates or fails and subsequently when full voltage or the supply is restored.

To achieve the degree of safety required it may be necessary to incorporate under voltage or null power relays in the control equipment to protect against the effects of variations in voltage or power and to provide time delay devices to ensure continued running during brief periods of low voltage where danger could arise.

Any delay device/s controlling a contactor must allow instantaneous opening of the contactor for control or protection and all devices must allow for starting conditions and be equiped with manual re-setting where appropriate if automatic re-setting of protective, safety or operational devices could cause danger.

Practice 9

Equipment

Accessibility

The fundamental safety requirement concerning access is given in Regulation 13-16. This requirement will be met if a positive answer can be given to the question: *"Is adequate safe working space and means of access available to persons who need to operate, inspect, maintain or attend to electrical equipment?"*

Regulation 13-16 is re-inforced by Regulation 513-1 which requires that all equipment installed to form part of an installation or system must be accessible to operate, inspect and maintain. Some joints in cables are exempted from this requirement – see Practice 3.

The Regulations concern themselves only with the situation which is current at the time equipment is installed. It is essential, however, to avoid the subsequent development of cramped conditions and inaccessible plant and equipment, that adequate provision be made for future extension of services, plant and equipment, so as to provide adequate access for operation and maintenance. Provision of extra space for such plant and services will of course be related to the probability of increased requirements occurring subsequent to the initial installation. A margin of up to one-third increase over net basic requirement may well be justified when at the design stage an assessment is made of possible future developments.

Figure 9.1 gives some basic data for access and operation which is related to the human frame.

Figure 9.1 is reproduced, by kind permission of Her Majesty's Stationery Office, from a Hospital Service Engineering Data Sheet published by the Department of Health and Social Security. Other DHSS literature, obtainable from HMSO, which covers accessibility and the provision of space for engineering services, is as follows:–

Hospital Technical Memorandum No.7, *"Electrical Services: Supply and Distribution"*.

Hospital Technical Memorandum No.23, *"Access and Accommodation for Engineering Services"*.

British Standard Code of Practice CP 413: 1973 *"Ducts for building services"* also deals with design and construction of access for building services.

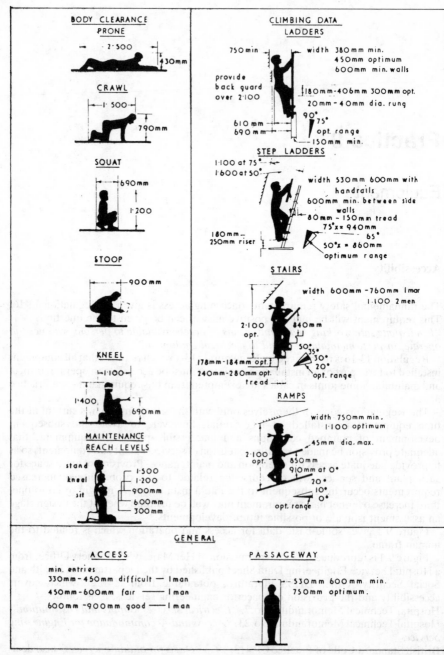

Figure 9.1 *Basic Anthropometric Data for Engineering Access and Operation as used by DHSS for practical application in Hospital Technical Memorandum Number 23 'Access of Accommodation for Engineering Services' (March 1972) published by HMSO.*

Transformers *(Regulations 551-1 to 551-3)*

The Regulations detail the requirements for the installation of the following types of transformers.
(a)   Step-up Transformers.
(b)   Auto-Transformers.
   When installing step-up transformers the Regulations require a link switch to be provided to isolate the unit from all conductors of the supply including the neutral. (See Figure 9.2).
   In a supply circuit incorporating a neutral conductor to an autotransformer, the common terminal of the transformer winding must always be connected to the neutral conductor (see Figure 9.3). It is not permissible to connect an autotransformer within an IT system.
   Transformers used to supply high voltage discharge lighting installations are required to meet the conditions detailed later in this Section for that type of installation. Inductors or transformers provided in discharge lighting installations shall be placed as close as possible to its associated discharge lamp.

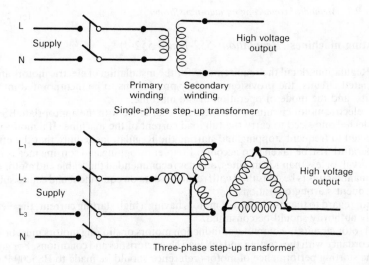

Figure 9.2   A linked switch is necessary to isolate a step-up transformer from all conductors of the supply (Regulation 551-3).

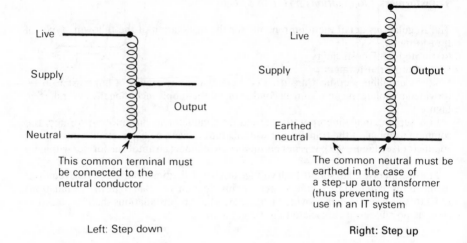

Left: Step down

Right: Step up

Figure 9.3   Method of connecting an auto-transformer.

Rotating machines *(Regulations 552-1 and 552-4)*

The Regulations detail the requirements for the installation of electric motors and their associated circuits, the provision of safety precautions to be incorporated into those circuits, and the mode of operation of the machine.

All electric motor circuits, when rated in accordance with the appropriate BS should be selected and sized to carry the full load current of the machine. If a motor is to be subjected to frequent stopping and starting the Regulations require that the effects of temperature rise be taken into account. Frequent stopping and starting means starting at intervals of less than 120 minutes, and it is recommended that cable and motor control gear manufacturers be consulted with regard to data on equipment and cables subjected to frequent starting operations.

With regard to the installation of motors having a high starting current, the electricity supply authority should be consulted.

All rotor circuits of commutator induction motors or slip ring motors must be chosen in accordance with the starting and full load characteristics and conditions. For guidance on the starting performance of motors reference should be made to BS5000 Part 99 – *"Machines for miscellaneous applications"*.

All motors rated at 0.37kW and above should be protected against overcurrent, unless it is a component part of and within an item of equipment complying with the appropriate British Standard. If the automatic restarting of a motor after a break in supply is likely to cause danger, the Regulations require that the equipment controlling the motor be provided with a no-volt device. This requirement does not apply where failure of a motor to start after a short interval would cause greater danger or if the frequency of starting is activated by an automatic control device and that adequate warning notices and other precautions are taken.

Figures 9.4 to 9.9 are diagrams of typical motor starters.

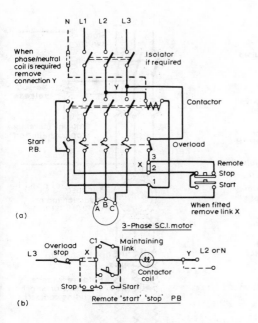

(a)

(b)

Figure 9.4 (a) Typical diagram for contactor-operated direct-on-line starter.
(b) Control circuit only.

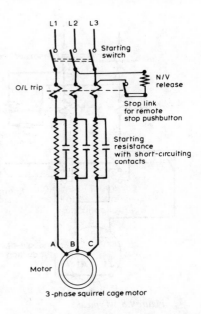

Figure 9.5 Typical diagram of stator resistance starter.

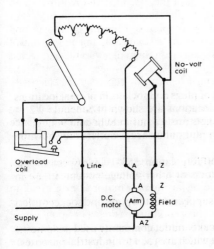

Figure 9.6 Typical diagram of d.c. faceplate starter.

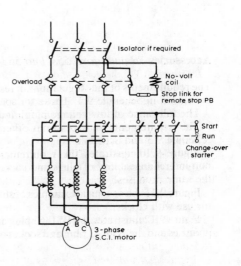

Figure 9.7 Typical diagram for hand-operated auto-transformer.

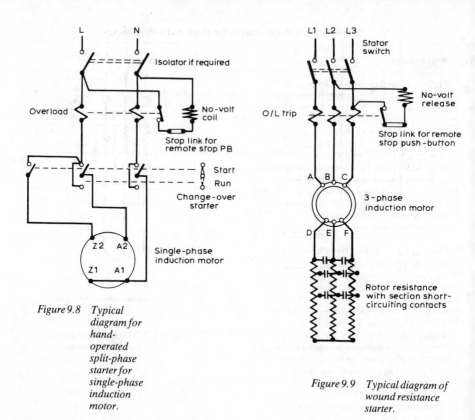

Figure 9.8 Typical diagram for hand-operated split-phase starter for single-phase induction motor.

Figure 9.9 Typical diagram of wound resistance starter.

Accessories (Regulations 553-1 to 553-20)

The requirements of the Regulations in respect of plugs and sockets in normal locations are shown in Schedule 9.1. Those for special locations are shown in Schedule 9.2.

The full range of low voltage plugs and sockets are set out in Schedule 9.4.

The requirements for accessories other than plugs and socket-outlets are shown in Schedule 9.3 and Schedule 9.5.

Figure 9.10 illustrates the requirements of Regulation 553-1 in respect of the non-interchangeability of plugs and socket outlets of other voltage systems in use in the same premises.

Figure 9.11 shows typical examples of shaver supply units and plugs and socket outlets for use with clocks.

Figure 9.12 illustrates the BS1363 plug and socket outlet commonly used in domestic premises and the BS4343 plug and socket outlet which are used for industrial purposes.

Schedule 9.1 – Requirements for plugs and socket-outlets

Requirement	Notes
Plugs, and socket-outlets, to be non-reversible with provision for protective conductor	
Plugs used with socket-outlets for which designed*	
Plugs should not be interchangeable with socket-outlets of other designs	See Figure 9.10 (b)
Plugs should not have any pin exposed to touch whilst an associated pin is engaged in a socket-outlet*	See Figure 9.10 (a)
Plugs in TT or TN to be designed so that no fused pin can be inadvertently connected to the neutral conductor	See Figure 9.10 (c)
Plugs, and socket-outlets, for low voltage circuits to be to BS1363, BS546, BS196, BS5550 or BS4343†	See Schedule 9.4
Plugs, and socket-outlets, in domestic premises preferably to be shuttered type to BS1363 (ac circuits)	See Figure 9.12**
Socket-outlets for shavers used elsewhere than bathrooms to be incorporated in BS4573 shaver unit	
Plugs and socket-outlets feeding portable appliances, or portable luminaires to be located in easily accessible position adjacent to appliance	When siting socket outlets, take account of supplies for fixed equipment before assessing and selecting positions for portable equipment. Have regard to user convenience and safety. Flexible cord length normally 1.5-2 metres
Socket-outlets mounted vertically should be at height suitable to reduce risk of mechanical damage	See Figure 9.13
Plugs and socket-outlets for clocks to be specially designed with plug having BS646 or BS1362 (up to 3A) fuse	Item 1 not applicable

† *Not applicable to circuits having special characteristics*
* *Not applicable to SELV circuits*
** *Ambient air temperature restricted to 35°C (average 25°C/24 hrs).*

Schedule 9.2 – Requirements for plugs and sockets in special locations

Location	Requirement	Notes
Caravan sites	To be 16A to BS4343 splash-proof type with earth contact in 6 o'clock position. If caravan's maximum demand above 16A, then higher rating to be used. One socket outlet to be within 20 metres of caravan intake position	See Figure 2.22
Bathrooms	To be incorporated in BS3052 shaver unit	With isolating transformer
Construction sites	To be to BS4343	Need not apply to site offices, toilets, etc.

Schedule 9.3 – Requirements for Couplers and Ceiling Roses

Requirement	Notes
Cable couplers to be to BS196, or BS1778 or BS4343, non-reversible, with means of connecting protective conductor and arranged so that plug portion is not live when disconnected. On construction sites to be to BS4343	Not applicable to SELV circuits
Ceiling roses to be installed in circuits up to 250V and to cater only for one flexible cord unless designed for multiple pendants	

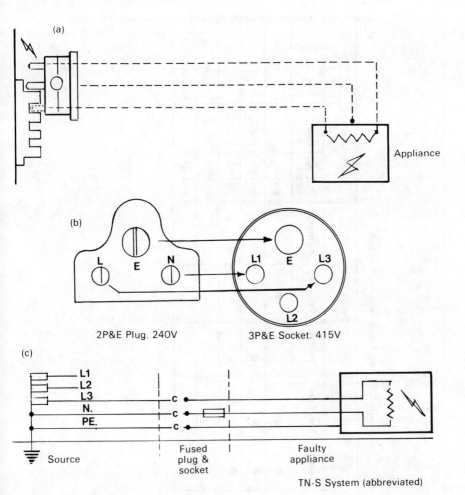

(a)

Appliance

(b)

2P&E Plug. 240V   3P&E Socket. 415V

L E N   L1 E L3

L2

(c)

L1
L2
L3
N.
PE.

Source

Fused
plug &
socket

Faulty
appliance

TN-S System (abbreviated)

Figure 9.10   Illustrating requirements of Regulation 553-1
(a) Non-exposure of any plug pin whilst another pin is energised.
(b) Non-interchangeability of plugs of differing type.
(c) Non reversible fused plugs in TT or TN system Overcurrent protection is removed when fuse is
placed in the neutral if plug is of the reversible type.

Schedule 9.4 – Low Voltage plugs and sockets

Duty			Rating (Amperes)	Plug		Socket Outlet			British Standard		Type
Poles	ac	dc		Fused	Non-fused	Normal	Protected	Shuttered	Plug & socket	Fuse	
2P & E	●	●	5, 15, 30	●	●		●		BS196		
2P & E	●	●	2, 5, 15, 30	●	●	●			BS546	BS646	
2P & E	●		13	●				●	BS1363	BS1362	
	●	●	15						BS5550		Theatre
	●	●	16, 32, 63, 125						BS4343		Industrial

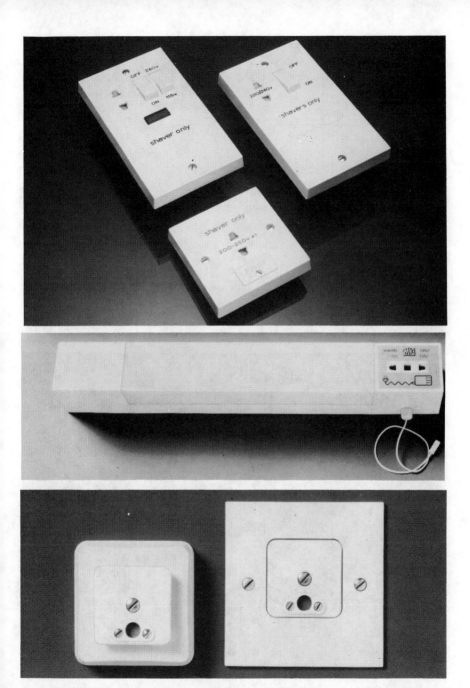

Figure 9.11 (Top and middle) Shaver supply units for bathroom to BS3535 and a shaver socket outlet for rooms other than bathrooms. (Bottom) Fused clock connector with 2A BS1362 fuse (Illustrations by courtesy of MK Electric Ltd).

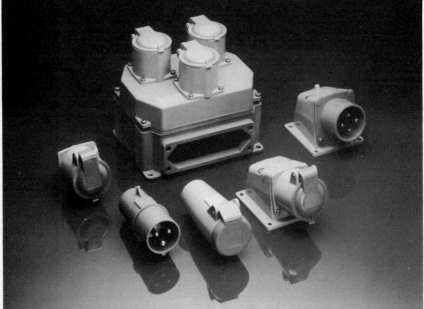

Figure 9.12 *(Top) Socket outlet to BS1363 (Bottom) Industrial socket outlets to BS4343 rated at 16, 32, 63 and 125A. Components are colour coded and have earth contact in different positions according to supply voltage (Photographs by courtesy of MK Electric Ltd.*

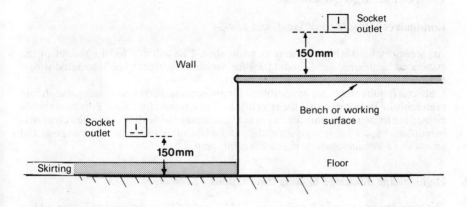

Figure 9.13 Recommended minimum mounting heights for socket outlets.

Schedule 9.5 – Requirements for lampholders

(Regulations 553-14 to 553-18)

Type of lampholder used †	Maximum rating of circuit overcurrent device		Notes and comments
	6A	**16A**	
BS5042 Part 1 (Bayonet cap) (Temperature rating T2*	B15	B22	Requirement does not apply if separate overcurrent protection provided (ie fused plug connected to a desk top luminaire) or lampholder and wiring enclosed in earthed metal or insulating material with 'P' ignitability characteristic. Lampholders in bathrooms to be fitted with BS5041 protective shield.
BS5042 Part 2 (Edison screw**)	E14	E27 E40	

---

*   *Unless lamp cap operating at less than 165°C when T1 rating can apply. See Appendix 'A', BS5042 for further guidance. For TN or TT systems centre contact connected to neutral conductor.*
†   *Lampholders for filament lamps normally used only in 250V circuits.*
**   *In TN or TT systems outer contact to be connected to the neutral conductor.*

Current using equipment

Luminaires *(Regulations 554-1 and 554-2)*

An accessory used with a lighting pendant should be suitable for the weight of the associated luminaire. See Schedule 3.9 for maximum weight to be associated with a flexible cord which supports a luminaire.

Special requirements are applicable to luminaires installed in caravans: these should preferably be installed so that the structure or lining is used for fixing. Provision should be made to fix pendant luminaires so as to avoid damage to flexible cord when caravan is in motion. A space for free air circulation should be left between the caravan body and an enclosed luminaire which uses a filament lamp.

High voltage discharge lighting installations *(Regulation 554-3)*

The main requirements of Regulations of 554-3 and BS559 are shown in Figure 9.14. It should be noted that the term "high voltage" used in this instance means any voltage between low voltage and 5kV ac (rms) to earth on open circuit. The necessary safety sign and warning notice are given in Practice 10. Questions relating to the Isolation and Switching are dealt with in Practice 8.

The following considerations also apply to high voltage discharge lighting installations:

1. Circuits operating from a transformer with input ratings above 500 watts need a means of automatic disconnection of the supply on short-circuit or for an earth leakage current of 20% of normal circuit current.

2. Ancillary equipment (transformer, capacitors, discharge resistors, etc.) need to be enclosed in earthed metal, or in a ventilated fire resisting enclosure.

3. No metallic connection should exist between high voltage and main supply circuits except for earth connections. Autotransformers, however, which supply a voltage not in excess of 1.5kV (rms) can be used if one point of the supply is earthed (TN or TT system) and both poles are capable of being isolated.

4. A means of isolation complying with the requirements for switching for mechanical maintenance should be provided (see Practice 8). Preferably the switch should have a lock or a non-interchangeable operating handle. Alternatively, the distribution board supplying the installation should be capable of being locked after fuses have been withdrawn.

5. Metal sheathed and/or armoured cable should be used for high voltage connections. This requirement need not be met for inaccessible exterior installations involving connections of 3 metres or less unlikely to suffer mechanical damage or in interior installed self-contained luminaires.

6. For window signs, bare or lightly insulated copper or nickel wire not less than 4mm² can be used for circuit series connections unlikely to be subject to mechanical damage, if less than 1 metre long and supported at 500mm intervals and if enclosed by glass tubing (not less than 1mm thick and 500mm diameter) or impervious insulating material with 'P' characteristic. The conductors must be in an enclosure accessible only to skilled persons.

7. For shop front fascias, bare or lightly insulated wire should be used only for connection in an earthed metal enclosure or between electrode housing terminals. Other connections should be made by armoured or metal sheathed cables.

8. Supports for insulated and braided cables or bare conductors must by of non hygroscopic insulating material and be supported at intervals of 500mm. Metal sheathed, non armoured cables must be supported at intervals of 800mm (horizontally) and 1250mm (vertically) Armoured cables must be supported at intervals of 1000mm (horizontally) and 1500mm (vertically). See Figure 9.15 for the length of cable supports and the airgaps required between metal and cables.

9. Figure 9.16 illustrates the requirement for cable supports close to each terminal connection.

10. The exposed insulation of metal sheathed or braided cables must be protected from ozone effects.

11. Armoured, or suitably protected, cables should be used if mechanical damage is likely. Where non-armoured cables pass through walls or floors they may be used by enclosure in short lengths of earthed metal conduit.

12. Low voltage cables may be used for return cables from electrodes to transformer terminals if not less than 2.5mm² (mechanically protected) or 4mm² (no mechanical protection).

13. Rotating device metalwork can be used as a return conductor (see Figure 9.17).

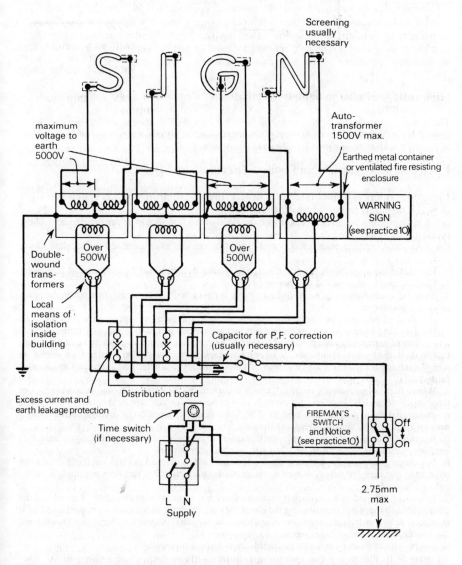

Figure 9.14   Illustrations of the requirements in a typical high voltage discharge lighting exterior installation with various means of isolation.

Earthed
metalwork,
woodwork
or surfaces
liable to
become damp

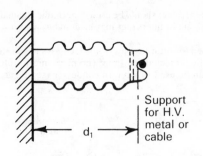

Support
for H.V.
metal or
cable

d_1

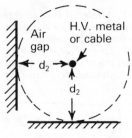

H.V. metal
or cable

Air
gap

d_2

d_2

Earthed metalwork,
woodwork or surfaces
liable to become damp

d_1 = kV x 10 minimum
(mm)

d_2 = kV x 4 minimum
(mm)

Figure 9.15   Illustration of creepage and clearance spacings required for h.v. metal and h.v. cables which are neither metal-sheathed nor armoured.

Electrode water heaters and boilers *(Regulations 554-20 to 554-26)*

Electrode boilers and electrode water heaters must be used only on a.c. systems and that they are required to comply with the following:–
(a) A multipole linked circuit breaker with overload protection should be provided to control the supply to each electrode.
(b) Additional earthing requirements and protection devices as detailed in the Regulations are met.
    The detailed requirements for electrode water heaters and boilers are as follows:
1. Shall be connected only to ac systems.
2. Shall be controlled by a multi-linked circuit breaker with overcurrent protection for each electrode conductor.
3. (a) Shell of heater to be bonded to metallic sheath or armour of supply cable.
    (b) Earthing conductor (eg protective conductor between installation main earthing terminal and means of earthing) to be connected to shell of heater. Its conductance should be not less than that of the largest phase conductor. If an earth-leakage protective device is fitted then minimum size of earthing conductor shall be 2.5mm^2 (if mechanically protected) or 4mm^2 (no mechanical protection).
4. Where high voltage supply involved, residual current device required to disconnect electrodes from supply if earth leakage current exceeds 10% of heater's rated current. If balanced conditions essential, that value may be increased to 15%. Time delayed operation of residual current device may be employed to prevent frequent tripping.
5. For three phase low-voltage supply, shell of boiler to be connected to neutral of supply as well as earthing conductor. Neutral to be same size as phase conductors.
6. For single phase supply, with one electrode connected to earthed neutral, shell of boiler to be connected to neutral of supply as well as the earthing conductor. But this does not apply if item 7 below followed.
7. If heater not piped to water supply or where there is no contact with any earthed metal and the electrodes and the water surrounding the electrodes are shielded with insulating material so that it is impossible to touch either, then fuse in phase conductor can be substituted for circuit breaker and the heater shell need not be connected to supply neutral.
8. Every type of heater for water or liquids must have a thermostat.
    Figure 9.19 illustrates the foregoing requirements in respect of a three phase low voltage installation. Figure 9.18 illustrates these requirements in respect of a low voltage single-phase installation.

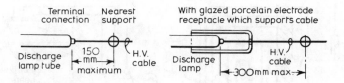

Figure 9.16   Distance between terminal connection of h.v. cable and first cable support.

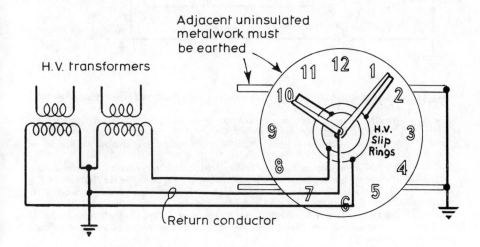

Figure 9.17   The hands of a clock used as a return conductor.

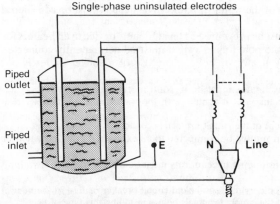

Figure 9.18   Essential safety requirements for low voltage single phase electrode boiler or heater installation.

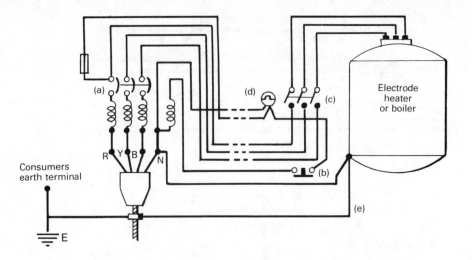

Figure 9.19   Essential requirements for safety in electrode water heater and boiler installations three phase low voltage supply.
(a) Multipole linked circuit-breaker with excess-current protection in each electrode conductor (shown remote from boiler).
(b) Means at boiler to open circuit-breaker instantaneously. Not specified in the Regulations.
(c) Isolator adjacent to heater or boiler, if circuit-breaker is remote (an alternative is a locking-out device on the circuit-breaker). Not specified in the Regulations.
(d) Indicating lamp adjacent to or on heater or boiler to show whether circuit-breaker is on or off. Not specified in the Regulations.
(e) Conductor bonding metallic sheath or armour (if any) of supply cable to shell of heater or boiler. (See Regulation 554-21), and earthing conductor (Regulation 554-21).
(f) Connection from the supply neutral to heater or boiler shell. (Regulations 554-24).

Water heaters – single-phase *(Regulations 554-29 and 554-30)*

It should be noted that before choosing a water heater or boiler having uninsulated elements the aggressive nature of the water or liquid to be heated must be considered and provided for.

A dangerous temperature must be prevented by an automatic device in all heaters for water or other liquids. A double pole linked switch must be permanently connected between the supply and every heater or boiler. The use of a socket outlet is not permitted.

The water pipe supplying the heater must be in solid metallic contact with
(a) All metal parts of the heater that are in contact with the water (note *not* the electrical conductors) and
(b) with earth potential independent of the circuit protective conductor.

The circuit protective conductor must be connected to all exposed metal of the heater or boiler.

In addition to the above the following precautions must be observed when installing this type of equipment:–
(a) Check that there is no single pole switch, non-linked circuit breaker or fuse in the neutral conductor between the heater and the supply terminals before installing this type of heater.

(b) Consult the local Water Authority and obtain their agreement.

(c) Do not install this type of heater or boiler if the water supply passes through a salt-regenerative water softener.

Figure 9.20 illustrates the requirements of the Regulations in respect of single-phase water heaters having immersed and uninsulated heating elements.

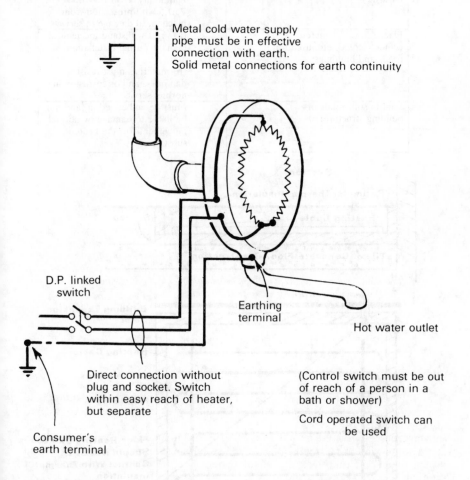

Metal cold water supply pipe must be in effective connection with earth.
Solid metal connections for earth continuity

D.P. linked switch

Earthing terminal

Hot water outlet

Direct connection without plug and socket. Switch within easy reach of heater, but separate

(Control switch must be out of reach of a person in a bath or shower)

Cord operated switch can be used

Consumer's earth terminal

Figure 9.20   Essential requirements for safety with water heaters and boilers having bare elements in the water.

Soil, road and floor warming *(Regulations 554-31 to 554-34)*

The requirements of the Regulations in respect of the locations of conductors and cables for soil, road and floor warming are set out in Schedule 9.6:

Schedule 9.6 – Requirements for heating cables used in particular locations

Situation of heating cables	Requirements
Near materials with a fire hazard:	Enclosure in material of ignitability 'P' in BS476, Part 5 with protection from mechanical damage in service.
Placed in soil, concrete, cement screed, etc. used for roads and buildings:	(a) must withstand mechanical damage during installation; and (b) materials must resist dampness and/or corrosion in normal service
Laid in soil, roads or building structure:	Must be embedded in, and not be liable to damage by normal movements of, the heated substance.

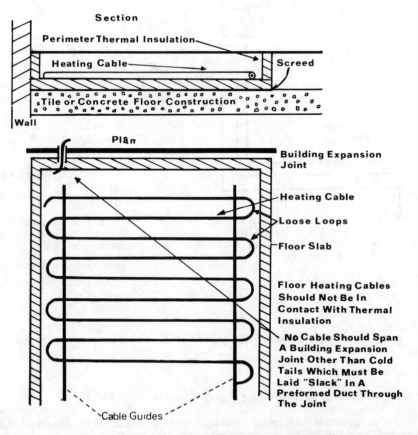

Figure 9.21   Layout of a typical floor warming section before final embedding in floor screed (Regulation 554-33).

Figure 9.21 shows part of a typical floor warming installation to which these Regulations apply.

The loading of floor warming cables must be limited by the following maximum operating conductor temperatures:

(a) *Cables suitable for a maximum temperature of 70°C:* General purpose pvc over conductors; Enamelled conductors: polychloroprene over enamel, pvc overall; pvc overall; pvc over enamel, lead alloy 'E' sheath overall.

(b) *Cables suitable for a maximum temperature of 85°C:* Heat resisting pvc over conductor; Nylon over conductor, heat resisting pvc overall; Butyl rubber or equal elastomeric insulation over conductor.

(c) *Cable suitable for a maximum temperature of 105°C or 135°C:* Mineral insulation over conductor, copper sheath overall, (depending on the type of seal used). If pvc sheathed – 70°C.

(d) *Cable suitable for a maximum temperature of 180°C:* Silicone-treated woven-glass sleeve over conductor.

Electric fence controllers *(Regulations 554-35 to 554-40)*

Compliance with BS2632 is necessary when installing electric fence controllers supplied from the mains and the controllers must ensure freedom from mechanical damage and unauthorised interference so far as is practicable. All controllers must be fixed on dedicated poles or supports. The use of poles supporting overhead power lines or telecommunication lines is not permitted.

The controller earth electrode must be completely separate from all other earthing systems and situated outside the resistance area of any other protective earthing electrode. Each fence shall only be provided with one controller. Figure 9.22 illustrates this requirement.

Contact between an electric fence with its wiring and controller, or any similar system, and any power or telecommunication lines, wiring or equipment must not be allowed to occur. This warning also applies to radio aerials and protective conductors.

The battery of a battery operated electric fence controller should be disconnected from the controller, before it is re-charged.

Figure 9.22 Showing the separation of an electric fence earth-electrode from any other electrode resistance area and typical fence controllers, (a) battery-operated, (b) mains-operated.

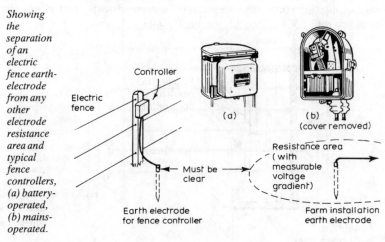

Thermal protection *(Regulations 421-1 to 423-1)*

The Regulations deal with the prevention of fire and burns and give guidance in the selection of equipment, appliances and their respective installation where heat is liable to be generated from their use in normal service. The selection of switchgear in this context must be made in accordance with the requirements of the Regulations so that arcing and overheating are avoided. The requirements for protections against overcurrent and consequently the prevention of overheating therefrom are covered in Practice 6.

Equipment selected and secured to the building fabric must be positioned so that its designed heat dissipation is not impaired nor must it constitute a hazard to adjoining building materials. Equipment with a surface temperature in excess of 90°C must be fixed away from flammable materials as shown in Figure 9.27 and Figure 9.28.

The Regulations are deemed to be complied with when luminaires, lamps and appliances have been installed in accordance with BS4533 and BS3456 respectively. Figure 9.23 illustrates the heating effect of various filament lamp positions.

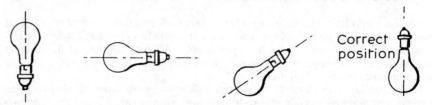

Figure 9.23   Overheating effect of filament lamp position. In inverted, horizontal and tilted position, cooling is less efficient and lamp becomes overheated.

Guards must be fitted to prevent contact between lamp or luminaire where contact with material is likely to occur. Shades must be suitable for the heat radiation from a lamp.

When partly enclosed distribution boards are installed they must not be fixed to combustible materials. The Regulation is deemed to be met if the material used complies with BS5486 Part 13, see Figure 9.24.

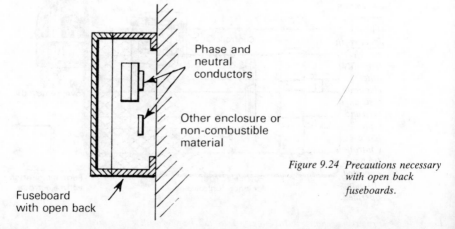

Phase and neutral conductors

Other enclosure or non-combustible material

Fuseboard with open back

Figure 9.24 Precautions necessary with open back fuseboards.

Where flammable liquid is contained within electrical equipment precautions shall be taken to prevent burning liquid and its products of combustion from spreading to other parts of the building. This is illustrated in Figure 9.25.

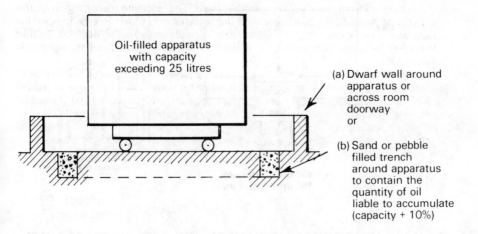

Oil-filled apparatus with capacity exceeding 25 litres

(a) Dwarf wall around apparatus or across room doorway
or

(b) Sand or pebble filled trench around apparatus to contain the quantity of oil liable to accumulate (capacity + 10%)

Figure 9.25   The precautions suggested in the note to the Regulation.

Positioning or guarding shall be provided to prevent accidental contact where the surface temperature of fixed equipment will exceed 80°C, see Figure 9.26. The Regulation can be disregarded providing the equipment complies with a British Standard which permits a temperature exceeding 80°C for an unguarded enclosure, for example the hob of an electric cooker where heating elements are exposed.

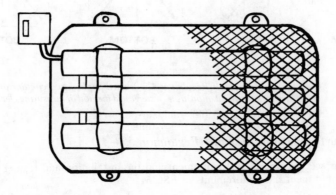

Figure 9.26   Protection against burns – nest of tubular heaters with wire guard.

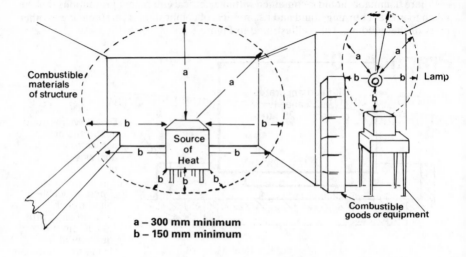

a – 300 mm minimum
b – 150 mm minimum

Figure 9.27   Shows the minimum spacing permitted between the heat source and unprotected combustible materials.

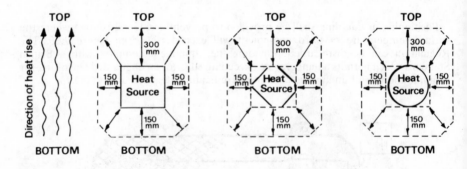

Figure 9.28   Shows the requirement of Regulation 422-2 when applied to a circular or irregular shaped heat sources and demonstrates a suggested method of measuring clearances for heat rise by natural convection.

Electric surface heating systems *(Regulation 554–41)*

Electric Surface Heating (ESH) equipment and the installation and testing of ESH systems should meet the requirements of BS6351.

Practice 10

Warning signs, notices, labels, drawings and certification

BS5378 Part 1: 1980 specifies a system for giving saftey information in the form of warning signs and supplementary signs, as well as prohibition, mandatory and safety condition signs. Generally, the signs referred to in the IEE Regulations are confined to those which give warning and these signs sometimes require a supplementary notice. The safety colour stipulated for triangular warning signs is yellow with the appropriate symbol and the surrounding triangular band coloured black.

The BS5378 sign which denotes "Caution, risk of electric shock" is shown at Figure 10.1. Supplementary notices are required by BS5378 to be oblong or square with background in white and text in black. Alternatively, and at least one IEE Regulation requires this, the background colour can be the same as the Safety Colour used in the safety sign it is supplementing, with the text in the relevant contrasting colour. An example of a supplementary notice is that used in conjunction with the safety sign associated with high voltage discharge lamp installations (see Figure 10.2).

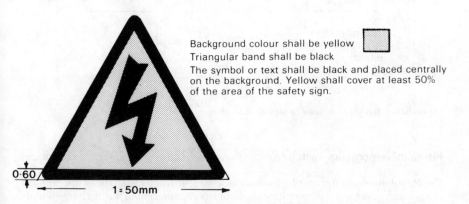

Background colour shall be yellow
Triangular band shall be black
The symbol or text shall be black and placed centrally on the background. Yellow shall cover at least 50% of the area of the safety sign.

0·60

1 = 50mm

Figure 10.1   The BS5378 safety sign which denotes "Caution, risk of electric shock".

Warning notices

High voltage discharge lamp installations

A safety sign indicating risk of electric shock must be fixed to every enclosure or contained associated with a high voltage discharge lamp installation e.g. inductors, resistors, capacitors and transformers. In addition, a supplementary sign must be placed below the warning sign. The warning sign is as shown in Figure 10.1. The supplementary notice is shown in Figure 10.2.

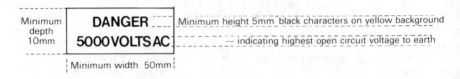

Figure 10.2   Supplementary notice used with safety sign, for high voltage discharge lamp installations.

Danger labels must be fixed to high voltage cables or their protective covering, as shown in Figure 10.3, at intervals of 1.5 metres (maximum).

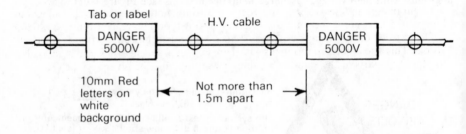

Figure 10.3   Method to be used to identify h.v. cables

Fireman's emergency switch *(Regulation 476-13 and 537-17;* see also Practice 8*)*

The Regulations require that for exterior discharge lighting installations operating at a voltage exceeding low voltage where the switch is not adjacent to the discharge lamp(s), a notice indicating the position of the related switch shall be fixed adjacent to the discharge lamps and a clear sign shall be fixed adjacent to the switch. The Regulations also specify that such a sign shall be of minimum size (150mm by 100mm) and the words 'FIREMAN'S SWITCH' in easily legible lettering not less than 13mm high. It is also desirable that the sign should contain the name of the installer and/or maintainer of the installation. Figure 10.4 shows the requirements for this notice.

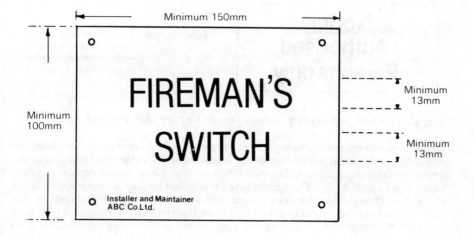

Figure 10.4   The warning notice to be fixed alongside a fireman's switch.

Warning notices – Voltage *(Regulation 514-4)*

When the voltage is in excess of 250V and is unexpected such as is found in a multi-gang lighting switch where more than one phase is present or where two lighting switches on different phases are closer than arms reach, a warning notice, similar to that shown in Figure 10.5 in conjunction with the safety sign shown on Figure 10.1 must be affixed adjacent to or on the means of access before access is achieved, so that it is clearly visible. This also applies to terminals which are in a separate enclosure and is accessible to other live parts at the same time; similar warning must be given.

Figure 10.5   Notice indicating presence of voltage in excess of 250V.

Warning notices – Emergency Switching *(Regulation 537-16;* see also Practice 8*)*

It should not be possible to re-energise equipment through the release of the related emergency switch, unless a warning notice is provided to indicate that the equipment concerned may be automatically restarted in that event.

Warning notices – Reserved access *(Regulation 471-25)*

Visible indication of areas reserved for access only by skilled or authorised persons is a requirement of the Regulations. A typical warning notice is shown in Figure 10.5(a).

```
┌─────────────────────┐
│      Notice         │
│   Authorised        │
│   Persons only      │
└─────────────────────┘
```

Figure 10.5(a) Notice warning that access to reserved areas is reserved for skilled or authorised persons.

Warning Notices – Isolation *(Regulation 461-3; see also* **Practice 8***)*

Unless interlocking arrangements ensure the isolation of all the circuits involved, the Regulations require the installation of a notice which warns of the need to use isolation devices when gaining access to live parts of equipment which are not capable of being isolated by a single device. This type of notice is required for, say, a consumer's isolating switch fuse (connections between cut-out and switch fuse are not isolated) or, for example, on a change-over contactor which is live from more than one source or indeed any type of equipment containing live parts connected to more than one separate supply. BS3476 gives the following as an example of the type of warning notice required where access to such live terminals is possible:
(i) "DANGER: (here give supply voltage)"
(ii) "Two (or more if applicable) supplies are taken into this equipment. Isolate both (all) before undertaking maintenance work"
   Figure 10.6 illustrates another type of notice which can be used in the above circumstances.

```
╭──────────────────────────────╮
│         CAUTION              │
│  More Than 250 Volts         │
│  Between  This  And          │
│  Adjacent Switchgear         │
╰──────────────────────────────╯
```

Figure 10.6 A warning notice which can be used to meet the requirements of Regulation 461-3.

Warning notice – Earth and bonding connections *(Regulations 514-7, 514-7(a) and 542-18)*

A label as shown in Figure 10.7, or similar must be attached firmly in a visible position, at the point of connection of:
1. Every earthing conductor to an earth electrode
2. Every bonding conductor to extraneous conductive parts

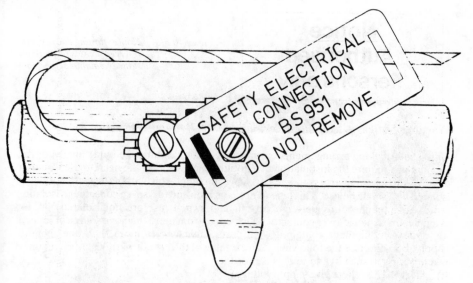

Figure 10.7   Warning notice for earthing and bonding connections as required by Regulation 514-7.

Warning notices – RCD *(Regulation 514-5(a))*

An 11 point warning notice shall be fitted by the main distribution board to read:- The installation, or part of it is protected by a device which automatically switches off the supply if an earth fault develops. Test quarterly by pressing the button marked 'T' or 'test'. The device should switch off the supply and should then be switched on to restore the supply. If the device does not switch off the supply when the button is pressed, inform your electrical contractor.

Warning notices – Equipment outside equipotential zone *(Regulation 514-8)*

A label must be fixed near a socket outlet, protected by a residual current device, used to connect equipment used outside the equipotential zone of a building (see Figure 10.8). The residual current device employed to provide protection for such socket-outlets may alternatively be incorporated into a consumer unit or distribution board but the label has to be fixed near to the socket outlet wherever the rcd is located.

Warning notice – Caravans *(Regulation 514-6)*

A notice as shown in Figure 10.9 must be fixed near to main incoming supply inside a touring caravan.

Labels and drawings *(Regulation 514-1 to 514-3)*

In order to avoid confusion or possible danger, the Regulations place great stress on the need to label and identify equipment. Apart from questions of safety, where the purpose of items of equipment is not obvious the Regulations require that such a purpose shall be clearly indicated. See Figure 10.10 and 10.11.

Figure 10.8 Socket outlet incorporating residual current device used to connect electrical equipment utilised outside the equipotential zone of a building, must have a notice fixed on or near the socket-outlet. (Photograph by courtesy of MK Electric Ltd).

INSTRUCTIONS FOR ELECTRICITY SUPPLY

To connect

1. Before connecting the caravan installation to the mains supply, check that:-

   (a) the supply available at the pitch supply point is suitable for the installation of the caravan and it's appliances.

   (b) the caravan main switch is in the "off" position.

2. Remove or raise any cover from the electricity inlet provided on the caravan, and insert the connector of the supply flexible cable.

3. Remove or raise any cover from the socket outlet provided at the pitch supply point and insert the plug at the other end of the supply flexible cable.

4. Switch on at the caravan main switch.

5. Check the operation of circuit breakers, if any, fitted in the caravan.

IN CASE OF DOUBT CONSULT THE CARAVAN PARK OPERATOR OR HIS AGENT.

To disconnect

6. Reverse the procedure described in paragraphs 2 to 4 above.

Periodically

7. Preferably not less than once a year, the caravan electrical installation should be inspected and tested and a report on its condition obtained as prescribed in the regulations for electrical installations published by the institution of electrical engineers.

Figure 10.9   Notice to be fixed inside a touring caravan near to the electricity supply intake position. (Reproduced by permission of the Institution of Electrical Engineers).

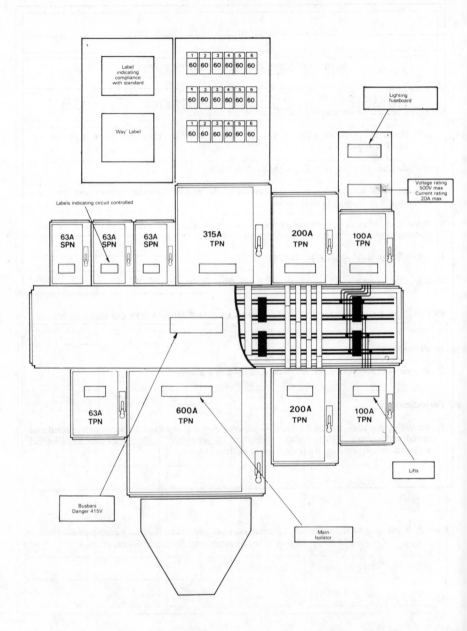

Figure 10.10   Labels must be provided to indicate usage of switch and control gear, unless there is no possibility of confusion (Regulation 514-1). (Illustration by courtesy of MEM Ltd).

Design to comply with B.S.5486: Part II: 1979			
List No.	Amps	Rated insulation voltage	Diversity factor
206MSN	**20**	**660**v	**0·9**

Fuse particulars

HRC cartridge fuse links use fuse links to BS 88 Part 2 1975		Semi-enclosed fuses use revireable insert only list No. 20MFRW designed to comply with BS 3036: 1958
Suitable MEM fuse links rated duty AC80 550V		Having category of duty S1A 415V
Type	Ratings	
SA2	2, 4, 6, 10,₅ 20, 20M25₅,* 20M32₅*	Recommended size of tinned copper wires

*High fusing factor fuse links for use on motor circuits			
Amps	**5**	**10**	**15**	**20**
SWG	**35**	**29**	**26**	**24**

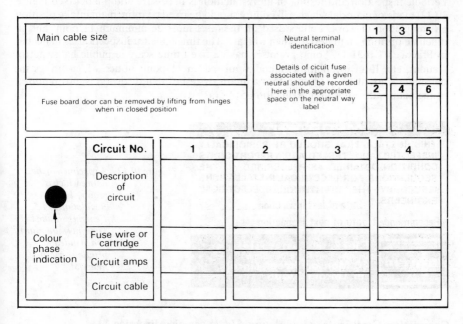

Main cable size		Neutral terminal identification	1	3	5
Fuse board door can be removed by lifting from hinges when in closed position		Details of cicuit fuse associated with a given neutral should be recorded here in the appropriate space on the neutral way label	2	4	6

	Circuit No.	1	2	3	4
Colour phase indication	Description of circuit				
	Fuse wire or cartridge				
	Circuit amps				
	Circuit cable				

Figure 10.11   (Top) typical SP & N fuse board label indicating compliance with Standards – fitted in conjunction with 'way' label shown (bottom) (Regulation 514-2). It is a recommendation that circuit protection devices should be incorporated into distribution boards and such schedules or 'way' labels should be provided.

Where equipment is not visible to an operator because it is remotely located, an indicating device to BS4099 *"Colours of indicator lights, push-buttons, annunciators and digital readouts"* needs to be provided.

Practice 3 gives information on the requirements for identifying conductors and cable cores.

The Regulations require that protective devices shall preferably be grouped together in a distribution board so that each protected circuit is marked for easy recognition.

A diagram, chart or table has to be provided showing the details of the installation and identifying all protective devices. For new installations or extensions comprehensive layout drawings will have to be provided, together with line diagrams and circuit schedules using symbols to BS3939. The size and type and composition of the mains cable has to be detailed together with its location.

It will also need to give details of main switchgear, sub-mains cables, distribution and protective equipment, means of switching and isolation, final circuits and points of utilisation. The character of the protective devices, earthing system, bonding, circuit and protective conductor impedances, fault levels, installed loads, diversities, maximum demands as appropriate will have to be provided to facilitate testing and inspection before and after commissioning. In a simple installation this can be provided in schedule form.

Periodic inspection and testing *(Regulations 514-5;* see also **Practice 11***)*

Periodic inspection and testing of an installation is necessary and a label (see Figure 10.12) made of material which will endure should be fixed near the main intake position on completion of work. Letters used on the label must be minimum 11 point and in indelible printing on material which will last. The time scale for inspections is indicated in Practice 11 (631-1). Some premises have a fixed time scale ie public halls, petrol stations, etc. If an installation embodies an rcd an 11 point notice which brings the consumer's attention to the need for a quarterly test of that device(s) is also required at the main intake position, Regulation 514-5(a).

IMPORTANT

THIS INSTALLATION SHOULD BE PERIODICALLY INSPECTED AND TESTED AND A REPORT ON ITS CONDITION OBTAINED, AS PRESCRIBED IN THE REGULATIONS FOR ELECTRICAL INSTALLATIONS ISSUED BY THE INSTITUTION OF ELECTRICAL ENGINEERS. Date of last Inspection _ _ _ _ _ _ _ _

Recommended date of next Inspection _ _ _ _ _ _ _ _

Electrical Installations
Electrical Engineers & Contractors
40 Monson Street, Lincoln.
Tel. Lincoln 37606

Figure 10.12   A specimen of the notice which is required by Regulation 514-5. Lettering should be 11 point (minimum) and in indelible printing on lasting material.

Completion Certificates *(Regulation 614-1;* see also **Practice 11***)*

A completion certificate shall be issued by the installer or any other person responsible for the construction of, or any alteration to an installation to the client as prescribed in the Regulations. A sample of such a certificate is detailed in figures 10.13 and 10.14.

COMPLETION CERTIFICATE
(as prescribed in the IEE Regulations for electrical installations)

Completion Certificate to be given by the contractor or other person responsible for the construction of the installation, or alteration thereto, or by an authorised person acting on his behalf.

I CERTIFY that the electrical installation at:

has been inspected and tested, in accordance with the Regulations for electrical installations, published by the Institution of Electrical Engineers (15th Edition)* and that, to the best of my knowledge and belief, the installation summarised in the drawings/schedule attached/overleaf† complies, at the time of my test, with the Edition of those Regulations current at the date of contract for the work, except as stated overleaf.

I RECOMMEND that this installation be further inspected and tested after an interval of not more than . . . . . . years‡.

Signed . . . . Date . . . .

 For and on behalf of: . . . .

. . . .

Address . . . .

. . . .

NOTE – This Completion Certificate does not cover portable appliances or equipment connected to socket outlets, for which an Inspection Certificate may be obtained.

---

* See Inspection Certificate attached.

† For simple installations, the particulars of the installation mentioned overleaf are regarded as a sufficient schedule for the purposes of Regulation 514–3.

‡ The space provided in the form for inserting the recommended number of years intervening between inspections should, for installations in general, be filled in by the figure 5 or such lesser figure as is considered appropriate to the individual case. For temporary installations on construction sites, the figure 3 should be inserted and the word 'years' changed to read 'months'. For caravan site installations, the figure should be 1, or such longer period (not exceeding 3 years) as is considered appropriate to the case. For agricultural premises the figure should be 3.

Figure 10.13   Front page of Completion Certificate (reproduced by permission of the Institution of Electrical Engineers).

Particulars of the installation covered by this certificate**

New installation.   Alteration/Extension to existing installation

Number of lighting points: Number of socket outlets:

Details of fixed current-using equipment:

Details of departures (if any) from the Regulations:

Comments (if any) on existing installation (where this certificate relates to an alteration or addition):

Applicable BASEC Certificate of Assessment number(s) (if any):

Figure 10.14   Obverse of Completion Certificate.

INSPECTION CERTIFICATE

(as prescribed in the IEE Regulations for electrical installations)

Inspection Certificate to be given by the contractor or other person responsible for carrying out an inspection and test of an installation, or part of an installation, or by an authorised person acting on his behalf.

I CERTIFY that the electrical installation at:

has been inspected and tested, in accordance with the IEE Regulations for electrical installations (15th Edition) and that the results are satisfactory in the respects mentioned below, except as indicated in the comments below.

I RECOMMEND that the installation be further inspected and tested after an interval of not more than . . . . . . years.*

Items inspected or tested:†

Type of earthing arrangements: TN)
                                   TT)   (Regulation 312–3)
                                   IT)

Type(s) of protective device: — overcurrent protective devices,
                               — residual current device(s),

Prospective short circuit current at the origin (Regulations 313–1 and 434–2)

Earth fault loop impedance at the origin (Regulation 313–1)

Continuity of ring final circuit conductors (Regulation 613–2)

Continuity of protective conductors and equipotential bonding (Regulation 613–3)

Earth electrode resistance (Regulation 613–4)

Insulation resistance of the fixed installation (Regulations 613–5 to 613–7)

Insulation resistance to earth of each item of equipment tested separately (Regulation 613–8)

Protection against direct contact, by insulation (Regulations 613–9 and 613–10)

Protection against direct contact, by barriers or enclosures (Regulation 613–12)

---

*The space provided in the Certificate for inserting the recommended number of years intervening between inspections should for installations generally, be filled with the figure 5 or such lesser figure as is considered appropriate to the individual case. For temporary installations on construction sites the figure 3 should be inserted and the word 'years' changed to read 'months'. For caravan site installations, the figure should be 1, or such longer period (not exceeding 3 years) as is considered appropriate to the case. For agricultural premises the figure should be 3.

†delete or complete items, as appropriate. Where a failure to comply with the Regulations is indicated further details should be entered, if necessary, overleaf.

Figure 10.15   Front of Inspection Certificate (reproduced by permission of the Institution of Electrical Engineers).

Inspection Certificate (contd.)

Resistance of non-conducting floors and walls, where relied upon for protection against indirect contact (Regulation 613–13)

Polarity, and position of single-pole devices for protection and switching (Regulation 613–14)

Earth fault loop impedance, for operation of devices relied upon for earth fault protection (Regulation 613–15)

Operation of residual current operated device for earth fault protection (Regulation 613–16)

Method of compliance with Regulation 413–3 (see also Regulation 413–4(i))

Protection against indirect contact by measures other than automatic disconnection (Regulations 613–10 and 613–11)

Condition of flexible cables and cords, switches, plugs and socket outlets (Regulation 612–1)

Sizes of live conductors and their methods of installation, in relation to design currents of circuits and to the operating currents of overcurrent protective devices (Regulation 612–1)

Equipment tested includes/does not include portable equipment.

Applicable BASEC Certificate of Assessment number(s) (if any):
Comments (if any) and departures from the IEE Regulations:

Signed . . . . Date . . . .

For and on behalf of: . . . .

. . . .

Address: . . . .

. . . .

. . . .

Printed copies of the inspection and completion certificates cannot be obtained from the Institution. There is, however, no objection to their being reproduced privately in any convenient form, provided the usual acknowledgement of their source is made.

Figure 10.16 Obverse of Inspection Certificate.

Inspection Certificates *(Regulation 631-1)*

Upon the completion of the inspection and testing procedure of an installation, or part of an installation, the person responsible for the inspection and testing of the installation shall issue an inspecting certificate to the client, or person requesting the work. A typical Inspection Certificate is shown in Figures 10.15 and 10.16. The format of a recording sheet used for earth tests made at the precommissioning stage of an installation is shown in Figure 10.17. Similarly, the format of a recording sheet for insulation resistance tests and earth loop impedance tests is shown in Figure 10.18.

ELECTRICAL PRECOMMISSIONING TESTS

EARTH TESTS

Contractor
Project

Contract No.
Sheet   of
Date
Site

Electrode Type Size	Location	Resistance	Copper Earth Tape Size	Ground Conditions	Witnessed by For	For Client

Figure 10.17   Recording sheet used for Earth tests.

INSPECTION AND TEST CERTIFICATE

SHEET   OF

Switchboard:
Section:
Manufacturer:

Project:
Contract No:
Elec. Sub-Contr.

Circuit Ref	Phasing RYBN	Insulation Resistance (Megohms)									Earth Loop Impedance (Ohms)			Checks
		Phase to Earth				Between Phases					Fuse Rating and Class	Max. Value Accepted	Value Recorded	
		RE	YE	BE	NE	RY	YB	RB	RBY/N				
INCOMER														
BUSBARS														
OUTGOING CIRCUITS														

INCOMER & BUSBARS:-
1. Operation of Switch
2. Fuse Class & Rating (if applic.) and tightness of fuse fixings.
3. Tightness of Cable Connections and Cable Glad.
4. Size of Incoming Cable.
5. Tightness of Busbar Connections.
6. Earthing of Panel & Cable Armouring & resistance of earth continuity conductors.
7. Labels.
8. No sign of overloading of conductors and accessories.

EACH OUTGOING CIRCUIT :-
At each Fuse Switch/Switch:-
1. Operation.
2. Fuse Class & Rating & Tightness of Fuse Fixings.
3. Tightness of Cable Connections and Cable Gland.
4. Size of Cable.
5. Earthing of Cable Armouring/ Conduit/ Trunking & resistance of earth continuity conductors.
6. Labels.
7. Locking Devices.
8. No sign of overloading of conductors and accessories.

I certify the equipment above has been inspected and tested in accordance with the current edition of the IEE Regulations and to the best of my knowledge complies with those Regulations.

Details of Departures from the Regulations ....

Inspected & Tested by.....................
Witnessed by.....................
Date.....................

For the Electrical Sub-Contractor
For

Figure 10.18   Recording sheet for insulation resistance tests and earth loop impedance tests.

Practice 11

Inspection and Testing

The fundamental requirements in respect of additions, alteration, inspection and testing are contained in Part 1 of the Wiring Regulations (Regulation 13-19 and 13-20). These are shown in Schedule 11.1.

Schedule 11.1 – Fundamental requirements in respect of additions, alteration and inspection and testing

(Regulations 13-19 and 13-20)

Positive answer required to the following questions	Notes and ASEE Comment
Has the rating and condition of existing equipment (including the supply authority's) been checked to determine that it is adequate to bear any extra load, before adding to or making alterations or additions to an existing temporary or permanent installation?	Bear in mind the need to verify and certify alterations and additions (see also Practice 10)
Are the earthing arrangements adequate for the additions or alterations?	
Have inspections and tests been made to check that all the requirements of Regulations 13-1 to 13-19 (See Principles 1) have been implemented	This needs to be undertaken on completion of an installation or when the installation is altered or extended.

Initial Inspection and Testing

General *(Regulations 611-1 and 611-2)*

The purpose of a recognised inspection and testing procedure is to ensure that the installation is safe to use and meets the requirements of the Regulations. Upon completion, every installation must be tested and inspected before it is connected to the supply, and it is important to ensure that the tests to be completed will not cause danger to persons or property.

The instruments used in testing should be checked and recalibrated regularly to ensure accuracy, and the instrument serial number should be noted with the results of the test.

It is a requirement that charts, schedules, diagrams, tables and calculations describing the installation, including details of devices used for isolation and switching, protection, and the characteristics of the protection devices for automatic disconnection of the supply shall be provided before inspection and testing procedures commence.

Visual inspection before commissioning *(Regulation 612-1)*

A visual inspection of the installation should be made to ensure all equipment and accessories comply with the relevant British Standards, and the materials and equipment have been selected and erected in accordance with the requirements of the Regulations. Verification is also required that no visible damage to the installed equipment has occurred.

Check list for initial inspections *(Appendix 14)*

The initial visual inspection should include those of the following items as are relevant to the installation:

Connections of conductors should be checked to ensure electrical and mechanically sound connections and that conductors have been identified with colours, sleeving or numbering as appropriate.

Selection of conductors for current carrying capacity and voltage drop, to confirm that the cross sectional area of the phase, neutral and protective conductors have been calculated to meet the requirements of the Regulations.

Check that the connection of single pole switches are in the phase conductor and for the correct connection of socket outlets and lampholders.

The correct installation of fire barriers and protection against thermal effects; it is important that rising main trunking or bus bar systems in high rise buildings are adequately protected by the use of the prescribed fire barriers.

Measures are required for protection against direct contact of live parts by the use of insulation, barriers or enclosures, obstacles, placing out of reach or by placing in a non-conducting location.

Checks must also be made regarding the presence of devices for isolation and switching.

The choice and setting of protective and monitoring devices should be checked.

That comprehensive labelling of all circuits, distribution boards, switches etc and danger and warning notices has been implemented.

Equipment and protective measures should be appropriate to the external influences.

The persons involved in the visual inspection should also have available all diagrams, as fitted drawings, and any other instructions or information to enable the inspection to be carried out in accordance with the requirements of the Regulations.

Testing

General *(Regulation 613-1)*

To ensure that the conductors in an installation have been installed and connected correctly, the sequence of tests shown in Schedule 11.2 should be completed before the installation is energised. The second Annexe hereto prescribes some of the testing methods to be used but other methods can be used if they are capable of producing correct results.

Schedule 11.2 – Sequence of tests and testing methods and requirements

Sequence	Test	Requirements and testing method
1	Continuity of ring final circuit conductors	See text which follows
2	Continuity of protective conductors, including bonding conductors	See text which follows
3	Earth electrode resistance	See text which follows
4	Insulation Resistance	See text which follows
5	(a) Insulation of site built assemblies – protection against direct contact (b) Insulation of site built assemblies – protection against indirect contact	See text which follows
6	Protection by electrical separation	Verify and test live parts of safety extra-low voltage equipment is electrical separate from live parts of other circuits. The separation should not be less than that between input and output windings of safety isolating transformers (see also Practice 2 – Electrical Separation)
7	Protection by barriers or enclosures during erection	Verify by test that enclosures or barriers have IP2X or 1P4X degree of protection where required (see Practice 2 – Safety Extra Low Voltage)
8	Insulation of non-conducting floors and walls	Resistance of floors and wall to main protective conductor to be measured at three points to be between 1 to 1.2m from any extraneous conductive part
9	Polarity	See text which follows
10	Earth fault loop impedance	See text which follows
11	Operation of residual current operated devices and fault-voltage operated devices	See text which follows

If any of the above tests shown in Schedule 11.2 indicates a fault condition, the fault must be rectified and that particular test (and the previous tests) repeated to ensure the installation complies with the requirements of the Regulations.

Continuity of ring final circuit conductors *(Regulation 613-2 and Appendix 15)*

Two methods of testing are recommended and in each case the test is made to verify the continuity of the phase, neutral and protective conductors of a ring final circuit.

Method 1 – Conductors of same cross sectional area and same metal

Stage 1. Check the continuity of each of the phase, neutral and protective conductors of the ring circuit at the distribution board termination between the ends of the conductors and record the resistance reading.

Stage 2. Note the resistance of the test leads.

Stage 3. Reconnect the conductors to complete the ring circuit, and using the long test leads measure the resistance of each conductor in turn between the distribution board termination and the appropriate contact of the socket outlet as near as possible to the mid point of the ring final circuit. The resistance value is noted and the resistance of the test leads deducted. The result should be approx one quarter of the value of the reading obtained in Stage 1.

Figure 11.1 illustrates this method of testing continuity in conductors of a ring final circuit.

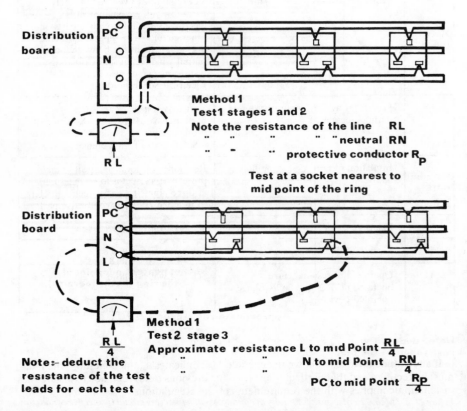

Distribution board PC N L

Method 1
Test 1 stages 1 and 2
Note the resistance of the line   RL
      "   "   "   " "neutral RN
      "   -   "   protective conductor R$_P$

R L

Test at a socket nearest to mid point of the ring

Distribution board PC N L

R L

Method 1
Test 2 stage 3
Approximate resistance L to mid Point $\frac{RL}{4}$
      "   "   N to mid Point $\frac{RN}{4}$
      "   "   PC to mid Point $\frac{R_P}{4}$

$\frac{R L}{4}$

Note :- deduct the resistance of the test leads for each test

Figure 11.1   Method 1 of testing continuity of conductors of a final ring circuit (conductors same csa and material).

Method 2 – Protective conductor of different composition to live conductors
Stage 1. Check the continuity of each of the phase neutral and protective conductors of the ring circuit the distribution board termination, between the ends of the conductors. Record the resistance reading.
Stage 2. Reconnect the conductors to complete the ring circuit, locate the socket outlet as near as possible to the mid-point of the circuit and bond the phase, neutral and protective conductors together at the point. Measure the resistance between phase and neutral conductors at the distribution board terminals. The resulting resistance should be approx half the value of the reading obtained in Stage 1.
Stage 3 If the protective conductor forms a ring, as in a pvc insulated twin and CPC cable the resistance is measured between phase and earth terminals at the distribution board, and the resulting resistance should be the sum of a quarter of the resistance of the protective conductor of the value of the reading obtained in Stage 1.

Figure 11.2 illustrates this method of testing continuity in conductors of a ring final circuit.

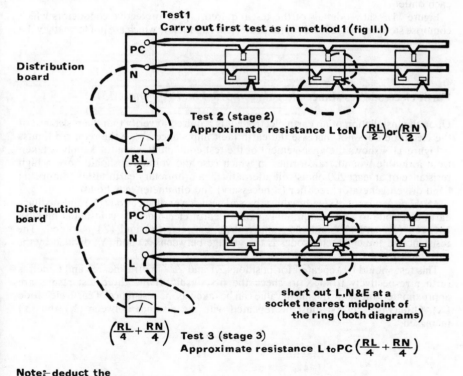

Test 1
Carry out first test as in method 1 (fig II.I)

Distribution board

PC
N
L

Test 2 (stage 2)
Approximate resistance L to N $\left(\frac{RL}{2}\right)$ or $\left(\frac{RN}{2}\right)$

$\left(\frac{RL}{2}\right)$

Distribution board

PC
N
L

$\left(\frac{RL}{4} + \frac{RN}{4}\right)$

short out L, N & E at a socket nearest midpoint of the ring (both diagrams)

Test 3 (stage 3)
Approximate resistance L to PC $\left(\frac{RL}{4} + \frac{RN}{4}\right)$

Note:- deduct the resistance of the test leads for each test

Figure 11.2   Method 2 of testing continuity of conductors of a final ring circuit (protective conductor not of equal csa or material as line or neutral conductors).

Continuity of protective conductors and equipotential bonding *(Regulation 613-3 and Appendix 15)*

Before the connection of an electrical installation to the supply it is required to verify that all protective conductors are connected correctly and electrically sound.

If the protective conductor forms part of a cable such as a core of a multicore pvc-insulated cable or a single protective conductor, a dc ohmmeter may be used to measure the resistance. Where steel conduit, trunking or other steel enclosures form the protective conductor the test shall be carried out by use of a high current test instrument at a voltage not exceeding 50 volts ac or dc and at a current approaching 1.5 times normal circuit current up to a maximum of 25A.

When using a dc test supply it must be noted that an inspection of the length of the protective conductor must be made to ensure that there are no inductors fitted.

It is preferable to use a hand generator, or other portable instrument to carry out the test so that the disconnected phase conductor can be connected to the consumer's earth terminal and the test can be made between phase conductor and protective conductor at each outlet.

Figure 11.3 shows details of the test required (a) for protective conductors which comprise steel enclosures and (b) for protective conductors which are not formed by the cable enclosure.

Earth electrode resistance *(Regulation 613-4 and Appendix 15)*

Upon the installation of an earth electrode it is required to verify that the resistance of the electrode does not increase the earth fault impedance above the required limits.

Figure 11.4 shows the arrangement of the test equipment when the supply is taken from a double wound transformer in which case the voltmeter should have a high resistance of at least 200 ohms/volt alternatively a proprietary earth tester comprising hand driven generator, rectifier (if necessary) and ohmmeter may be used.

Method. A current of steady value is passed between earth electrode (X) and auxiliary earth electrode (Y). An additional auxiliary earth electrode (Z) is installed midway between (X) and (Y) and the voltage drop between (X) and (Z) recorded. The resistance of the earth electrodes is the voltage between (X) and (Y) divided by the current flowing.

This test should be repeated for positions Z1 and Z2 6 metres nearer and 6 metres further respectively from X to check the first result. If the three test results are approximately the same the mean value can be taken as the resistance of earth electrode (X). Otherwise the test must be repeated with the distance between (X) and (Y) increased.

(a) Testing of protective conductors comprising steel enclosures.

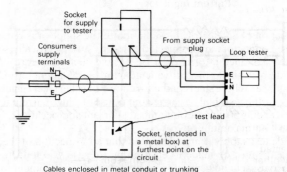

(b) Testing of protective conductors, not part of an enclosure.

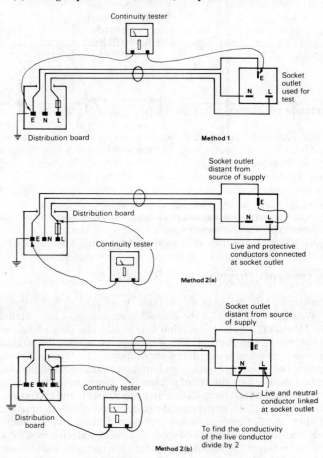

Figure 11.3   Continuity tests of protective conductors in a radial circuit.

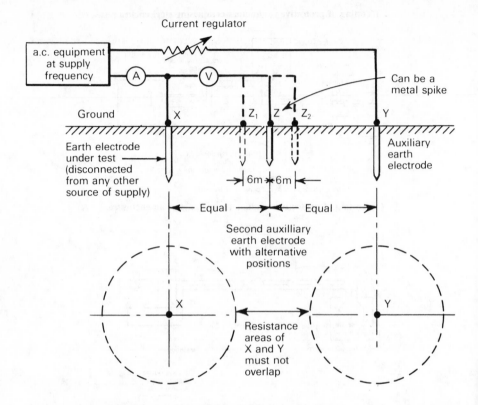

Figure 11.4   Method of measuring earth-electrode resistance.
Note: The resistance area is one within which it is possible to measure the voltage gradient with a commercial measuring instrument.

Insulation resistance *(Regulations 613-5 to 613-8)*

Before a completed installation or an alteration to an existing installation is connected to the supply, a test to determine the insulation resistance of the installation must be carried out. However, a large installation may need to be divided into sections, each containing not less than fifty outlets. This is because it is not possible to achieve accurate low voltage readings when testing large installations. The term outlet meaning every switch, lighting fitting, socket outlet, and appliance incorporating a switch. The test voltage applied shall be a dc voltage of not less than twice the declared voltage, that is a maximum of 500 volts dc test for installations up to 500 volts and 1000 volts. To carry out the test, all fuses must be in, switches and circuit breakers closed, appliances and fixed equipment disconnected and all lamps removed. Because of the increased use of electronic devices such as dimmers and speed controls for electric motors, which may be damaged by test voltages the Regulations permit the temporary disconnection of these devices while testing is being carried out. The results of the tests shall be recorded and shall be not less than one megohm between all poles of a system to earth, (with the exception of a TNC system), and one megohm between all poles or phases of a system. The insulation resistance between exposed conductive parts and live parts shall be tested to comply with the appropriate British Standard for that equipment but if there is no British Standard the insulation resistance shall not be less than 0.5 megohm.

The testing voltages are shown in Schedule 11.3.

Schedule 11.3 – Insulation resistance testing voltages

Testing Voltage: twice designated voltage but need not exceed	For nominal circuit voltage (rms for ac)
500Vdc 1000Vdc	up to 500V between 500V and 1000V

The requirements of Regulations for insulation resistance test are shown in schedule 11.4

Schedule 11.4 – Insulation Resistance Tests

Conditions of test	Minimum insulation resistance
Insulation to earth with all fuses in place, switches closed (including main switch if practicable) and all poles or phase conductors connected together.*	1 megohm
Insulation between any two poles or phase conductors, with all lamps removed and apparatus disconnected, but all switches closed.**	1 megohm
Insulation of fixed apparatus that is practicable to disconnect for test (a) between case or framework and all normally live parts (tested separately)	0.5 megohm
(b) between poles or phases	0.5 megohm†

*   The last part of the test is not applicable to installations with earthed concentric wiring and TN-C systems.
** Where it is impracticable to remove lamps or disconnect other apparatus their switches must be open to obtain the same conditions of test.
†   If not specified in an appropriate British Standard for the equipment.

Insulation of site built assemblies *(Regulations 613-9 to 613-10)*

Protection against direct contact provided by insulation applied to live parts during erection (see also Practice 2 "Insulation of live parts") shall be tested to ensure that the insulation is able to withstand without breakdown an applied test voltage equal to that specified in the relevant British Standard for factory built assemblies BS5486. Full details are given in that British Standard and should be consulted. However, it can generally be stated that for the verification of dielectric properties, BS 5486 requires the test voltage to be applied between all live parts and the frame of the assembly and between each pole and all other poles connected to the frame of the assembly. If the assembly includes a protective conductor, the conductor should be regarded as a separate circuit. The test voltage should be steadily raised to its full value over a few seconds. Main circuit test voltage depends on the voltage rating of the applied insulation and ranges from 1000V to 3500V ac. The test is considered to have been successful if there is no puncture or flash over.

When protection against indirect contact is provided by additional insulation installed during erection it must be verified that the insulated enclosure gives a protection of not less than IP2X to BS5490 and that the insulating enclosure should be able to withstand without breakdown or flashover an applied voltage test equal to that specified in the British Standard BS5486 *"Factory Built Equipment"*. For enclosures made of insulating material, BS5486 requires an additional dielectric test to be carried out by applying a test voltage of between 1500V to 5200V. The test is between metal foil laid on the outside of the enclosure over opening and joints and the interconnected line and exposed conductive parts within the enclosure located next to the opening and joints.

Verification of dielectric properties is not required by BS5486 for those parts which have already been type tested provided their dielectric strength has not been impaired by their mountings.

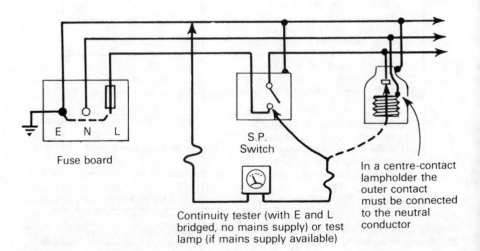

Fuse board

S.P. Switch

Continuity tester (with E and L bridged, no mains supply) or test lamp (if mains supply available)

In a centre-contact lampholder the outer contact must be connected to the neutral conductor

Figure 11.5   Method of testing polarity of circuits.

Polarity *(Regulation 613-14)*

This test shall be carried out to ensure that:–
(i)   All fuses and single pole control devices are connected in the phase conductor only
(ii) The centre contact of an edison screw lampholder is connected to the phase conductor and the outer metal threaded part is connected to neutral conductor
(iii) Socket outlets are connected with the phase conductor on right when inspected from the front.

Tests are carried out with all switches closed, lamps and equipment removed. Figures 11.5 and 11.6 show the testing methods.

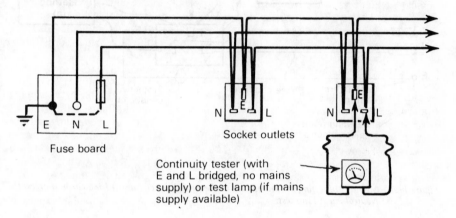

Figure 11.6   Method of testing polarity of socket-outlets.

Earth fault loop impedance *(Regulation 613-15 and Appendix 15)*

The earth fault current path, phase to earth loop, starting at the point of fault comprises:– circuit protective conductor consumer's earthing terminal and earthing conductors; the metallic return path in TN systems, or the earth return path in TT and IT systems; the path through the earthed neutral point of the supply transformer and transformer winding; and the phase conductor from the transformer back to the point of fault.

The symbol for earth loop impedance is Zs. The symbol for earth loop impedance external to installation is Ze.

The test is usually carried out by using a proprietary earth fault loop impedance test instrument which is plugged into a socket outlet to test the earth loop impedance. The instrument operates at a current of approx 20A applied for 25-50ms, with indicator lights to show the condition of polarity and continuity. It is necessary to verify the continuity of the protective conductor, this would prevent the loop current from flowing and the whole of the protective conductor would be connected to the phase conductor.

When using an instrument with ac at less than 10A or rapidly reversed dc and the protective conductor is mainly steel conduit two tests shall be made, a test at the farthest point of the installation with the protective conductor connected (Zs), and a test at the main consumer's supply position with protective conductor disconnected (Ze). The loop impedance value being double the value of the first test minus the value of the second test.

See Figures 11.7 and 11.8.

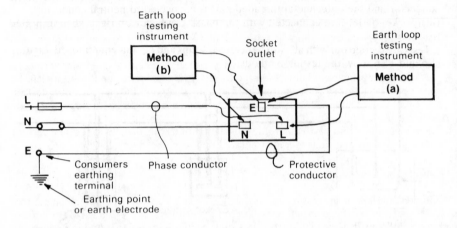

Figure 11.7 Methods of testing the impedance of the earth loop circuit (a) Line-earth loop test (b) Neutral-earth loop test.

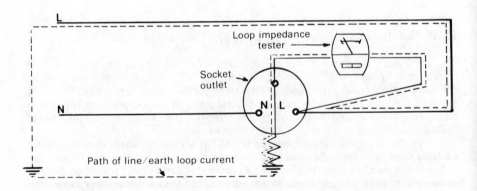

Figure 11.8 Shows that the loop impedance tester checks the actual path of a fault current.

Operation of residual current operated and fault voltage operated protective devices* *(Regulation 613-16 and Appendix 15)*

Both the residual current operated protective device and the fault voltage operated protective device are manufactured with testing facilities, but a test to check for instantaneous operation by external means is required.

The testing device shall be a single-phase, double-wound mains transformer with an output voltage not exceeding 50 volts rms alternating current, having a short period rating of not less than 750VA; and shall be connected across the circuit line conductor and the cpc of an residual current operated device, or the neutral and frame terminals of a fault voltage operated device. In the former case the device should trip within the time delay declared by the manufacturer (usually 0.2s) and in the case of the test on the f.v.o. device should trip instantly. A more satisfactory test with more elaborate equipment is detailed in CP1013.

See Figure 11.9 and 11.10 regarding connection of testing devices to residual current operated devices and fault voltage operated devices.

Completion Certificates *(Regulation 614-1)*

Upon completion of the testing and inspection of an electrical installation completion and inspection certificates shall be issued to the customer by the contractor or person responsible for the work. The certificates shall be in the form illustrated in Practice 10 and signed by the contractor or an authorised person acting on his behalf.

Any defects revealed during the inspection and testing of the installation shall be rectified before the issue of any certificate and the client shall also be reminded of the importance of periodic re-testing and re-inspection of the installation.

Alterations and their certification *(Regulations 621-1 and 622-1)*

Where alterations to, and additions to, an existing installation take place it is necessary for the contractor to verify that the work complies with the IEE Regulations and does not impair the safety and operation of the existing installation.

Completion certificates are required to be issued in respect of additions or alterations to the installation in the same way as is previously mentioned but the contractor is also required to report to the customer any defects found in an associated section or sections of the existing installation.

Periodic inspection and testing *(Regulation 631-1)*

Those reponsible for the construction of an installation are recommended to advice the customer of the importance of period re-inspection and re-testing. Any re-inspection and re-testing undertaken is required to meet the conditions for inspection and testing already set out in this Section. The results obtained should be documented on the inspection certificate (see Practice 10) and issued to the client by the contractor, or authorised person acting on his behalf.

Electrical installations should be tested periodically to minimise the potential risk of shock or fire and the interval between tests should vary according to the type and function of the building concerned. It is therefore recommended that the following

*See note to Schedule 2.15.

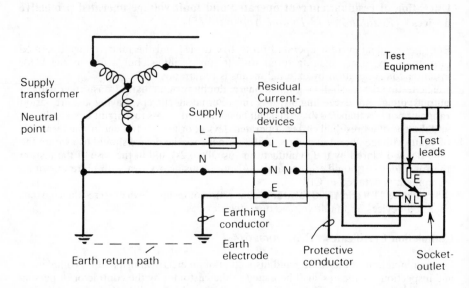

Figure 11.9 *Method of testing a residual current-operated device.*

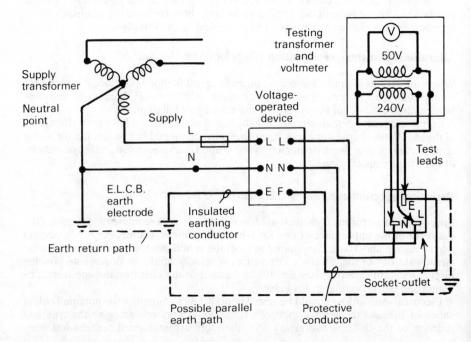

Figure 11.10 *Method of testing a fault voltage-operated device.*

types of installations be re-inspected and re-tested at the intervals stated, unless shorter durations are specifically required by manufacturers' instructions, or other mandatory requirements:

5 yearly intervals: private houses; hotel and boarding houses; schools and colleges; shops; offices and general commercial properties.

3 yearly intervals: factories; caravan sites underground cables, etc; workshops, etc; agricultural installations.

annually: petrol stations; theatres and cinemas; public laundries and launderettes; caravan sites; night clubs and discotheques; public houses; churches.

three monthly intervals: construction sites; temporary installations.

Note the following in respect of the intervals between inspections of particular types of installations:

Annual inspections – recommended: emergency lighting systems; fire alarm systems.
Annual inspections – mandatory: cinema installations; petrol filling stations.

ASSOCIATION OF SUPERVISORY AND EXECUTIVE ENGINEERS

ENQUIRY

For details of any of the ASEE services please complete and return this enquiry form to ASEE Head Office, Wix Hill House, West Horsley, Surrey, KT24 6DZ.
Tel No.: Guildford (0483) 222383

Membership ....

Diploma in Engineering Management ....

DEM by Distance Learning ....

PUBLICATIONS

ASEE Management Handbooks (Please state number of copies required).

Management & Communication £9.50 ....
Production Planning & Control £9.50 ....

Industrial Relations £5.00 ....

Human Resources Planning £5.00 ....

ASEE Guide to the Wiring Regs. 15th Ed.
(Including 1987 amendments)
Terms (cash with order, post free)
1–4 copies (U.K. £5.00 O'seas £6.50 each)
5–19 copies, 10% discount ....
20 or more copies, 20% ....

ASEE Journal Electro-Technical News
(Issued free to members)
Non-member subscriber U.K. £12.00 p.a. ....
Non-member subscriber O'seas. £20.00 p.a. ....

Please supply information on publications as indicated. I enclose cheque/cash for £

Name (Block Capitals) ....

Address ....

....

....

Postcode ....   Tel No ....

Date ....   Signed ....

ASSOCIATION OF SUPERVISORY AND EXECUTIVE ENGINEERS

A professional association for **SUPERVISORY AND EXECUTIVE ENGINEERS: SENIOR EXECUTIVES: MANAGERS: DIRECTORS AND PRINCIPALS engaged in the Engineering** and allied industries with large industrial and commercial users of engineering services, and with H.M. Forces.

ASEE PROVIDES MEMBERS WITH:

* **An Engineering Identity**

- On satisfying the membership requirements, members may use the appropriate entitlements following their name: e.g. Member – MASEE: Associate Member – AMASEE

* **Engineers Registration**

- Registration at the appropriate level with the Engineering Council (T Eng or Eng Tech.) available to corporate members see overleaf
* Opportunities to keep in touch with technical developments.

- Lecture programme and work visits
- Technical information and library service
- Technical publications
- Electrotechnical News Bi-monthly Journal
* Diploma in Engineering Management

- A scheme of management education for those who have completed their technical education – leads to widely recognised Management Diploma.

-

    DEM College based
- DEM by Distance Learning scheme (UK only at present)
- DEM Management Handbooks (Distance Lerning Texts)

* A forum for social and professional contacts

- Social and technical events organised nationally and by Branches.

* **A variety of practical services**

- Patents Advice
- Appointments bureau
- Legal advice on employment problems
- Welfare assistance via the EEIBA
- Subscription tax deductible
- Insurance schemes, BUPA, financial counselling, investment services.

ASSOCIATION OF SUPERVISORY AND EXECUTIVE ENGINEERS

Association Membership

The Association invites applications for membership (see enquiry form) the Membership qualifications are as follows:-

Corporate Membership
Member
25 years + Minimum Qualifications:
Accredited BTEC/SCOTVEC HND/HNC in engineering subjects or equivalent e.g., C & GLI Full Technological Certificate or Part III in certain Technician Engineering subjects or accredited ordinary unclassified degree in engineering subjects and competence in english. **Training and Experience**: suitable training not less than eight years in relevant post of a responsibility demonstrably higher than that expected for Associate Member.

Associate Member
23 years + Minimum Qualifications:
Accredited BTEC/SCOTVEC ND/NC (OND/ONC) in engineering subjects or equivalent e.g., C & GLI Part II Technician Certificate in certain subjects or Part III Craft Certificate (e.g., El Install 'C') and competence in English.
Training and experience: suitable training and at least two years in relevant post.*

Non-Corporate Membership
Associate
25 years + Eligibility: not possessing qualifications for corporate grades.
Experience: Holding a post at a suitable level of responsibility in the engineering field for a sufficient period of time.

Student
17–25 years. Studying recognised qualification.

Notes:
H.M. Forces applicants: Rank held as shown by discharge papers assists with placing such applicants. The Engineering Council's guidance is observed.

Engineer's Registration
The ASEE is a body Nominated by the Engineering Council to recommend the Registration of suitable applicants by the Engineering Council and applicants for membership of the Association will be invited to seek registration through the Association. Registration is regarded by the Association as being of the utmost importance to the status of Engineers in society.

Corporate Members with requisite qualifications will usually be registrable as either Technician (Incorporated) Engineer or Engineering Technician.

ELECTREX

INTERNATIONAL ELECTRICAL & ELECTRONICS EXHIBITION

National Exhibition Centre
Birmingham
England

A MARKET PLACE OF CONCENTRATED TECHNOLOGY

All enquiries regarding Electrex should be sent to:

ELECTREX LTD
Wix Hill House, West Horsley, Surrey KT24 6DZ, England
Telephone Guildford (0483) 222888
Telefax (0483) 224321

ELECTREX

INTERNATIONAL ELECTRICAL & ELECTRONICS EXHIBITION

National Exhibition Centre
Birmingham
England

Please send further information

NAME: . . . . , ...

COMPANY: . . . .

ADDRESS: . . . .

. . . .

Send to: Electrex Limited, Wix Hill House, West
Horsley, Surrey, KT24 6DZ, U.K.
or: Telephone Guildford (0483) 222888,
Telex 859460
Telefax (0483) 224321

INDEX